Marine Biomes

GREENWOOD GUIDES TO
BIOMES OF THE WORLD

Introduction to Biomes
Susan L. Woodward

Tropical Forest Biomes
Barbara A. Holzman

Temperate Forest Biomes
Bernd H. Kuennecke

Grassland Biomes
Susan L. Woodward

Desert Biomes
Joyce A. Quinn

Arctic and Alpine Biomes
Joyce A. Quinn

Freshwater Aquatic Biomes
Richard A. Roth

Marine Biomes
Susan L. Woodward

Marine BIOMES

Susan L. Woodward

Greenwood Guides to Biomes of the World

Susan L. Woodward, General Editor

GREENWOOD PRESS
Westport, Connecticut • London

Library of Congress Cataloging-in-Publication Data

Woodward, Susan L., 1944 Jan. 20–
Marine biomes / Susan L. Woodward.
p. cm. — (Greenwood guides to biomes of the world)
Includes bibliographical references and index.
ISBN 978-0-313-33840-3 (set : alk. paper) — ISBN 978-0-313-34001-7 (vol. : alk. paper)
1. Marine ecology. I. Title.
QH541.5.S3W68 2008
577.7—dc22 2008027512

British Library Cataloguing in Publication Data is available.

Library of Congress Catalog Card Number: 2008027512
ISBN: 978-0-313-34001-7 (vol.)
978-0-313-33840-3 (set)

First published in 2008

Greenwood Press, 88 Post Road West, Westport, CT 06881
An imprint of Greenwood Publishing Group, Inc.
www.greenwood.com

Printed in the United States of America

The paper used in this book complies with the Permanent Paper Standard issued by the National Information Standards Organization (Z39.48–1984).

10 9 8 7 6 5 4 3 2 1

Contents

Preface

Preparing this book was a journey of discovery for me. I'm pretty much a landlubber. What I learned by writing let me see with new eyes and fascination the land and organisms affected by the sea. Fortunately, both for the book and for the writer, in the midst of the process I had opportunities to comb rocky coasts in South Africa and a desert coast in Namibia and to snorkel in the Galapagos. All three experiences heightened my awareness of a world that lies largely hidden from view. I'm ready for more.

Aquatic biomes in general are difficult to define, because they do not fit the mold prepared for terrestrial ones, which are delineated according to vegetation. Marine biologists and oceanographers continue to seek consensus on the best way to recognize boundaries in the sea. This book uses a fairly conventional organization, dividing the marine environment into coastal, continental shelf, and deep sea biomes. Separate chapters are devoted to each. The first chapter introduces key elements of the ocean as habitat and includes discussions of the physical factors influencing life in the sea as well as the chief forms of life and ecological relationships. Each ocean basin is introduced with a description of its size, major landform features, and broad circulation patterns.

Individual biome chapters begin with an overview of the biome under consideration that describes the physical environment and the types of organisms that commonly inhabit such areas. Ocean habitats are distinguished according to water temperatures, ocean currents, distance from land, and characteristics of the seabed. Selected regional variants are described to demonstrate these influences as appropriate to the biome under discussion. Usually, latitudinal variations (polar, temperate, and tropical) were chosen. For comparison, different ocean basins and different sides of the same basin were also included.

The number of species and even higher taxa—up to and including the level of phylum—are too diverse in the seas to include examples of everything. Creatures are often identified only to family level. Many marine organisms do not have common names, so it was impossible to avoid some use of scientific names in the body of the text.

Maps, diagrams, photographs, and line drawings are plentiful to enhance the reader's appreciation of the great variation found in what initially may appear to be a vast, uniform, borderless world ocean. Advanced middle school and high school students are the intended audience, but undergraduates and anyone else intrigued by the vast oceans of the Earth will find the material of interest.

What lies beneath the surface of the ocean is strange and unfamiliar to most people. In recent years the BBC has produced *Blue Planet, Seas of Life*, a series of videos on life in different marine habitats. Since these may be the only way most of us can experience the undersea world, relevant programs are listed at the end of each chapter, as are Internet sites where images of marine life are readily available.

The ocean is one of the last frontiers for scientific exploration on Earth. New knowledge and understanding come with every expedition. Much is yet to be learned. The best that can come out of a book such as this is that some young people will become enthralled enough with the wonders already revealed beyond the shoreline—and all that still awaits discovery—that they will embark on their own quests to find out more about the sea and the life within in it.

I would like to thank Kevin Downing of Greenwood Press for his insights and constant support in bringing this project to fruition. Jeff Dixon deserves much credit; his illustrations are a major contribution, and he was a wonderfully cooperative collaborator in the book's production. Bernd Kuennecke of Radford University's Geography Department prepared the excellent maps that guide the reader to the ocean habitats discussed. To these folks and to the people who freely provided pictures to be used in the book goes my deepest appreciation.

Blacksburg, Virginia
January 2008

How to Use This Book

The book is arranged with a general introduction to marine biomes and a chapter each on the Coast Biome, the Continental Shelf Biome, and the Deep Sea Biome. The biome chapters begin with a general overview at a global scale and proceed to selected regional descriptions. Each chapter and each regional description can more or less stand on its own, but the reader will find it instructive to investigate the introductory chapter and the introductory sections in the later chapters. More in-depth coverage of topics perhaps not so thoroughly developed in the regional discussions usually appears in the introductions.

The use of Latin or scientific names for species has been kept to a minimum in the text. However, the scientific name of each plant or animal for which a common name is given in a chapter appears in an appendix to that chapter. A glossary at the end of the book gives definitions of selected terms used throughout the volume. The bibliography lists the works consulted by the author and is arranged by biome and the regional expressions of that biome.

All biomes overlap to some degree with others, so you may wish to refer to other books among Greenwood Guides to the Biomes of the World. The volume entitled *Introduction to Biomes* presents simplified descriptions of all the major biomes. It also discusses the major concepts that inform scientists in their study and understanding of biomes and describes and explains, at a global scale, the environmental factors and processes that serve to differentiate the world's biomes.

The Use of Scientific Names

Good reasons exist for knowing the scientific or Latin names of organisms, even if at first they seem strange and cumbersome. Scientific names are agreed on by international committees and, with few exceptions, are used throughout the world. So everyone knows exactly which species or group of species everyone else is talking about. This is not true for common names, which vary from place to place and language to language. Another problem with common names is that in many instances European colonists saw resemblances between new species they encountered in the Americas or elsewhere and those familiar to them at home. So they gave the foreign plant or animal the same name as the Old World species. The common American Robin is a "robin" because it has a red breast like the English or European Robin and not because the two are closely related. In fact, if one checks the scientific names, one finds that the American Robin is *Turdus migratorius* and the English Robin is *Erithacus rubecula.* And they have not merely been put into different genera (*Turdus* versus *Erithacus*) by taxonomists, but into different families. The American Robin is a thrush (family Turdidae) and the English Robin is an Old World flycatcher (family Muscicapidae). Sometimes that matters. Comparing the two birds is really comparing apples to oranges. They are different creatures, a fact masked by their common names.

Scientific names can be secret treasures when it comes to unraveling the puzzles of species distributions. The more different two species are in their taxonomic relationships the farther apart in time they are from a common ancestor. So two species placed in the same genus are somewhat like two brothers having the same father—they are closely related and of the same generation. Two genera in the same family might be thought of as two cousins—they have the same grandfather, but different fathers. Their common ancestral roots are separated farther by time. The important thing in the study of biomes is that distance measured by time often means distance measured by separation in space as well. It is widely held that new species come about when a population becomes isolated in one way or another from the rest of its kind and adapts to a different environment. The scientific classification into genera, families, orders, and so forth reflects how long ago a population went its separate way in an evolutionary sense and usually points to some past environmental changes that created barriers to the exchange of genes among all members of a species. It hints at the movements of species and both ancient and recent connections or barriers. So if you find a two species in the same genus or two genera in the same family that occur on different continents today, this tells you that their "fathers" or "grandfathers" not so long ago lived in close contact, either because the continents were connected by suitable habitat or because some members of the ancestral group were able to overcome a barrier and settle in a new location. The greater the degree of taxonomic separation (for example, different families existing in different geographic areas) the longer the time back to a common ancestor and the longer ago the physical separation of the species. Evolutionary history and Earth history are hidden in a name. Thus, taxonomic classification can be important.

Most readers, of course, won't want or need to consider the deep past. So, as much as possible, Latin names for species do not appear in the text. Only when a common English language name is not available, as often is true for plants and animals from other parts of the world, is the scientific name provided. The names of families and, sometimes, orders appear because they are such strong indicators of long isolation and separate evolution. Scientific names do appear in chapter appendixes. Anyone looking for more information on a particular type of organism is cautioned to use the Latin name in your literature or Internet search to ensure that you are dealing with the correct plant or animal. Anyone comparing the plants and animals of two different biomes or of two different regional expressions of the same biome should likewise consult the list of scientific names to be sure a "robin" in one place is the same as a "robin" in another.

1

Introduction to the Ocean Environment

The oceans are a mysterious realm to most of us, a place of unfamiliar lifeforms and conditions hostile and even unimaginable for land-dwelling organisms such as ourselves. Yet oceans cover 71 percent of the planet's surface; and—if one considers the enormous volume of water contained in them as habitat—they contain 99 percent of the habitable space on Earth. Almost all phyla first appeared in the sea, and many continue to live only there.

To a person standing on land and looking out to sea, the ocean looks like a continuous, uniform water world that stretches miles and miles beyond the horizon. In truth, a multitude of different and complex habitats lie hidden in its vastness and each harbors life. A single ocean may contain several distinct water masses, separated one from the other by underwater mountain ranges, strong currents, and different water densities due to differences in temperature and salinity. The water column, an imaginary slice of water from sea surface to the ocean bottom, has distinct layers; and these play an important role in determining the availability of nutrients for the ocean's tiniest inhabitants. The marine environment changes with distance from the Equator (latitude), with distance from the edge of land, and with depth below sea level. It varies as light, salinity, temperature, pressure, currents, waves, tides, and nutrient input vary. These environmental conditions—other than temperature—are not major concerns in describing the land-based biomes we live in, so this first chapter discusses each and describes how each varies across distance, with depth, and/or from one time of year to the next according to latitude. It also introduces some of the forms of life found in the sea and some of the ways habitats and organisms are classified.

Five Oceans and the Seven Seas

Since 2000, five oceans are recognized. The newest, by decision of the International Hydrographic Organization, is the Southern Ocean surrounding Antarctica. It extends from the coast of that continent north to the 60° S parallel. Accordingly, it coincides with the limits of the Antarctic Region accepted internationally in the Antarctic Treaty, which manages resources and scientific research in that icy area owned by no single country. The four other traditionally recognized oceans are the Pacific, Atlantic, Indian, and Arctic oceans. The Pacific, the largest by far, covers nearly half (46 percent) of the planet.

Ancient peoples of the Mediterranean World spoke of "the Seven Seas." These were the bodies of saltwater that they knew: the Mediterranean itself, the Adriatic Sea, Black Sea, Caspian Sea, Red Sea, Persian Gulf, and Indian Ocean. Today the Caspian is considered a lake, though its waters are salty. Indeed, it is the world's largest lake. The distinction between sea and ocean is not absolute, and the two terms are often used interchangeably. However, in proper names, smaller bodies nearly enclosed by land are usually called seas and the great bodies of open water are called oceans. Connected to each other, the five oceans can also be thought of as a single world ocean.

The Oceans

Each of Earth's five oceans has distinct physical characteristics that influence the organisms that inhabit it. Some of the major features are described here.

Pacific Ocean

The world's largest ocean, the Pacific, with a surface area of 60,667,000 mi^2 (155,557,000 km^2), covers approximately 28 percent of Earth's surface, a greater area than all the landmasses combined and twice the size of the Atlantic Ocean. It includes the Bering Sea and Bering Strait, the Gulf of Alaska and Sea of Okhotsk, the Sea of Japan, East China Sea, South China Sea, Philippine Sea, Gulf of Tonkin, Coral Sea, and Tasman Sea.

The Pacific is essentially cut off from the Arctic Ocean, but it exchanges water with the cold Southern Ocean via the Antarctic Circumpolar Current. As a result, the clockwise gyre of the surface waters of the North Pacific is dominated by warm water, while the counterclockwise gyre south of the Equator is dominated by cool water. Sea ice covers the Bering Sea and Sea of Okhotsk in winter. Sea ice from Antarctica reaches its northernmost extent in October, but fails to reach the South Pacific.

The ocean floor in the eastern Pacific is dominated by the East Pacific Rise and a series of transverse fracture zones, whereas the western Pacific is cut by a number of deep oceanic trenches. The lowest point in the Pacific (−35,837 ft or −10,924 m) lies in Challenger Deep in the Mariana Trench. Indeed, this is the deepest part of Earth's entire crust. In 1960, in the deep-sea submersible *Trieste*, Jacques Piccard and Don Walsh saw flounder-like flatfish and shrimps living at the bottom of the trench.

Plate movements have been shrinking the Pacific Basin for some 165 million years. Although new seafloor is being created at the East Pacific Rise, along the margins of the ocean, plates are subducting. The result is not only oceanic trenches, but also frequent earthquakes and active volcanoes in the Pacific's "Rim of Fire." Several of the plates that make up the Pacific seafloor pass over hot spots in Earth's mantle, giving rise to chains of seamounts and volcanic islands such as the Hawaiian Islands and Galapagos Islands.

Covering such a large proportion of the planet's surface, the Pacific plays a major role in global climate patterns. The oceanic component of El Niño/La Niña phenomena, for example, occurs in the equatorial Pacific but affects weather worldwide.

Atlantic Ocean

The Atlantic is the second largest ocean, but with a surface area of 29,937,000 mi^2 (76,762,000 km^2), it is only half the size of the Pacific. Included in the Atlantic are the Baltic, Black, Mediterranean, North, and Norwegian Seas in the eastern North Atlantic; the Labrador Sea, Caribbean Sea, and Gulf of Mexico in the western North Atlantic; and the Drake Passage and most of the Scotia Sea in the South Atlantic. The clockwise, warm-water gyre in the Northern Hemisphere is dominated by the warm western boundary current, the Gulf Stream, and its northeastward extension, the North Atlantic Drift. Some of this water penetrates into the Arctic Ocean, but most circulates within the gyre to form the eastern boundary current, the cool-water Canary Current. In the smaller basin of the South Atlantic, the western boundary current of the South Atlantic gyre is the weak warm Brazilian Current, while the cold Benguela current—drawing water from the Antarctic Circumpolar Current—forms the eastern boundary current.

In the north, sea ice may cover the Labrador Sea and coastal parts of the Baltic from October to June. In the south, sea ice extends from Antarctica north to about 55° S latitude, well within the bounds of the South Atlantic.

The seafloor of the entire Atlantic basin is split by the Mid-Atlantic Ridge, the center of active seafloor spreading. The ridge rises above sea level to form Iceland. The deepest point in the basin, some 28,233 ft (8,605 m) below sea level is in the Milwaukee Deep in the Puerto Rico Trench, where the Caribbean Plate is subducting beneath the Atlantic Plate.

Indian Ocean

The Indian Ocean covers about 26,737,000 mi^2 (68,556,000 km^2) of Earth's surface and is third largest in size, but nonetheless covers a greater surface area than the planet's largest continent, Eurasia. It includes the Red Sea and Gulf of Aden, Persian Gulf and Gulf of Oman, the Arabian Sea; Bay of Bengal, Andaman Sea, and Strait of Malacca; Java Sea, Timor Sea, and Great Australian Bight; and the Mozambique Channel. North of the Equator, ocean currents are complicated by the changing winds of the Asian monsoon, which results in a unique seasonal reversal in the direction the ocean currents flow. From December to April, the northeasterly winter monsoon blows surface waters to the southwest; in summer (June to October), a southwesterly flow of air pushes surface currents to the northeast.

South of the Equator, the South Indian Gyre moves in a counterclockwise direction throughout the year.

The seafloor of the Indian Ocean is divided by three mid-oceanic ridges (Mid-Indian Ridge, Southeast Indian Ridge, and Southwest Indian Ridge), which merge to form a more or less Y-shaped undersea mountain range. Another interesting rise is Ninetyeast Ridge, which traces the path the Indian edge of the Indo-Australian Plate took over a hot spot before India docked to the Eurasian continent some 50–55 million years ago. The lowest part of the Indian Ocean Basin lies 23,377 ft (7,125 m) below sea level in the Java Trench, where the Australian Plate—now apparently moving independently of a separate Indian Plate—is subducting beneath the Eurasian Plate. Plate movement in this zone was responsible for the great Indian Ocean tsunami of December 2004.

Southern Ocean

Encircling the continent of Antarctica, the Southern Ocean links the Pacific, Atlantic, and Indian oceans. Its equatorward or northern limits have been set at 60° S latitude by international convention. With a surface area of roughly 7,927,500 mi^2 (20,327,000 km^2), it is the world's fourth-largest ocean. Circulation is dominated by the world's strongest ocean current, the Antarctic Circumpolar Current, also known as the Westwind Drift, which is driven by some of the strongest and steadiest winds on Earth. The Southern Hemisphere's mid-latitude Prevailing Westerlies blow uninterrupted by major landmasses. During the heyday of the tallships, sailors named these southern latitudes the "Roaring Forties," Furious Fifties," and "Screaming Sixties." The winds force water at a rate of 4.8 million ft^3/sec (135,000 m^3/sec) through the Drake Passage between the southern tip of South America and Antarctica.

Sea surface temperatures (SST) in the Southern Ocean range from 50° F (10° C) to 28° F (−2° C). In winter the surface freezes from the coast of Antarctica northward to 65° S just south of the Pacific Ocean but into the Atlantic Ocean to 55° S. The size of the ice pack increases sixfold between March, when it covers more than 1 million mi^2 (2,600,000 km^2), and September, when its covers more than 7 million mi^2 (18,800,000 km^2), an area nearly twice the size of Europe. In addition to sea ice, ice shelves—the floating edges of glaciers, occur along 44 percent of Antarctica's coastline. Their landward margins are anchored to the shore and also attached to the seafloor. The front part of ice shelves, however, floats and rises and falls with the tides. Cracks develop and large icebergs calve off. The thickness of the floating ice ranges from 330–3,300 ft (100–1,000 m); about 90 percent of this mass lies below water. Ross Ice Shelf, about the size of Spain, extends 190,000 mi^2 (500,000 km^2) over the Ross Sea and is the largest. The Ronne Filchner Ice Shelf on the Weddell Sea is a bit smaller at 160,000 mi^2 (430,000 km^2). The ice of the shelves melts and evaporates at the top but new ice forms on the underside. The sea beneath the shelves is just beginning to be explored, so what lives there is still mostly unknown.

The Southern Ocean Basin is a single geological structure edged by rift zones from whence the other plates dispersed with the breakup of Gondwana. Depths are generally 13,000–16,000 ft (4,000–5,000 m) below sea level. The Antarctic continental shelf is unusually deep; the weight of the Antarctic ice cap depresses much of the continent's bedrock surface well below sea level. Water depth on the shelf varies from 1,300–2,600 ft (400–800 m), whereas on other continents, the average depth of the shelf areas is about 435 ft (133 m).

Arctic Ocean

The Arctic measures about 5,482,000 mi^2 (14,056,000 km^2)—almost the same size as Antarctica on the opposite side of the Earth—and is the smallest ocean. Mostly north of the Arctic Circle (66.5° N latitude), it is almost entirely enclosed by land. Included in this ocean are the Greenland Sea, Baffin Bay, Hudson Bay, Hudson Strait, and Beaufort Sea on the North American side; and the Chukchi, East Siberian, Laptev, Kara, and Barents seas on the Eurasian side. In some ways, the Arctic can be considered an extension of the Atlantic Ocean, with which it exchanges 80 percent of its water. The other 20 percent comes through the narrow Northwest Passage, which connects it to the Pacific.

Two surface currents dominate the ocean. The Beaufort Gyre moves clockwise north of Alaska over the Canada Basin. The Transpolar Current moves more or less along the 180th meridian in the Chucki Sea past the North Pole and into the Greenland Sea. It is influenced by the huge amounts of freshwater that in spring and summer flow out of the great rivers of Siberia and float on the surface of the sea.

At intermediate depth, relatively warm saline water enters the Arctic Ocean from the Atlantic. As it cools and ice forms, the water becomes saltier and denser and moves as a deep sea current back out of the Arctic and into the Atlantic. This bottom current is an important part of global deep sea circulation.

The Arctic Ocean is covered in winter by a drifting ice pack that until recently was some 10 ft (3 m) thick. The polar ice is surrounded by open water in summer, when it is less than half its winter size. It moves slowly in a clockwise direction within the Beaufort Gyre. One complete circling of the pole takes about four years. Under today's changing climate, the ice is thinning and shrinking, and predictions are that none will be left by the end of this century.

Life in the Ice

Pack ice is usually brown. It is only the fresh snow on top that is white. The color comes from all the bacteria, diatoms, flagellates, foraminiferans, flatworms, and copepods living in the ice. In the Arctic, they are joined by abundant rotifers and nematodes. In the Antarctic, turbellarians are common members of the ice community. These tiny organisms are caught between ice crystals or are trapped in brine channels. Their concentrations are actually greater than in the surrounding seawater.

Photosynthesis takes place in the top 6 ft (2 m) of the ice, where diatoms adapted to low light levels abound. Dissolved organic matter (DOM) accumulates in pools to enter microbial food chains. The single-celled ice-bound animals graze the bacteria, diatoms, and flagellates, while pelagic animals—amphipods, copepods, krill, and ice fish—come to feed at the edges of the pack ice or in cracks and crevices or where the ice is melting. Many of the ocean species have tailored their seasonal patterns and even life histories to the pack ice's annual rhythms.

Melting of the Arctic Ocean Sea Ice

Change is coming rapidly to the Arctic. Summer 2007 saw the surface area of Arctic Ocean sea ice at its lowest point since modern climatic patterns were established. Only 2.4 million mi^2 (4 million km^2) remained, down 23 percent from the previous low recorded just two years earlier. Not only is the area of the ice cap shrinking, but its thickness is also diminishing. The total volume of summer ice in 2007 was 50 percent less than in 2004.

Ice reflects sunlight back to space, so a large ice cover kept polar air temperatures stable. But open water absorbs summer sunlight and converts it to heat energy, warming the air above. The more water to collect heat, the faster the ice pack melts. Arctic surface temperatures have risen by 3.6° F (2° C) in the past 100 years, twice the global average.

Warming of the Arctic affects wildlife and humans. Marine mammals such as walruses and ringed seals lose their habitats. Walruses, which once stayed on the sea ice much of the summer, now crowd onto Russian shores of the Bering Strait. (Ringed seals, totally aquatic animals, do not have this option.) Startled by polar bears—themselves endangered by the loss of summer sea ice—or low-flying aircraft, walruses stampede back into the sea, often with deadly consequences. Several thousand mostly young animals were reportedly crushed in one event alone.

Native peoples living on Arctic coasts depend on being able to venture onto the ice with dog sleds and snowmobiles to hunt marine mammals. Their ways of life will disappear. For nations, open water means new sea lanes (the long sought Northwest Passage was actually ice free in October 2007) and new fishing grounds and access to the oil and gas beneath the Arctic seafloor. The scramble is on to establish ownership of this once-closed-off seabed. Such economic considerations combined with worries about the defense of newly open coastlines create political dilemmas for countries surrounding the ocean.

Fifty percent of the seafloor of the Arctic Ocean is continental shelf. On the Asian side of the basin, the shelf is unusually wide, extending in places some 1,000 mi (1,600 km) beyond the shoreline. On the North American side, the shelf is narrow, like most continental shelf areas in the world, and ranges from 30 to 75 mi (30–125 km) wide. The central basin of the seafloor is divided into four smaller basins by three undersea ridges. The Lomonosov Ridge passes close to the North Pole as it runs between Asia and Greenland and cuts the ocean basin in half. Alpha Cordillera lies west of the Lomonosov Ridge, separating the Makarov Basin from the larger Canada Basin; and the Nansen or Gakkel Ridge lies to the east, separating the Fram and Nansen basins. The geographic North Pole lies at a depth of 13,000 ft (3,962 m) below sea level at the eastern edge of the Fram Basin. In contrast, the South Pole is 9,300 ft (2,835 m) above sea level atop the Antarctic ice cap. Numerous smaller basins exist between Scandanavia and Greenland.

Life Zones of the Ocean

The physical and biological features of the seas have clear horizontal and vertical patterns. The horizontal (distance from shore) pattern results largely from the geological structure of continents and ocean basins, including the precipitous change in the depth of the ocean at the geologic edge of continents (see Figure 1.1). A coastal zone exists wherever tides continually alter sea level and the sea bottom is exposed to the air for some period of time each day. Life in this zone must be able to deal with a habitat that is alternately flooded with saltwater and waterlogged for hours of time and then exposed and dried out for hours. Since differences between high-tide and low-tide water levels include fluctuations in temperature, salinity, food availability, and shelter, organisms living in this zone have to tolerate a broad range of environmental conditions or be able to move and avoid those conditions that could prove lethal. Other terms applied to this zone include littoral, nearshore, and intertidal. (See Chapter 2 for more information.)

Beyond the low-tide mark, the rest of the marine habitat is the open water of the pelagic zone. Within this vast region, the waters overlying continental shelves—the gently sloping margins of landmasses—make up the neritic zone. Here the sea bottom is no more than about 600 ft (200 m) below the surface, and sunlight is able to penetrate the entire water column. The edges of continents plunge steeply and abruptly to the true geological ocean floor as the continental slope. Water depths now greatly exceed the level to which sunlight reaches and new sets of environmental conditions become established in what is known as the oceanic zone. Darkness and tremendous pressure are dominant factors for life existing beneath the surface waters, and life zones based on depth become important.

Vertical life zones in the open sea or oceanic zone appear in Table 1.1 and Figure 1.1. The surface of the water itself makes up the neustic zone. Floating or "skating" organisms inhabit this thin film or "skin." In the tropics, especially, this can be a severe environment because of the high levels of ultraviolet (UV) radiation received with the

Who Owns the Ocean?

The notion of freedom of the seas, that the ocean belongs to all nations, held sway from the 1600s to the mid-twentieth century. Coastal countries claimed territorial rights 3 mi (4.8 km) offshore, the reach of land-based cannons. After World War II, territorial claims expanded to protect fisheries and oil and gas reserves on the continental shelf. The United States and others set new limits 12 nautical miles (nm) from shore. Chile, Ecuador, and Peru extended their control 200 nm (230 mi or 370 km) to safeguard fisheries in the Humboldt Current. By the early 1980s most countries had followed suit and established Exclusive Economic Zones (EEZ) 200 nm wide.

The United Nations Convention on the Law of the Sea recognized the 200 nm limit and gave coastal countries the sole right to exploit natural resources in those waters. Foreign nations maintained the right to pass through or fly over. Territorial waters, in which a country establishes laws and regulations on use and itself has the sole right to use any resource, was set at 12 nm. Landlocked countries retained the right to pass through coastal waters. The Law of the Sea became a reality in 1994, when Guyana became the sixtieth country to ratify the treaty. To date, 155 countries have joined as signatories. The United States has yet to ratify it.

One provision of the Law of the Sea allows claims up to 100 nm farther out to sea if the continental shelf extends beyond the EEZ border. Outside the EEZ, a state has the sole right to take nonliving materials from the shelf. Thus, Russia claims that Lomonosov Ridge is part of their continental shelf, so they may have rights to oil and gas under a large part of the Arctic seafloor. With access to these reserves now possible, the United States is reconsidering its stand on the Law of the Sea.

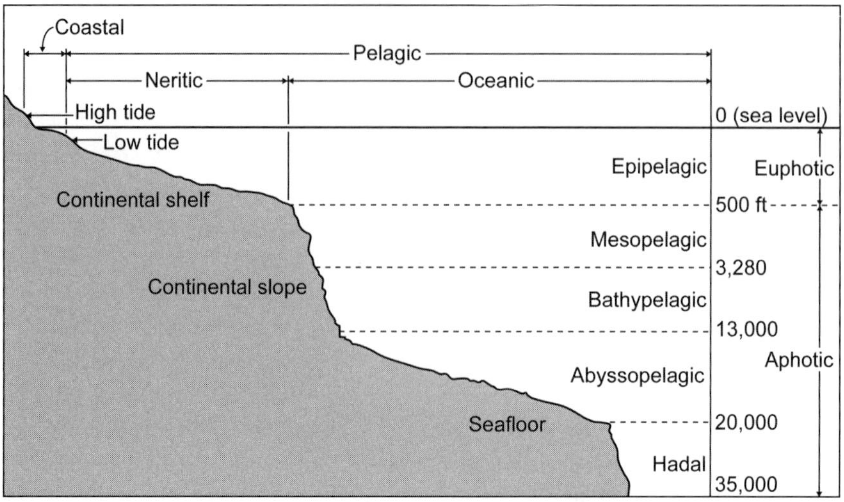

Figure 1.1 Life zones of the ocean environment. *(Illustration by Jeff Dixon. Adapted from Kaiser et al. 2005.)*

vertical rays of the sun. Many of its inhabitants are blue from pigments they contain to reflect the harmful UV rays. Immediately below the surface is the epipelagic zone, which extends to depths where there is still enough light for photosynthesis to take place. For this reason it is commonly referred to as the euphotic zone ("good light"). Beneath the euphotic zone are the several zones of the ocean deep. Here, except for chemosynthetic microorganisms, living organisms are either scavengers feeding on a rain of organic detritus from above, or consumers feeding on sinking photosynthetic algae and bacteria or on the vast array of invertebrates and vertebrates that inhabit the ocean deep.

In all the life zones just mentioned, except for the neustic zone, organisms drift or swim in the water column itself. A major distinction occurs between the habitats of the open water and those of the substrate, the benthic zone, where life burrows into or crawls upon the bottom materials.

Table 1.1 Oceanic Depth Zones

	Depth (feet)	Depth (meters)
Neustic zone	The surface film	The surface film
Epipelagic Zone (= Euphotic zone)	0–500 ft	0–150 m
Mesopelagic Zone	500–3,280 ft	150–1,000 m
Bathypelagic	3,280–13,000 ft	1,000–4,000 m
Abyssopelagic Zone	13,000–20,000 ft	4,000–6,000 m
Hadal Zone	20,000–35,000 ft	6,000–10,000 m

Major Environmental Factors in Marine Biomes

Light

Almost all food chains in the ocean begin with microscopic, single-celled organisms that photosynthesize. They combine water and carbon dioxide in the presence of chlorophyll (or other light-absorbing pigments) and sunlight to produce organic compounds and a store of chemical (metabolic) energy that they use for their own life functions and reproduction. When consumed, they pass the chemical energy on to the animals in the food chain. Changes in light intensity and duration (photoperiod) affect primary production and influence algal blooms. Light, or lack thereof, determines the daily and seasonal vertical migration patterns of the plankton. And light affects visibility in terms of both seeing and being seen.

Sunlight is able to penetrate water since it is transparent, but there are limits to just how deep different wavelengths can go. Solid particles and dissolved ions in the water—often the very nutrients that the photosynthesizing cells need—absorb and scatter visible light. The longest wavelengths (at the red end of the light spectrum) are absorbed first, near the surface, so that red and orange light is no longer available below the top 50 ft (15 m) of the water column. Most other wavelengths are absorbed within the next 130 feet (40 m). The short blue and violet wavelengths penetrate the deepest and make the ocean look blue on a sunny day.

The depth to which any light reaches depends on the clarity of the water. In the waters of the open ocean, where particulates are few, sufficient light for some photosynthesis to occur can reach depths of 325–650 ft (100–200 m). In the clearest coastal waters, free of most particulates (and hence nutrients), only 10 percent of the light received at the surface will be left 160 ft (50 m) below the surface. In nutrient-rich and therefore more murky waters, the 10 percent level may be reached at a depth of about 30 ft (10 m).

A significant threshold for the algae and cyanobacteria absorbing sunlight is reached at the point at which only 1 percent of the light reaching the surface remains. At this low light level, photosynthetic organisms can fix only enough energy to support their own needs. Nothing is left over for growth or reproduction. The depth at which this occurs is known as the compensation level, and it marks the bottom of the uppermost layer in the water column, the euphotic zone. In general, this level occurs at about 650 ft (200 m). Below the euphotic zone, many organisms bioluminesce; that is, they produce their own light.

The euphotic zone is the shallow uppermost layer of the ocean in which there is enough light for most photosynthesizing organisms—those that almost all other creatures depend on—to survive and reproduce. Ninety-five percent of ocean habitat lies below the euphotic zone. Some short wavelengths of light do extend deeper. Five hundred feet down, in very clear water, 0.1 percent of the original light striking the seas surface is left. One hundred and fifty feet deeper and only 0.01 percent remains. Divers and true marine animals can still perceive the light when looking skyward at depths up to 2,600 ft (800 m). Until a depth of about 800 ft (250 m),

Figure 1.2 Snell's circle allows marine organisms to track the position of the sun and navigate at depths as great as 800 ft below the surface. *(Photo © Dennis Sabo/Shutterstock.)*

they can see a bright circle of light called Snell's circle or Snell's window (see Figure 1.2) and use it to track the position of the sun in the sky and thereby navigate in the deep.

Below approximately 3,000 ft (1,000 m) there is no light. Since most oceanic habitat lies at depths near 13,000 ft (4,000 m), darkness is a major environmental factor and well-lit waters are an exception. The euphotic zone is a very different habitat than the waters beneath it. Not only does it receive light from the sun, but that light is converted to heat energy when it is absorbed, warming the zone. (See section on temperature below.) Since warm water is less dense than colder water, the surface layer floats on top of the sea and resists mixing with deeper water.

Pressure

At sea level, the weight of the air above exerts 14.7 lbs/in^2 (1 kg/cm^2) of pressure on surface objects. This pressure is known as 1 atmosphere. In the ocean, pressure increases by 1 atmosphere for every 33 ft (10 m) increase in depth because of the added weight of the overlying water. This fact limits the depth to which divers can go and requires special construction of manned and unmanned submersible vehicles. On the deep seafloor, pressure may be more than 500 atmospheres, and it is even greater in the depths of oceanic trenches. Surprisingly, there are forms of life well adapted to withstand such pressure. Sea mammals such as whales and sea elephants may dive down 1,000 or 2,000 ft (600 m) or more, displaying an amazing ability to withstand tremendous and rapid changes in pressure. Other forms of life spend their entire lives at great depths and pressures and have proven difficult to collect and study because they cannot withstand great or rapid pressure decreases.

High pressure compresses the gases in their blood and stomachs, and when they are brought to the surface, they seem to explode into a gory, gooey mess of popped eyes and extruded stomachs when these gases expand.

Oceans as Carbon Sink

The mechanisms by which CO_2, a major greenhouse gas, is absorbed and stored in the oceans and the quantities involved are still being studied. Many organisms, from phytoplankters (especially the algae known as coccolithophorids) to corals to molluscs, combine carbon with calcium to form their exoskeletons. Upon the death of the organisms, these exoskeletons precipitate to the seafloor, where they may accumulate as sediments that act as long-term pools of carbon and could represent the removal of excess carbon from the atmosphere (where it occurs as CO_2). However, the chemical reaction that produces the calcium carbonate of which the exoskeletons are composed actually releases CO_2 and is sensitive to pH, so it may not be as significant or reliable in removing excess CO_2 from the atmosphere as first thought.

Gases Dissolved in Seawater

The gases essential for life—oxygen (O_2), carbon dioxide (CO_2), and nitrogen (N_2)—are dissolved in seawater. Amounts of oxygen and carbon dioxide vary in accordance with the activities of living organisms, since they are involved in photosynthesis and respiration. At the surface, in contact with the atmosphere, water is able to dissolve significant amounts of oxygen. The colder the water, the more dissolved oxygen it can hold. Cold, oxygenated water is dense and moves downward in currents to the ocean bottom. Therefore, unlike the situation in many lakes, the bottom waters of oceans are usually well oxygenated. However, intermediate waters—at depths between 300 ft (100 m) and 3,300 ft (1,000 m) and isolated from surface and deep waters—contain the least amount of dissolved oxygen, a condition that can limit life in that zone.

Carbon dioxide levels may be lowered in the euphotic zone because it is absorbed by photosynthetic algae and bacteria. The highest levels are therefore at depth. The ocean's ability to take carbon dioxide from the atmosphere plays a role in global climate and is of major concern to those trying to understand and predict future climate change.

Nitrogen gas is not the form of nitrogen utilized by most forms of life. Instead, as on land, most plants assimilate nitrate (NO^{-3}), which must be fixed by microorganisms. Nitrogen is thus a major limiting factor in the marine environment (see below under "Nutrients").

Water

Water, of course, is the main component of the marine environment. The unique properties of water, however, make it more than just a passive medium in which life floats or swims. Water molecules are made up one atom of oxygen sharing the electrons of two atoms of hydrogen. The larger oxygen atom pulls the hydrogen atoms' electrons toward it, leaving the hydrogen part of the asymmetrical water molecule slightly positive in charge and giving the oxygen part a slight negative charge. The result is an attraction of water molecules for each other and the formation of hydrogen bonds that link them together. The attractive force of hydrogen bonds causes the surface tension that permits a neustic zone to occur. It also results in a high specific heat or high heat capacity. In chemistry, specific heat is a measure of the amount of heat energy required to raise the temperature of 1 cc of a substance 1° C. Temperature is a measure of the average movement or vibration of the molecules making up a substance. The hydrogen bonds between water molecules hold them together and make it difficult for movement to happen. Much heat must first be used to weaken or break the bonds (this is latent or undetectable heat) and allow vibrations to increase before a rise in temperature (felt as sensible heat) can occur. As a result, water warms (and cools) more slowly that an equivalent area of land at the same latitude. Water holds or stores the latent heat as ocean currents move, so this heat is transported around the Earth and only slowly is given off as sensible heat to warm the atmosphere above. Transferring heat from equatorial regions toward the poles, the oceans moderate temperatures around the globe. The effect is most keenly felt near coasts.

The strength of hydrogen bonds and the heat energy required to break them lets water exists in three phases or states on Earth: ice, liquid water, and gaseous water vapor. In ice, the water molecules are rigidly bond together in a hexagonal crystalline lattice. The space at the center of each hexagon makes ice slightly less dense than water, so that ice floats at the surface of the seas. In liquid water—or simply water, some of the bonds are weakened or broken so that the molecules clump together in tight groups. In the gas phase, the bonds are completely gone and individual molecules of water float free. Evaporation involves removing sensible heat from water or air to add enough latent heat to break the bonds and form water vapor. Evaporation is thus a major cooling process both on land and in the sea.

Another impact of the existence of negative and positive poles on the water molecule is the ability of water to dissolve a large number of other compounds. Solution means that molecules are disassociated or broken into their component ions, as each part is attracted to the opposite charge on a water molecule. Ions of many substances make up the major nutrients of the primary producers in the sea, the first step in marine food webs.

Nutrients

Photosynthesizing organisms, in addition to light, require many nutrients. These include the macronutrients carbon, nitrogen, phosphorus, silica, sulfur, potassium, and sodium. Traces of other elements, so-called micronutrients, are also essential. Among these micronutrients are iron, zinc, copper, manganese, and certain vitamins. Nitrogen and phosphorus, when they become depleted in surface waters, are usually the nutrients that curtail algal growth. In some places, however, a lack of dissolved iron may lower or prevent the take up of nitrogen and phosphorus even when they are abundant. Such appears to be the case in the subarctic Pacific, equatorial Pacific, and Southern Ocean. Though rich in essential macronutrients, these bodies of water are deserts in terms of algal growth. Iron dissolved in seawater originates on land and is transported to the sea as runoff or as windblown dust. The lowest levels of atmospheric dust deposition in the world occur in the Southern Ocean and the vast equatorial Pacific, both far removed from land sources. The tropical Atlantic, on the other hand, receives much iron from dust storms blowing out of the Sahara.

Carbon, the key element in life processes, is never in short supply. Inorganic carbon is transformed to organic carbon during photosynthesis as plants fix energy to fuel life and create complex molecules to build living structures. The familiar, simplified equation of photosynthesis shows the key role of carbon and its transformation from simple inorganic forms to complex organic compounds:

$$6CO_2 + 6H_2O + \text{light energy} \rightarrow 6O_2 + C_6H_{12}O_6$$

Dissolved inorganic carbon occurs in four forms: as carbon dioxide gas (CO_2), as carbonic acid (H_2CO_3), as bicarbonate ions (HCO_3^{-1}), and as carbonate ions (CO_3^{-2}). In average seawater with a salinity of 35 and pH between 8.1 and 8.3, 90 percent of inorganic carbon is held in bicarbonate ions. Carbon dioxide is the main ingredient in photosynthesis, but it occurs in very small amounts in seawater. Many algae therefore supplement the carbon dioxide they take up by converting the abundant bicarbonate ions to carbon dioxide. This is accomplished by special enzymes in the cells or on their outer surfaces. It is unknown which pathway—the direct use of carbon dioxide or the indirect route from bicarbonate—is most frequently employed.

Nitrogen, the most common limiting factor in algal growth, is present in seawater in inorganic form as dissolved nitrogen gas (N_2) and ions of ammonium (NH_4^{+1}), nitrite (NO_2^{-1}), and nitrate (NO_3^{-1}) and in organic compounds such as urea and amino acids. In average seawater, 95 percent of the nitrogen occurs as ammonium. Nitrate, however, is the main form taken up by algae, which then convert it to ammonium by enzymes in the cells. Some cyanobacteria can assimilate nitrogen gas directly, and they are most abundant where other forms of dissolved nitrogen are scarce. In the coastal biome, seagrasses and saltmarsh grasses have nitrogen-fixing bacteria in or on their roots, and free-living cyanobacteria dwell in soft shore sediments.

Phosphorus is the second most common limiting factor for algal growth. Phosphorus occurs in inorganic form as free phosphate ions (HPO_4^{-2}, PO_4^{-3}, and $H_2PO_4^{-1}$), as well as in organic phosphates. The last can be broken down in the cells of many algae to release the needed phosphorus.

Sulfur is rarely limiting, since sulfate (SO_4^{-2}) is extremely abundant in seawater. Sulfur is essential for the production of amino acids and proteins.

Temperature

Water temperature varies with depth and with latitude. Infrared wavelengths (heat energy) of solar energy are absorbed in the top 3 ft (1 m) of the sea. Waves mix this warmed layer with the water immediately below it and distribute the heat to depths

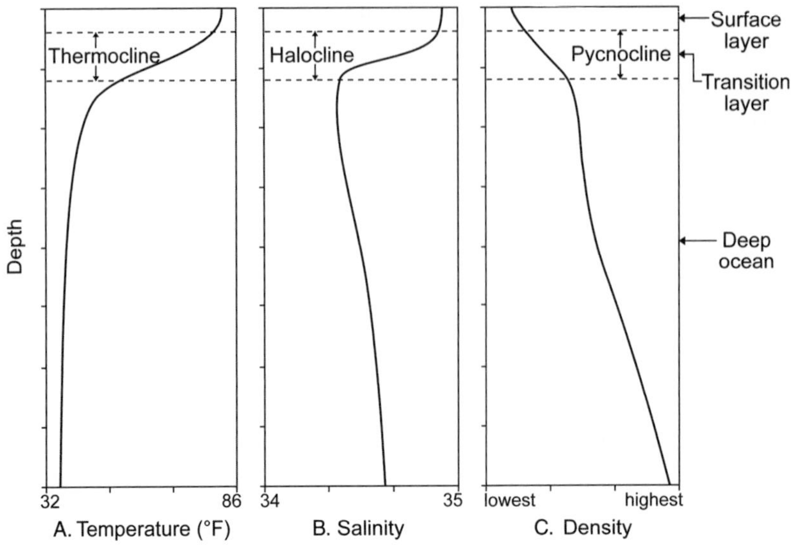

Figure 1.3 Layers form in the ocean as a result of differences in water temperature, salinity, and density. The transition zone between surface waters and the deep is a region where rapid changes occur: (a) The thermocline marks the depth at which temperature changes; (b) the halocline marks the depth at which salinity changes; (c) the pycnocline marks the depths at which water density changes. *(Illustration by Jeff Dixon.)*

of 30 ft (10 m) or more. The layer of mixed water constitutes the surface zone and the temperature is the same throughout it. Underneath the surface zone is a transition layer in which temperatures rapidly decrease with depth. This is the thermocline. Beneath the thermocline is the deep zone, where temperature changes only very slightly with greater depth (see Figure 1.3a). In most of the deep zone, the temperature stays at 37° F (3° C) all year long. The coldest waters are near the seafloor and are between 33° and 35.5° F (0.5° to 2.0° C). Due to its salt content, seawater does not freeze until 28.5° F (−1.9°C). Nearing freezing, water density suddenly decreases and the coldest water rises toward the surface. Ice forms at the surface in polar seas, not at depth.

SSTs are primarily a consequence of latitude. In polar regions water will be close to freezing or 28.5° F (−1.9° C), while in tropical seas surface waters will commonly reach 79°–86° F (26°–30° C). Some of the highest temperatures (95° F or 35° C) occur in the shallow waters of the Persian Gulf. Due to the peculiar chemistry of water, the oceans can absorb much heat energy without a change in water temperature and can store that heat over long periods of time. Thus, there is little change in surface-water temperature between day and night, and what does occur is limited to the uppermost part of the surface layer. In shallow coastal waters, the daily range of temperature may be about 5.5° F (3.0° C), but in the open sea it is a mere 0.5° F (0.3° C).

Salinity

The amount of dissolved material (salts) in seawater is measured as salinity. Average salinity of the ocean is 35 grams per liter (g/L) or 35 parts per thousand (ppt). In other words, on average, 96.5 percent of seawater is water and 3.5 percent is dissolved matter. Salinity is now often recorded in practical salinity units (psu). Average salinity is simply written as 35. Dissolved salts occur as electrically charged particles or ions. Most ions (55.3 percent) are chlorine (Cl^{-1}); sodium (Na^{+1}) is the second most abundant ion (30.8 percent). All elements occur in at least trace amounts.

Salinity varies across the oceans in relation to precipitation amounts (high amounts lower salinity), discharge from rivers (again, high amounts of freshwater entering the ocean lower the salinity of the sea), and evaporation (high rates, typical year-round in the tropics and during summer in the mid-latitudes, increase salinity). In polar regions, ice formation increases salinity, since only the water freezes. The salinity of surface waters changes from season to season as temperature (which affects evaporation rates) and rainfall amounts change and as snow melts. At depth, however, salinity remains pretty much the same all year. There is an observable transition zone in terms of salinity between surface waters and the deep that is called the halocline (see Figure 1.3b).

Density

Both temperature and salinity affect the density of a particular mass of water. Warmer water is less dense than cooler water and will float on top of it. Freshwater is less dense than salty (high salinity) water and will sit on the surface. Differences in density can develop, especially seasonally, that prevent the mixing of surface water and deeper water. Usually a transition zone occurs between the surface layer and the deep in which density changes rapidly. Called the pycnocline, this zone serves as a strong barrier to the exchange of nutrients between the euphotic zone occupied by the producers (algae and cyanobacteria) and deeper waters below (see Figure 1.3c), but it also helps prevent the phytoplankton from sinking below the sunlit surface waters.

Particles in water have a tendency to sink. When inorganic and organic particles settle out of the euphotic zone, they are lost to the photosynthesizing organisms that would convert them to the food used by animals living in that layer. Mixing of the layers and upwelling will return sunken particles to the surface. Under warm, calm conditions, surface water becomes lower in density and resists mixing and thus can quickly become depleted of essential nutrients. This is a year-round condition in the tropics and a common summer phenomenon in the middle latitudes. Separate stable layers develop and the water column becomes stratified. Only some physical or mechanical process will bring denser water—and the nutrients that have been sinking into it—up from below (see Figure 1.4). Storms accomplish this, as does upwelling. The temperature changes brought on by autumn and winter in the middle latitudes will break down the stratification, and wind and

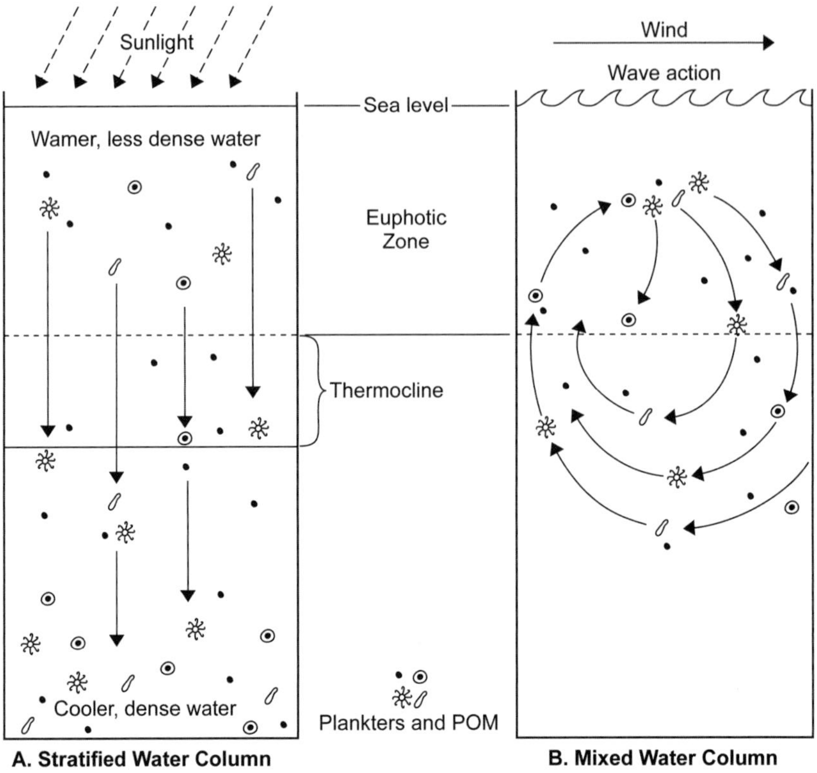

Figure 1.4 (a) Stable layers (stratification of the water column) develop when surface waters are warmed and become less dense than the water below. Stratification makes the upward return of particles settling out of the euphotic layer impossible and can lead to nutrient-poor conditions. (b) The water column can be mixed by the action of wind and waves. Mixing breaks down the stratification and allows nutrients and phytoplankters to recycle back to the well-lighted zone near the surface. *(Illustration by Jeff Dixon.)*

waves will mix the layers. In warm tropical waters, however, there is no great seasonal temperature change, and the seas may stay stratified all year. The surface waters therefore are often depleted of nutrients by the phytoplankton, keeping their numbers low and resulting in relatively sparse marine life.

Waves

Winds roil the surface of the sea and make waves. A wave is actually energy moving through the water from sea to shore. The water molecules themselves only move up and down in clockwise circular orbits (see Figure 1.5). The circling water transfers energy to underlying molecules setting them into orbits of their own. Each orbit lower down in the chain has less energy and a smaller diameter than the one directly above. At the bottom of the chain of orbits, at a depth 1.2 times the wave

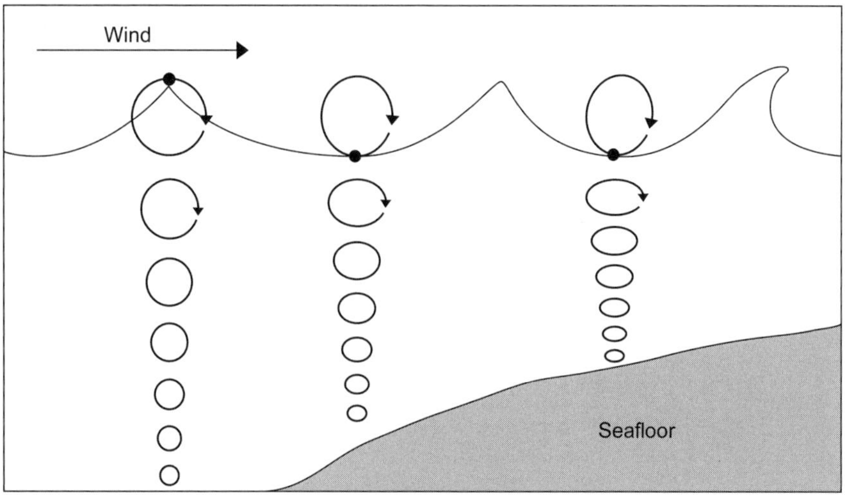

Figure 1.5 Wave motion involves the circulation of water molecules in ever smaller circular orbits between the surface and deeper waters. In deep water, no forward movement occurs in the water itself, only in the wave form. In shallow water, the orbits become deformed into ellipses and waves steepen and become unstable, eventually collapsing forward as breakers. *(Illustration by Jeff Dixon.)*

height, no energy is left. Any deeper water or seabed is beyond the action of the waves and, by definition, beyond the coast.

When orbiting water molecules do contact the bottom in shallow water, they stir up sediments. Smaller particles will become suspended in the water column and enrich the nutrient supply for the phytoplankton. Together with the shallowness of the water, which allows light to penetrate to the seabed, wave action is a major reason for the normally high primary productivity in the coast biome.

As a wave moves into shallow water, there may not be enough depth for a series of circular orbits to develop. The orbit shape changes to elliptical (see Figure 1.5) and the energy builds up into steeper and steeper waves. In the lowest orbits, water molecules are essentially moving back and forth and friction at the seabed causes the deeper water to slow. The crest of the wave gets ahead of the base, spills over, and breaks. Breakers form and create a surf zone on their landward side. The wave's remaining energy raises the water level and thrusts water onto a beach or against a headland. As the water rushes to shore, it picks up sands and other sediments that act like sandpaper and scrape against rocks and shells and any other solid materials over which they pass.

Wave crests, although they approach the coast parallel to shore, usually become bent as lower orbits come into contact with the sea bottom. Their shape will reflect the contours of the seabed. This bending or refraction of the wave crest focuses a wave's energy on protruding headlands and reduces it in bays or coves (see Figure 1.6). The headlands become places where erosion creates steep cliffs,

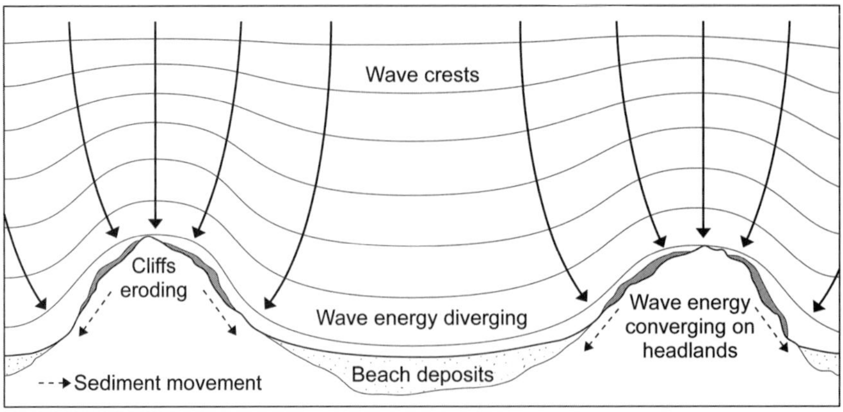

Figure 1.6 Wave crests bend as they approach a headland. Energy is concentrated at the headland, creating an environment of high surf and erosion. Energy dissipates away from a headland, creating an environment of diminished wave action and deposition. *(Illustration by Jeff Dixon.)*

while neighboring inlets are places of deposition and low-sloping sandy beaches. Two distinct habitats are created side-by-side.

Wave-cut platforms. As a headland or rock cliff wears back, a horizontal rock surface is left in its place (see Figure 1.7). Also called wave-cut terraces, marine terraces, and rock benches, these features are often exposed at low tide. Wave action first cuts a long notch at the base of a cliff where the force of waves is concentrated. Breakers pummel the shore with sediments and abrade it, and changes in hydraulic pressure as waves crash against the headland and then recede blast away at weak points. Deep notches expand to become sea caves on both sides of the headland. Eventually the caves converge and create arches. When the arch collapses, a flat surface sometimes punctuated with sea stacks results. The sea stacks are pinnacles of rock, the final remnants of the arch. Some platforms may be covered with sediments eroded from the shore, but many of these materials will be removed by storm waves. Wave-cut platforms and the landforms that precede them provide numerous coastal habitats for benthic sea life.

Tides

Tides are created by the gravitational pull of the moon and sun on the oceans. The moon, being so much closer to Earth than the sun, exerts the greater gravitational pull on the oceans and plays the leading role in determining the timing and height of tides. The Earth and moon rotate around the same center point. Any place on the surface of either body has two forces acting upon it. Centrifugal force pulls away from the center point; gravitational force pulls toward the other body. Thus the oceans on the side of Earth facing the moon bulge toward it, while those on the

Figure 1.7 The solid rock bench exposed at low tide here in the Galapagos Islands is a wave-cut terrace. A masked booby rests after foraging at sea. *(Photo by author.)*

opposite side feel less effect of the moon's gravitational pull and more of the pull of centrifugal force, so bulge away from the planet's surface (see Figure 1.8). One can think of Earth rotating through these two areas of high tide each day to cause a continuous change in local water levels, the ebb and flow of tides experienced on most coasts.

The largest tidal ranges at a given site occur at full moon and new moon. These are called spring tides, although they occur in all seasons. During spring tides,

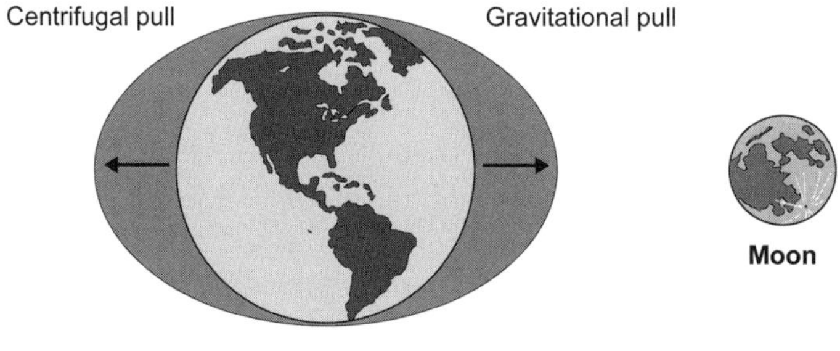

Figure 1.8 Tides are generated primarily by the moon. Gravity pulls ocean water toward the moon on the side of Earth facing the moon, while centrifugal forces pull water away from Earth on the opposite side. *(Illustration by Jeff Dixon.)*

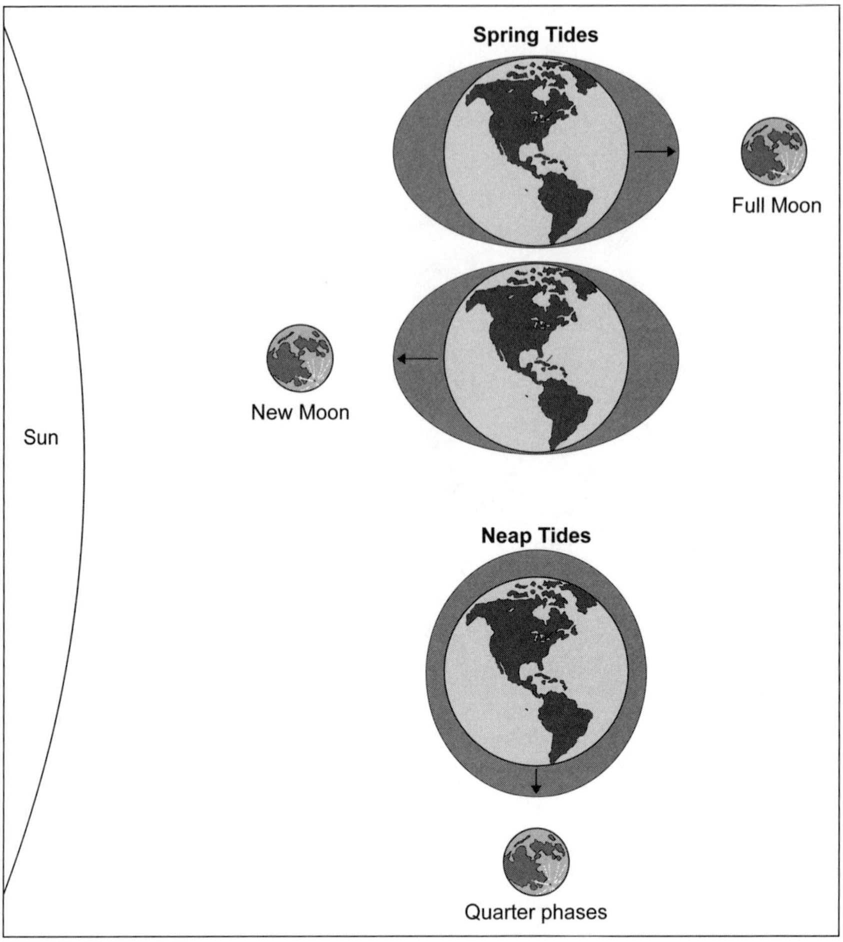

Figure 1.9 When the sun and moon are aligned, as during the phases of full moon and new moon, the highest high tides and lowest low tides—spring tides—occur. When the sun and moon are perpendicular to each other during first-quarter and third-quarter phases of the moon, their gravitational influences tend to cancel each other out. At these times, the lowest high tides and highest low tides—neap tides—occur. *(Illustration by Jeff Dixon.)*

coasts experience their highest high tides and lowest low tides. The opposite conditions are set up during first-quarter and third-quarter phases of the moon, when the lowest high tides and highest low tides occur, the so-called neap tides (see Figure 1.9). The difference between spring and neap tides is greatest near an equinox.

The orientation and shape of a coastline and its seafloor determine water levels and the frequency of high tide and low tide. Most coasts, but not all, experience two high tides and two low tides over a period of 24 hours and 50 minutes. The two high tides may be equal in height (a semidiurnal tide), or unequal in height (a mixed tide). Unequal tides are a product of the 23.5° tilt of Earth's axis and the 5° declination of the moon's orbital plane relative to Earth's orbital plane. Along a few coasts only one high tide and one low tide occurs each day (a diurnal tide). This phenomenon occurs in the Gulf of California and on some coasts along the Gulf of Mexico.

Tidal ranges. The differences in elevation between the high-tide mark and the low-tide mark on the shore experienced around the world vary enormously. On coasts surrounding the Mediterranean and Baltic seas the difference between high tide and low tide is barely noticeable. In the Bay of Fundy, between New Brunswick and Nova Scotia, Canada, on the other hand, water level changes 52.5 ft (16 m) between high and low tide, the greatest tidal range on Earth. In the open sea, the effects of the moon and sun are spread over vast areas, and tidal ranges are less than 0.24 in (0.5 cm).

Surface Currents

The surface waters of oceans are in motion, in large part driven by the wind and directed by the rotational force of the Earth (Coriolis Force). Heat gained in tropical ocean waters flows poleward in warm surface currents. The strong easterly Trade Winds of tropical latitudes push surface waters westward until they come up against a continent. The east coasts of the landmasses block the water and divert it poleward into the middle latitudes. The result is a warm boundary current on the western sides of oceans (see Figure 1.10). The surface waters continue to move in a clockwise direction in the Northern Hemisphere and counterclockwise in the

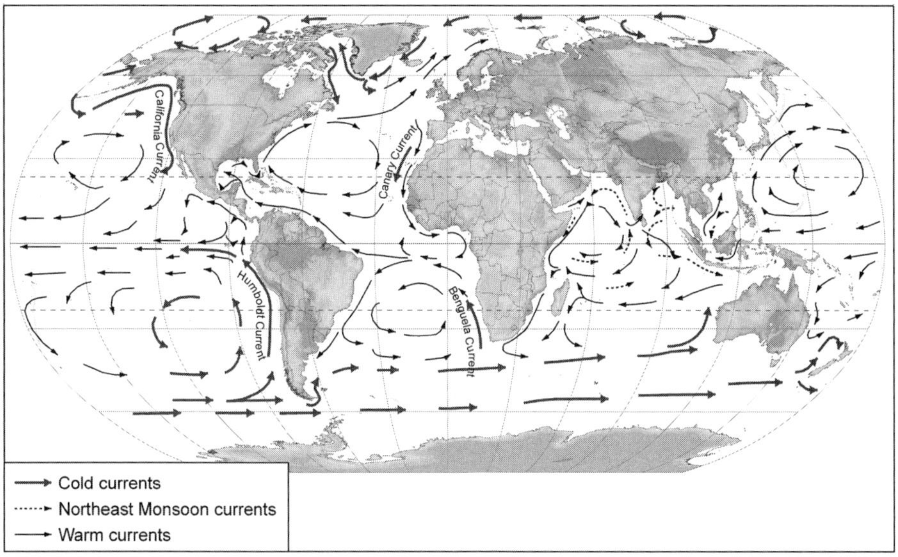

Figure 1.10 The major surface currents and oceanic gyres. *(Map by Bernd Kuennecke.)*

Southern Hemisphere to form the great circular currents known as gyres that flow around each major ocean basin. These so-called anticyclonic gyres are centered in the subtropics near 30° latitude where semipermanent high-pressure cells dominate in the atmosphere. Poleward of the subtropical gyres and moving in the opposite direction are smaller cyclonic gyres.

The Trade Winds, in their easterly flow, push the warm surface waters off the west coasts of continents away from the land and expose the colder water underneath. From depths of 300–650 ft (100–200 m), water from below the thermocline will well upward to replace the surface zone and produce cold boundary currents on the eastern sides of oceans. Temperatures in the cold currents may be 10° F (5.5° C) or more cooler than expected for the latitude. The Benguela Current off the coast of southwestern Africa, for example, has water temperatures of 54°–57° F (12°–14° C), whereas typical water temperatures between the latitudes of 15° and 30° S are 68° F (20° C). Upwelling brings nutrients that had settled into lower waters back to the surface. These nutrients nourish plankton, which in turn feed huge numbers of fish. In the Benguela Current, as well as the Humboldt Current off Peru, the most abundant fish are anchovies, sardines, and horse mackerel.

Another important area of upwelling occurs in the Southern Ocean 5°–10° of latitude north of Antarctica, more or less along the 70th parallel. Two circumpolar ocean currents move in opposite directions at this location. The more poleward or southern current, the East Wind Drift, moves east to west, driven by the Polar Easterlies. Equatorward, or to the north, the Antarctic Circumpolar Current (or West Wind Drift) flows west to east, driven by the strong Prevailing Westerlies. Separation or divergence of water in the contact zone permits upwelling and a concentration of nutrient-rich surface waters.

Cold water also flows in currents such as the Labrador Current and Falklands Current, which move out of polar seas toward lower latitudes. Wherever two masses of water with very different physical properties meet, the contact zone or boundary is often sharp. These sharp boundaries are called fronts. When cold currents contact warm currents, turbulence results and moves nutrients upward to concentrate at the front. As a result, some of the world's major fisheries are associated with ocean fronts. The great cod fishery of the Grand Banks off Newfoundland, though now depleted due to overfishing, was one such example.

Langmuir circulation is another phenomenon of the surface layer. Steady gentle wind causes a series of long parallel, rolling cylinders of water to form in the upper 70 ft (20 m) (see Figure 1.11). Like meshing gears, adjacent cylinders rolls in opposite directions and create alternating bands of upwelling and downwelling. Nutrients and hence phytoplankters get swept into streaks between adjacent rolls.

Deep Oceanic Circulation

Differences in water density force a slow surface-to-depth circulation of waters in the world ocean. Dense water off the coast of Antarctica sinks to the seafloor, and Antarctic Bottom Water flows toward the Equator at great depth. This water is

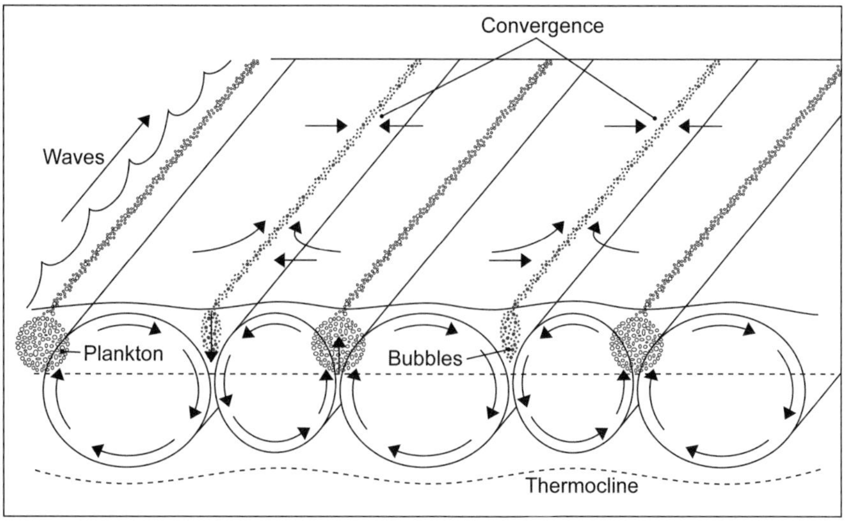

Figure 1.11 Langmuir circulation concentrates plankton in long streaks on the ocean surface. They and alternating lines of bubbles orient in the general direction of the wind. *(Illustration by Jeff Dixon.)*

dense in the summer because of low temperature: it is primarily ice melt. It is dense in winter because of high salinity: only the water in seawater freezes leaving behind unfrozen waters of greater and greater salt content. Another deep current of cold, saline water begins in the Arctic Ocean off Greenland. The North Atlantic Deep Water Current has been traced as far south as 40° S latitude. The two currents are parts of a great conveyor belt that slowly moves seawater around the Earth (see Figure 1.12). The waters rise again to the surface in the upwelling zones along the west coasts of continents and where seamounts obstruct their passage. A complete trip around the circuit might take a given water molecule 2,000 years.

The circulation of water from surface to seafloor is important for life in the deepest parts of the sea. While at the surface in polar seas, the water is exposed to the atmosphere and, being cold, is able to dissolve significant amounts of life-giving oxygen. These descending currents carry oxygen with them as they descend toward the ocean floor; the bottom waters of oceans are usually well oxygenated and hence amenable to life.

Ocean Life I: Drifters, Swimmers, Crawlers, and the Firmly Attached

Life in the oceans is obviously different from that living on the continents. Flowering plants, insects, and four-legged vertebrates so dominant on land are nearly absent. Yet the oceans are rich in life: 29 of the 34 known phyla of animals have members living in the sea. Fourteen animal phyla only occur in the oceans.

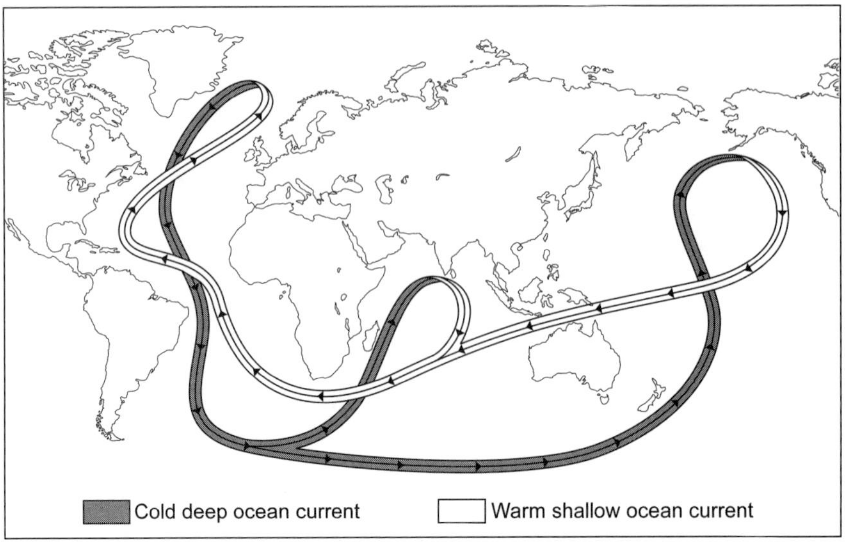

Figure 1.12 Ocean waters slowly circulate in a vertical pattern that unites the waters of all oceans. This deep sea circulation is sometimes likened to a giant conveyor belt and is believed to be linked to global climate patterns. *(Illustration by Jeff Dixon.)*

Interestingly, the great diversity found at the phylum level is not repeated at the species level. Some 20 million species may exist on Earth. Fewer than 250,000 are described from the sea and most of these inhabit the benthic zone. Discovery of new species continues, but identification of new phyla and classes does also. Since 1980, the phyla Loricifera and Cycliophora have been described by scientists. A new class of crustacean (Remipeda) and a new class of cocentricycloid echinoderms have also been discovered. The most recently heralded discoveries are of microorganisms, primarily viruses and bacteria. More accurately, what has been reported is the existence of millions of previously unknown gene sequences that suggest the existence of unknown millions of new microbes.

Marine organisms are often classified according to size, mobility, and location in the water column or bottom materials (see Table 1.2). The pleuston live half in and half out of water. Buoyant creatures, best exemplified by the Portuguese man-of-war and the by-the-wind sailor, they are blown about by the wind. Both of these colonial cnidarians have gas-filled sacs that act as sails.

The neuston is composed of a small number of carnivorous animals able to cling to the water surface. Most are tropical in distribution. One of the rare insects of the sea, the sea strider, like its freshwater relative the pond strider, is supported by the surface tension of the water and lives its entire life above water, the only marine organism to do so. A few other animals hang just below the surface. The gastropod *Ianthina* makes its own raft of froth to hang onto, while another gastropod, *Glaucus*, keeps air bubbles in its gut to stay buoyant.

Table 1.2 Groupings of Marine Life According to Location and Mobility

Type	Location	Mobility	Examples
Pleuston	Straddle surface	Wind-blown	Portuguese man-of-war
Neuston	At surface	Drift at or "walk" on surface	Sea skater or ocean strider
Plankton	Mostly in euphotic zone	Float with the currents; zooplankton able to move vertically in water column with the aid of flagella	Single-celled algae and cyanobacteria; copepods, salps, krill; larvae of invertebrates and some vertebrates that are part of nekton as adults
Nekton			
Pelagic	In upper parts of water column	Swim	Squid, sharks, herring, tuna, bluefish, whales
Demersal	In lowest parts of water column	Swim	Cod, rockfish, flounder, groupers, skates, rays
Benthos			
Motile	In or on substrate	Crawl	Horseshoe crabs, polycheate worms, seastars, anemones, lobsters
Sessile	On substrate	Attached	Kelps, sponges, coral polyps

Plankton refers to those small organisms that float in the water without the ability to propel themselves against tides or currents. Many can move up and down in the water column, however. Plankton are commonly separated into types according to their taxonomic relationships: the phytoplankton are the plants (really algae and some cyanobacteria); the zooplankton are animals.

The nekton consists of active swimmers. They are large enough or strong enough to be able to move against the force of waves, tides, and currents. This is a diverse group that includes cephalopod molluscs, crustaceans, sharks, fishes, and whales. Members range in size from less than an inch to more than 65 ft (20 m) in length. The nekton can be subdivided into those forms that live close to the sea bottom, the demersal types, and those that live higher in the water column, the pelagic forms.

Plants and animals confined to the benthic zone are called the benthos. Macroalgae (algae visible to the naked eye), such as kelps, attach themselves to the bottom, as do the seagrasses, true flowering plants. Some multicelled animals, such as sponges, coral polyps, and barnacles, also attach themselves to the bottom materials; most only become sessile as adults. Other animals of the benthos, such as worms, seastars, anemones, mussels, and crabs, are motile and move through or on top of the substrate.

The Plankton

The plankton consists of a number of different organisms, individuals of which are called plankters. They can be classified according to evolutionary or taxonomic relationships (for example, whether bacteria, algae, or animals), according to size (see Table 1.3), and according to their position or role in marine food chains. Marine viruses are the smallest. Consisting of clumps of RNA encased in a protein coating, viruses are not truly living organisms, but they are extremely abundant in the ocean and produce dissolved organic matter (DOM) that enters the microbial loop, an important part of oceanic food chains.

Bacterioplankters are decomposers and the beginning of all important detritus food chains in the sea. There are two main kinds. Smaller (<1 μm), free-living bacteria consume DOM. Larger forms clump onto particulate organic matter (POM), the debris and garbage of other living organisms. POM can be dead cells from phyto- and zooplankters, molted exoskeletons, leftovers from the meals of herbivores, or feces. The plankters excrete a mucus-like substance that glues organic particles together. The resulting globs sink to the bottom as "marine snow." Caught on the snow, perhaps accidentally, are bacteria that ride down with it. The bacteria break down POM into its inorganic components to maintain nutrient cycles in the sea. The bacteria themselves are significant food for zooplankters. Stuck to the POM, they are also consumed by larger marine animals.

The phytoplankters have the capacity for photosynthesis and live in the euphotic zone. Fewer than 2,000 species are known. They are either one-celled algae with chlorophyll and other light-sensitive pigments or cyanobacteria, tiny organisms ranging in size from 0.2 to 200 μm. For comparison purposes, a red blood cell is about 7 μm in diameter. A particle 50 μm in size is just barely visible to the naked eye. Phytoplankters are the chief producers in the open sea and the beginning of grazing food chains. Not only do they manufacture food during photosynthesis, but they leak cell contents and yield DOM, which is itself a food source for many marine organisms. Small size offers several advantages to organisms that must live in the surface waters where light is available. For one thing, small

Table 1.3 Classification of the Plankton According to Size

Size class	Length (in μm)	Types of organisms in group
Femto- or Ultraplankton	0.02 to <0.2	Viruses
Picoplankton	0.2 to 2.0	Cyanobacteria; bacteria
Nanoplankton	2.0 to <20	Small flagellates, both autotrophic and heterotrophic
Microplankton	20 to <200	Phytoplankters: diatoms and dinoflagellates Zooplankters: radiolarians and foraminiferans
Macroplankton	200 to <2,000	Zooplankton: copepods
Megaplankton	≥2,000	Larvae of crustaceans and finfishes

organisms sink more slowly than larger, heavier ones. For another, small size maximizes the ratio between surface area and volume, especially if the shape of the organism is not spherical. A large amount of surface area compared with volume allows for fast and efficient absorption of nutrients from the water. Small phytoplankters have short life spans but can reproduce quickly. An organism 10 μm in size has a generation time of one hour. This means that every hour a single cell divides into two daughter cells. These single-celled organisms use energy to produce new individuals rather than to grow the cell or original individual to a larger size. This lets the species as a whole react rapidly to environmental changes such as a sudden increase in nutrients. It also allows a population to survive high rates of consumption by the animals that feed upon them. New cells are produced more quickly than older ones die or are eaten.

Cyanobacteria are part of the picoplankton. The genus *Synechococcus* is found in all but polar waters. Since they are able to absorb blue wavelengths, they tend to concentrate in the deeper sections of the euphotic zone. Species in the genus *Prochlorococcus*, though only 0.7 μm in diameter, are significant primary producers in the open sea. Another genus, *Trichodesmium*, thrives in warm tropical waters; its blooms are the reason the Red Sea is red.

Among the nanoplankton are some autotrophic flagellates, tiny single-celled organisms with a few whip-like appendages that enable them to move in the water column. These microalgae are difficult to collect and see under standard light microscopes, but they may account for nearly 90 percent of the total living matter (biomass) of the phytoplankton and contribute more than half of the primary production in marine ecosystems.

Diatoms are the main taxonomic group within marine algae (see Figure 1.13). They dominate in nutrient-rich waters. Each individual is encased in a rigid exoskeleton consisting of upper and lower pieces that fit together like a box and its lid. The glassy opal cases come in a wondrous diversity of textures and shapes that let scientists identify diatoms rather easily to the level of genus.

Dinoflagellates (see Figure 1.14) make up another important group of algal phytoplankters. They are larger than diatoms and motile. They tend to have

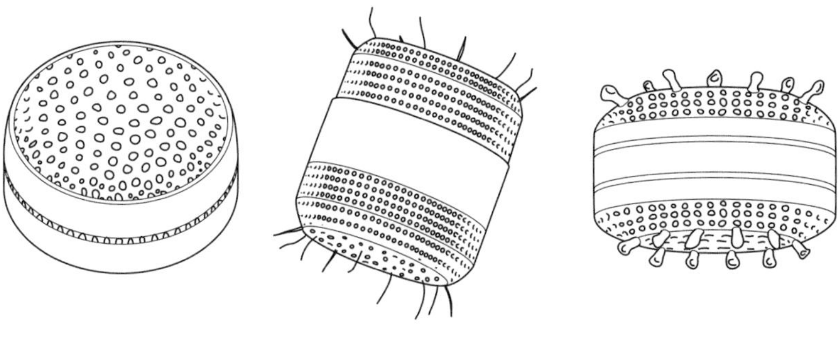

Figure 1.13 One type of diatom, exhibiting the box-and-cover structure of its exoskeleton. *(Illustration by Jeff Dixon.)*

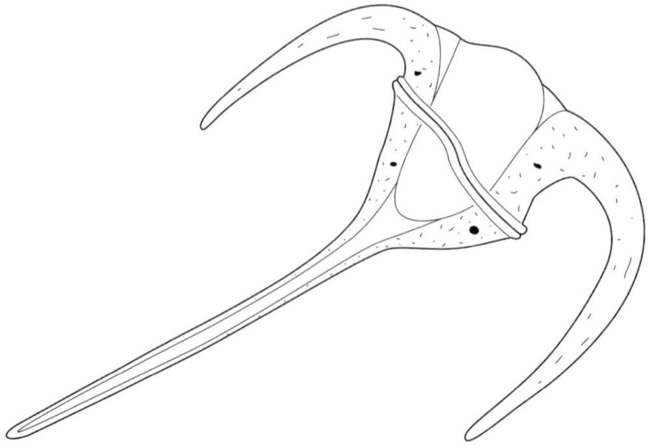

Figure 1.14 One type of dinoflagellate, showing the flagella that allows it to whirl up and down the water column. *(Illustration by Jeff Dixon.)*

various projections and odd shapes to increase surface area and maximize absorption of nutrients. This is especially true of dinoflagellates living in nutrient-poor tropical waters. Some have two whip-like flagella that are fixed perpendicular to each other. These flagella produce a spiraling motion that lets them swim up to light ("dinos" means "whirling"). They may move up the water column as much as 30 ft (10 m) and typically undergo daily migrations, rising into the euphotic zone for photosynthesis and sinking to lower depths to capture nutrients. Some dinoflagellates bioluminesce and create phosphorescent surf and other light shows in surface waters.

Phytoplankters have complex life cycles that include periods of rapid cell division known as blooms and resting periods when they are encysted spores. Diatoms typically have blooms in the spring in the mid-latitudes. Dinoflagellates often bloom in the autumn, although they do sometimes have massive blooms in the spring that cause so-called red tides. Dinoflagellates leak the toxic by-products of their metabolism that, in high concentrations, poison shellfish. These nerve poisons accumulate in the tissues of clams and oysters and can kill humans who eat seafood so contaminated. Dinoflagellates also are the algae that form symbiotic relationships with coral polyps, giant clams, and nudibranch snails. In that role, they are referred to as zooxanthellae.

Zooplankters (see Table 1.4) are the free-living animals that generally "go with the flow," unable to drive themselves against currents and tides. As a group, they can be subdivided into protozooplankers, the single-celled forms, and metazooplankters, the multicelled animals. Protozooplankters include ciliates such as the *Tintinnids* as well as foraminiferans and radiolarians (see Plate I). They feed on either DOM or bacteria. An estimated 60 percent of the energy flowing through marine ecosystems passes through the so-called microbial loop (see Figure 1.15),

Table 1.4 Selected Phyla Represented in the Zooplankton

Protista	Single-celled protozoans: flagellates; ciliates; foraminifera; radiolaria
Cnidaria	Gelatinous forms armed with stinging cells (include hydromedusae, jellyfish)
Ctenophora	The comb jellies
Crustacea	Copepods usually dominate; also includes amphipods, euphausids (krill), decapods (true shrimps)
Chordata (subphylum Urochordata)	Tunicates or sea squirts
Salps (pelagic tunicates)	Tube-shaped, gelatinous organisms with cellulose stiffening body; have flap-valves at either end of tube
Class Appendicularia	Adults resemble the larvae of tunicates, are also called Larvaceae

wherein DOM is consumed by bacteria that are then consumed by flagellates and ciliates that leak DOM which is taken up by bacteria and the cycle starts again.

Other protozooplankters are true herbivores, feeding upon members of the phytoplankton. They become especially abundant during and after the spring blooms of diatoms, but they are also associated with upwelling regions and red tides. Some large foraminiferans have developed symbiotic relationships with algae and carry with them so-called gardens of dinoflagellates.

Many different types of organism comprise the metazooplankton. These multicelled organisms can be subdivided into two ecological groups, those that are suspension-feeders and those that are raptorial, that is, they grab their prey with some kind of clawlike device. The suspension-feeders extract particles from the water by forcing it through sieve-like apparatuses. They include some copepods, euphausids such as krill, thaliceans (large, gelatinous creatures), and the larvae of a number of invertebrates such as polychaete worms, molluscs, decapod crabs, and barnacles.

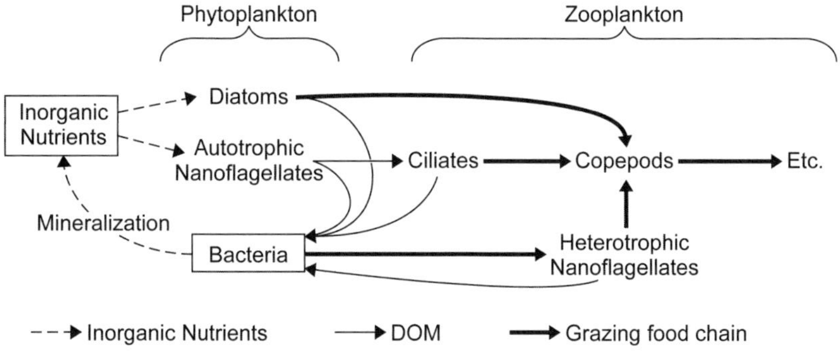

Figure 1.15 The microbial loop. *(Illustration by Jeff Dixon.)*

The raptorial metazooplankters can be selective in what they catch. They include other copepods, chaetognaths or arrow worms, cnidarians, ctenophores or comb-jellies, and the larvae of nudibranches or sea slugs. The larvae of some fish are part of the raptorial metazooplankton.

Zooplankters are able to move up and down the water column with the aid of cilia and flagella. The smaller ones migrate up to 1,300 ft (400 m), while larger forms may move vertically 2,000–3,000 ft (600–1,000 m). Typically, zooplankters will spend the daylight hours in deeper water and rise toward the surface at dusk. In the middle of the night, they may be dispersed throughout the water column, but they concentrate near the surface before dawn and then descend into deeper water at sunrise. The purpose of this daily migration pattern is not well understood, but it may be a way for the herbivores to access ungrazed patches of the sea. The thought is that grazers deplete the phytoplankton in part of the surface layer during the night. At sunrise they move into deeper water. The surface water is pushed away from the area by wind; but the deeper water stays in place. When the zooplankters rise the following night, they stand a better chance of encountering "new" water with a more abundant supply of food than if they had stayed close at the top of the water column and been blown along with the surface waters.

The phytoplankton is distributed in distinct concentrations or patches in the surface layer rather than as a continuous and uniform chlorophyll soup. One way that phytoplankters become concentrated is a result of Langmuir circulation. Phytoplankters also get concentrated in eddies that spin off warm western boundary currents. Such eddies from the Gulf Stream can be 150 mi (250 km) in diameter and 3,000 ft (1,000 m) deep and may stay intact for up to three years. Other places where phytoplankters concentrate are at the fronts at the margin of continental shelves, where well-mixed coastal waters contact stable, stratified waters of the open sea. Concentrations of phytoplankters attract animals, not only zooplankter but large predators as well. They become predictable feeding sites for carnivorous fish, seabirds, and sea mammals.

Animals of the Nekton

Nonattached forms of life in the oceans are either plankton or nekton. The forms that swim make up the nekton. Among them are a host of invertebrates, including squid and shrimp, as well as about 2,000 kinds of vertebrates. Cartilaginous fishes such as sharks and bony fishes or teleosts are members of this group, as are reptiles (such as sea turtles, sea snakes, and saltwater crocodiles), seabirds, and marine mammals.

Seabirds all nest on land, but a number fly or swim great distances out to sea to feed and become—temporarily to be sure—members of the nekton as they plunge into the sea or dive from the surface and swim after prey. Shearwaters, Storm Petrels, and albatrosses spend much of their lives on the wing. Others, such as the boobies and tropicbirds, return to land to roost each day. Gulls, terns, pelicans, and cormorants feed in nearshore waters close to their rookeries. Some seabirds are (or were) flightless. Penguins, restricted to the Southern Hemisphere, swim after krill, squid, and fish. A now-extinct flightless bird in the Northern Hemisphere, the Great Auk, lived in a similar fashion.

Perhaps the best-known members of the nekton are three orders of marine mammals: Sirenia, Pinnipedia, and Cetacea. Plant-eating dugongs, manatees, and the now-extinct Stellar's sea cow are sirenians and spend their entire lives in the sea, inhabiting coastal waters and estuaries, and sometimes freshwater rivers. All pinnipeds, on the other hand, must haul out onto land or ice to breed. The five different kinds of pinniped are sea lions, fur seals, eared seals, true seals, and walruses. Whales, dolphins, and porpoises comprise the cetaceans. They are the mammals best adapted to life in the open sea. Two basic types or suborders exist. The so-called baleen or whale-bone whales have fringed plates of a horny material known as baleen hanging from their upper jaws instead of teeth, and they use the plates to filter their food—crustaceans and other plankton—out of the seawater. They are further distinguished from the other group by having two blowholes and a symmetrically shaped head. The blue whale, the largest animal ever to exist, is an example. The other suborder consists of the toothed whales, which have a single blowhole and asymmetrically shaped heads. Selective hunters, toothed whales are carnivores. The sperm whale feeds on fish and squid; narwhals and orcas feed heavily on fish and squid but will take marine mammals and penguins when they can. Dolphins and porpoises are other toothed whales.

Animals of the Benthos

A number of animal phyla are represented in the benthos. Sponges (Porifera) and cnidarians such as sea anemones, corals, sea pens, and hydroids attach themselves to the substrate, as do bivalves molluscs such as oysters and mussels. Mobile members of the benthos include gastropod molluscs such as snails and cephalopod molluscs such as octopus and giant squid, as well as crustaceans such as lobsters and crabs, cartilaginous fishes such as skates and rays, and bony fishes such as flounder and hake.

Ocean Life II: Ecological Subdivisions

Producers

Primary producers are those organisms that fix solar energy into organic compounds from which it can later be released and used for life's processes. Most primary producers photosynthesize; that is, they use sunlight and dissolved inorganic carbon to produce the stuff and energy of life. The producers use some of the energy they fix to fuel their own metabolism and some of the fixed carbon to maintain their cells. What is left over goes into growth of the individual cell or organism or into the formation of new offspring or daughter cells—that is, reproduction. The energy and matter stored temporarily as the living tissue of the producers is food for the consumers and, later, the detritus-feeders of the sea (see Figure 1.16).

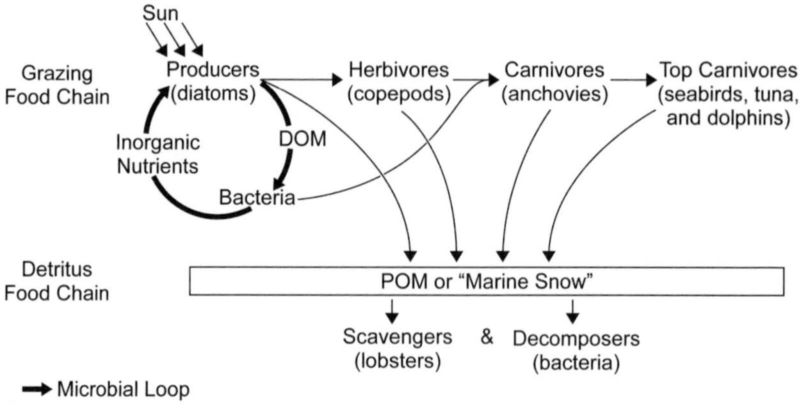

Figure 1.16 A simplified marine food chain. *(Illustration by Jeff Dixon.)*

In the oceans, seagrasses, seaweeds, single-celled algae, and cyanobacteria are the primary producers. The main ones are members of the phytoplankton, mostly single-celled algae and cyanobacteria floating in the surface waters. As is true of all photosynthesizing organisms, algae contain certain light-absorbing pigments, primarily chlorophyll-a (Chl*a*). Cyanobacteria also use Chl*a*. (Since Chl*a* absorbs red and blue wavelengths and reflects green, its presence can be sensed remotely by satellite imagery.) The amount of Chl*a* in a water sample is used to estimate the abundance of algae and monitor algal blooms from space. Other pigments are also present in algal cells, and algae can adjust the amounts of these pigments to maximize the absorption of those wavelengths available at different water depths. Wavelengths of visible light in the 400–700 nanometer (nm) range are photosynthetically active radiation (see Table 1.5).

Primary production is controlled by the availability of light and nutrients. In addition to carbon and sunlight, algae need many other nutrients. Nitrogen and phosphorus are usually the elements in limited supply that end algal blooms, but a lack of trace amounts of iron and certain vitamins such as B_{12}, biotin, and/or

Table 1.5 Wavelengths Absorbed by Different Pigments

Pigment	Wavelengths best absorbed	Color of light absorbed
Chlorophylla-a (Chl*a*)[a]	410 nm and 655 nm	Blue and red
β-carotene, Chlorophyll-b	400–520 nm	Blue-green
Phycoerythrins	490–570 nm	Green
Phycocyanins	550–630 nm	Yellow-green
Allophycocyanins	650–670 nm	Orange-red

Note: [a]Chl*a* is most common in phytoplankters.

thiamine can also slow or prevent primary production and hence the growth and reproduction of the algae. For phytoplankters, two other environmental conditions are necessary for them to perform their ecological roles as primary producers. First, the surface water layer must be stable. This stability will keep the tiny cells in the euphotic zone, where they have access to sunlight. The second requirement is at least periodic mixing of the surface waters with water from below. As the algae population grows, it depletes the surface layer of essential nutrients. Mixing brings more nutrient-rich water from beneath the euphotic zone up to the phytoplankters, replenishing their supply.

Macroalgae are slimy, multicellular forms of algae usually called seaweed. Most are attached by means of holdfasts to the substrate and do not move from the site on which they grow. Some grow in the surf zone, exposed to the air and sprayed by breakers. Others are always submerged. Among more common forms are sargassum, kelps, sea lettuce, and the so-called Irish moss, an edible dark purplish alga harvested from rocks in the intertidal zone on both sides of the North Atlantic.

Seagrasses are true flowering plants rooted in the substrate and thus limited to shallow waters where sunlight is available. They obtain their nutrients through roots and rhizomes, just as land plants do.

In addition to photosynthetic primary producers, some chemosynthetic primary producers known as chemolithotrophs occur in the ocean. These are bacteria that use inorganic chemicals such as hydrogen sulfide (H_2S), ferrous iron (Fe^{+2}), nitrite (NO_3^{-1}), or ammonium (NH_4^{+1}) instead of sunlight as a source of energy. They obtain carbon from carbon dioxide dissolved in seawater. An interesting example of a chemosynthetic species is the sulfur-oxiding bacterium *Beggiatoa* that lives in the tissues of hydrothermal vent animals and allows them to thrive at depths well beyond the reach of sunlight.

Consumers

Grazers or herbivores are the so-called first-level consumers—that is, the first to utilize the energy and carbon fixed by the producers and not used by the primary producers themselves. Herbivores in the sea are mostly zooplankters and vary in size from the smallest protozoans (hetertrophic nanoflagellates and ciliates) to copepods, salps, and krill. Second-level consumers are carnivores that feed on herbivorous zooplankton and include squid, fish, and baleen whales. Top carnivores consume mainly second-level consumers and include cod and tuna, seals, and toothed whales.

Scavengers and decomposers are members of the detritus food chain. Lobsters are typical scavengers, feeding on dead organisms. Bacteria are the chief decomposers, breaking organic debris into its inorganic components. These so-called chemotrophs receive their carbon not from dissolved inorganic compounds but by breaking down organic compounds.

Marine Biomes

Unlike the more familiar terrestrial ecosystems in which energy flow is initiated primarily by flowering plants, oceanic ones are dominated by invisible single-celled algae and some even smaller cyanobacteria. This difference not only makes for different food chains in the ocean compared with land, but also creates problems in applying the biome concept to the marine ecosystems. The biome concept was originally designed to separate regions of continents covered with distinctive types of vegetation that reflected or were adapted to each region's climate. A whole new set of criteria needs to be determined for oceanic biomes, and these are not wholly agreed upon at this time. A brief description of two schemes proposed to delimit marine biomes is presented below. One or both may become the way marine biomes or regions are organized in the future.

Biogeographic Regions or Biomes of the Sea: Two Proposed Classifications

In 1974, the American marine biogeographer John Briggs built upon the studies of the Swedish marine biologist Sven Ekman (1876–1964), who had viewed temperature as the most important factor in the distribution of animals in the sea. Since a strong correlation exists between latitude and water temperature, Briggs divided the oceans into seven latitudinal zones, and then proposed one or more biogeographic regions in each zone. His latitudinal zones, from north to south, are Arctic, Cold-Temperate Northern Hemisphere, Warm-Temperate Northern Hemisphere, Tropical, Warm-Temperate Southern Hemisphere, Cold-Temperate Southern Hemisphere, and Antarctic. The circulation patterns of oceans, which are determined by global winds and the positions of the continents, create distinct groups of animals in each ocean within a given zone; and each area with a distinctive group represents a separate biogeographic region.

To some degree, not only many animals but also large algae (especially kelps) and seagrasses (true flowering plants) sort themselves out according to latitude. Kelps are found only in Temperate, Arctic, and Antarctic waters. Different kinds of seagrasses are found in tropical waters than elsewhere. Coral reefs and mangroves are essentially limited to tropical seas. While Briggs's regions are not widely used as organizing factors in oceanographic research, the names are commonly used to describe different parts of the world ocean.

In 1998, oceanographer Alan Longhurst defined four primary marine biomes according to the physical conditions that determine the depth of the mixed layer—factors such as light penetration, nutrient supply, the depth and timing of vertical mixing, and the seasonal responses (that is, blooms) of the phytoplankton to changing physical conditions (see Table 1.6).

Longhurst named his four biomes the Trades Biome, Westerlies Biome, Polar Biome, and Coastal Biome and identified 57 subprovinces. Each ocean has two or more biomes represented. Each biome consists of several water masses separated

Table 1.6 Longhurst's Marine Biomes

Biome	Controlling factor(s)	Plankton response	Location
I. Polar	Light (winter periods with no sunlight and no photosynthesis); reduced salinity of surface waters due to ice melt and runoff	Single midsummer peak	Arctic and Southern Oceans where sea ice occurs all year or seasonally
II. Westerlies			
A. Subpolar	Iron limitation; seasonal mixing	Two peaks in production: spring and fall	North Atlantic Ocean (north of Gulf Stream); North Pacific Ocean; subantarctic parts of Southern Ocean beyond range of sea ice.
B. Subtropical gyres	Semipermanent subtropical high pressure cells; permanent pycnocline at 400 ft (120 m) prevents vertical mixing; summer thermocline at 150–250 ft (50–70 m); surface waters nutrient-poor; water clarity depresses compensation level to about 400 ft (125 m)	Winter to spring production	Located between approximately 25° and 45° latitude; includes Saragasso Sea; maximum chlorophyll near bottom of euphotic zone mostly in cyanobacteria.
III. Trades	Constant easterly winds moving across large distances push warm surface waters westward; upwelling and cold boundary currents on eastern sides of ocean basins	Low production all year, except in areas of upwelling	Tropical oceans between 5° and 25° latitude
IV. Coastal	Complex processes, including nutrient inputs from land and upwelling; tidal mixing; and type of substrate		

from one another by land barriers (see Table 1.5). Versions of Longhurst's scheme are appearing in the newest marine ecology textbooks, so these biomes may become better accepted as the biomes of the sea in the future. A similar concept, that of large marine ecosystems (LME), is used in fisheries biology.

Marine Biomes: Traditional Habitat-Based Classification

Scientists have long recognized three general habitat types in the world's oceans: the coastal or intertidal zone, the subtidal region in the shallow waters above continental shelves, and the open seas of deep water. When the biome concept was first applied to aquatic ecosystems, marine biologists and others used these three habitat types as the equivalents of terrestrial biomes, even though they understood that they were not really the same kind of ecological unit. Nonetheless, it is common today to identify marine biomes in this way. As we learn more about the sea and life in it, this way of classifying marine biomes may lose popularity and be replaced with something more like what Longhurst has proposed (see above), but this book will continue to use the traditional approach.

Each of the three biomes has different aspects or expressions. In the Coast Biome, the type of substrate (rocky shores versus soft sediment shorelines) makes for important distinctions in the assemblage of organisms occupying different areas. Latitude (tropical, temperate, or polar) also matters, since it affects climate and thus some nearshore processes. Subdivisions of the Coast Biome strongly influenced by latitude include salt marshes and mangrove forests.

Early Exploration of the Ocean Environment

Seaside vacations became popular at the beginning of the nineteenth century in Victorian England, and beachcombers began amassing sizeable collections of seashells. Scientific interest in the sea grew out of this pastime, and by 1839, marine biology research stations were being established in Europe. In the United States, the first such station was set up at Wood's Hole, Massachusetts, in 1888. Oceanography as a science that investigated the physical characteristics of the sea traces its beginnings to the voyage of the British research vessel *HMS Challenger* (1872–1876). Sailing all the oceans except the Arctic, the ship recorded information on tides, currents, water chemistry, and water temperature.

At first, research on life in the sea was generally restricted to studying coasts at low tide, although primitive diving gear that consisted of pumping compressed air from the surface through a hose into a hard helmet worn by the diver was available by 1819. Augustus Siebe's improved diving suit (1837), with the air pump still located onboard ship, allowed researchers to descend all of 60 ft (18 m). It was another hundred years, during World War II (1939–1945), before divers could finally swim free and untethered using the Self-Contained Underwater Breathing Apparatus (SCUBA) invented by Jacques Costeau and Emile Gagnan. Breathing air from refillable tanks on their backs, SCUBA divers could go to depths of 130 ft (40 m). Later, specialized mixtures of gases in the tanks permitted descents greater than 400 ft (130 m).

Modern technological advances permit today's scientists to study the oceans both directly and remotely. Descent into the deepest ocean trench has been achieved, but important information also comes from far above the sea in data retrieved from Earth-orbiting satellites such as GEOSAT and the Global Ocean Observing System (GOOS).

The Continental Shelf Biome is subdivided according to the type of substrate upon and within which the benthos must exist. Inputs of nutrients governed by ocean currents, stratification of the water column, and runoff from continents are also important considerations, as are temperature patterns.

The Deep Sea Biome is the deep water pelagic zone where temperature, pressure, and nutrient availability are significant factors in determining the distribution patterns of life and hence major subdivisions of the biome. Hydrothermal vents are just one patch in the mosaic of ecosystems that make up this biome.

Oceans and People

Nearly four-fifths of the human population lives in 60 mi (100 km) wide strip bordering the world's oceans and seas, and everyone is affected by the role oceans play in world climate. Considerable research continues on how ocean and atmosphere interact and what this means for global climate change. Though vast and seemingly indestructible, oceans are being changed by human activities. Pollution, overfishing, and climate change are among the ways people are altering the ocean habitat and the life that flourishes within in it.

Further Readings

Book

American Museum of Natural History. 2006. *Ocean.* New York: DK Publishing. Includes facts about oceans and seas and the life residing in them, plus excellent photos, maps, and diagrams.

Internet Sites

NOAA's OceanExplorer. 2001–2008. http://oceanexplorer.noaa.gov/explorations/explorations.html. Logs of expeditions beneath the sea, result summaries, and photo galleries.

Sanctuary Integrated Monitoring Network (SIMoN). 2008. http://www.mbnms-simon.org/index.php. Access to information on all ecosystems of Monterey Bay National Marine Sanctuary.

The Virtual Ocean. n.d. http://www.euronet.nl/users/janpar/virtual/ocean.html; or Micropolitan Museum. n.d. http://www.microscopy-uk.org.uk/micropolitan/marine/index.html. Exquisite photos of planktonic life.

Videos

BBC. 2002. *Blue Planet, Seas of Life.* Almost as good as being there. Available on DVDs. bbc.co.uk/nature/programmes/tv/blueplanet. Especially good for an introduction to marine habitats and conditions are the following programs: "Introduction," Programme 1; "Open Oceans," Programme 3; "Frozen Seas," Programme 4; "Seasonal Seas," Programme 5; and "Deep Trouble," Programme 9.

2

Coast Biome

Overview

The Coast Defined

The coast is where land merges with the sea. It begins where salt spray from breaking waves affects terrestrial plants and animals and extends out through the surf to that depth at which even storm waves do not disturb the seabed. Commonly the outer edge occurs at depths of about 200 ft (60 m).

Life on a coast demands adaptations to a complex set of environmental factors that change across space (see Plate II), that is, that form gradients from one extreme to another. The three most significant gradients are those from wet to dry, related to the length of time an area is submerged or exposed; the strength of wave action against the coast; and the particle sizes of the substrate. A host of species are adapted to at least some part of the Coast Biome. Some are able to tolerate exposure to the air for longer periods than others, and some tolerate being submerged for longer periods of time. Some must avoid the pounding of the surf; others are able to withstand it. Some are best able to thrive on hard rock substrates; others only survive buried in the finest of sediments. Whatever their habitat requirements or preferences, almost all had their origins in the ocean and must return to the sea at some stage to complete their life histories.

The complexity of the coastal environment translates into the greatest variety of habitats and microhabitats found anywhere on the planet. These habitats tend to organize themselves into zones at different heights above or below mean sea level and running roughly parallel to the shoreline. Each zone is occupied by a characteristic group of organisms, although different geographic areas have different assemblages of species. This chapter introduces the major plant and animal communities in various coastal habitats around the world.

Environmental Factors

Regardless of whether the coast is made of solid rock or soft, loose particles and regardless of whether the transition from land to sea is abrupt or gradual, the coastal environment is influenced by the mechanical force of waves and longshore currents and by ever-changing water levels resulting from ebbing and flowing tides. Organisms living in upper zones along the coast must be able to tolerate being sprayed or submerged in saltwater for certain lengths of time and also to being exposed not only to dry air for varying periods of time, but also to freshwater whenever it rains. In addition, they need to deal with the force of moving water—with waves, surf, longshore currents, and tides.

Wave action. Organisms living in the surf zone must be able to survive both the weight of the water thrust at them and the abrasive action of sediments carried in that water. Waves sweep higher up a shore with a steep slope than one with a gentle rise and so extend the reach of sea spray and thus humidity higher on cliffs and headlands. This results in an upward expansion of the range of many species that live on such landforms.

Coasts composed of loose, unconsolidated sands and gravels have unstable, ever-shifting substrates frequently disturbed by wave action. Waves will remove sediments from one location and drop them somewhere else. Water moves onto and up the beach as swash. Swash usually moves at an angle other than perpendicular to the shoreline because wave crests bend in shallow water. When the water in the swash loses its forward momentum, gravity takes over and pulls the water back down the beach at a right angle to the coastline. The water returning to the sea is called backwash. When it flows back out to sea across a sandy coast, the backwash water passes beneath incoming waves, forming an undertow. The alternating back-and-forth movement of swash and backwash moves loose particles along the beach and moves seawater along the coast. On land the process results in beach drift; in water it creates longshore drift or currents.

Longshore currents, pushed by the waves, flow parallel to the coast in the same direction that the waves approach the shore. The currents move both sediments and water molecules and build sand spits and bars wherever the flow is slowed. During storms, they may contribute to significant beach erosion. Where barriers obstruct the longshore current or where waves of different strength come into contact, the longshore flow may turn and circulate out to sea as a rip current. This seaward flow is often strong and carves a channel into the seabed through which it moves across the surf zone and out beyond the breaker line.

Wave action is a major control in the distribution of coastal organisms. Although difficult to measure precisely, coastal exposure to wave action ranges from fully exposed to sheltered. The communities of organisms living on coasts vary according to how exposed the coastline is. Wave action is also largely responsible for the width and height above mean sea level of the conspicuous bands or zones of organisms so characteristic of rocky shores.

Tidal action. Organisms living in the intertidal zone of the coast biome must contend with the varying lengths of time they will be exposed or submerged during each lunar cycle. (See Chapter 1 for an explanation of tides.) Dessication is an obvious consequence of being exposed to the air. Animals able to retreat into shells or crevices can keep themselves from drying out. Existing in or moving to shaded areas is another option, for evaporation rates are lower there than on sunlit rocks. A thick cover of algae can maintain high humidity for animals exposed at low tide.

Exposure to air also means organisms will experience a greater range in surface temperatures than occurs in the sea itself. Heat overload is a common threat to surface-dwelling organisms. How high a temperature is experienced at low tide depends on latitude, season, color of the rock, and aspect (the direction a surface faces) and may account for the presence or absence of certain species on a particular coast. In summer, especially, a rapid drop in temperature occurs each time the tide flows in.

Particle size. The type of bottom material or substrate that underlies coastal waters is critical to the kind of living organisms that can inhabit a given locale. The most general subdivision is between rocky coasts and soft-sediment coasts (see Table 2.1). Included among rocky coasts are those of exposed solid bedrock and those with boulders too large to be dislodged by wave action. Soft-sediment coasts are

Table 2.1 Some Key Differences between Rocky Coasts and Sandy Coasts

ROCKY COASTS	SANDY COASTS
ENVIRONMENTAL FACTORS	
Desiccation at low tide	Water held in sediments at low tide
Wide diurnal range in temperature, humidity, salinity, and pH	Small diurnal range in physical and chemical factors
Stable substrate	Unstable substrate
Two-dimensional habitat	Three-dimensional habitat
BIOLOGICAL RESPONSES	
Thick shells are defense against predators and desiccation	Burrowing into sand is defense against predators and desiccation
Macroalgae abundant	Microalgae abundant
Attached (sessile) forms dominant	Motile forms dominant
Epifauna dominant	Infauna dominant
Filter-feeders dominate	Deposit-feeders dominate
Distinct life zones clearly visible based on present of characteristic species	Difficult-to-observe or vague and shifting life zones

Table 2.2 Particles Sizes and Some Equivalent Soft Sediment Shore Organisms

Particle	Size	Shore life of similar size
Cobbles	2.5–10 in (64–256 mm)	Crabs, polychaetes
Pebbles	0.6–2.5 in (4–64 mm)	Amphipods
Coarse gravels	0.078–0.6 in (2–4 mm)	Juvenile invertebrates
Sands	0.002–0.078 in (0.063–2.0 mm)	Copepods
Silts[a]	.0002–0.002 in (4–63 μm)	Diatoms
Clays[a]	0.00004–0.0002 in (1–4 μm)	Bacteria

Note: [a]Silts and clays together constitute muds.
Source: Adapted from C. Little, 2000, *The Biology of Soft Shores and Estuaries.*

made of sands and muds (see Table 2.2) into which organisms can burrow. In between are cobble and shingle beaches, the particles of which are constantly tumbled around by waves and are too unstable and hazardous for most forms of life.

On large particle, rocky coasts lifeforms live *on* the substrate. An epifauna of snails, limpets, and barnacles and a flora of encrusting algae or kelps with strong holdfasts dominate such habitats. In fine particle soft-sediment coasts an infauna of burrowing clams and shrimps is usual with smaller organisms such as nematodes, copepods, and flatworms living between the sediment particles.

Finer sediments accumulate in low-energy situations in which currents are slow and wave action minimal. However, currents and wave action are only part of what determines the different types of shores found along a given coast. The type of sediment available to the shore is equally important. Present-day erosion of headlands supplies some of the particles, but vast accumulations of glacial sands and gravels dating from the Pleistocene and now located off the shores of previously ice-covered regions also contribute small particles to certain coasts, so sand and shingle beaches may occur even under conditions of strong wave action. Muds will be deposited only in the most sheltered coastal environments, such as in bays and estuaries or behind sand bars and barrier islands. Their origins lie in both the sea and the land, from which large amounts are carried by rivers. Muds may be frequently resuspended in coastal waters and transported to other locations in the same inlet. On the other hand, plant roots and algae can bind the fine grains together and hold them in place for long periods of time.

Zonation. Zonation at a local scale is a universal fact in coastal habitats. Life zones with different organisms living at different heights above and below tidal levels are quite visible on rocky coasts due to the colors of the most abundant species. In soft-sediment coasts such as sandy beaches and tidal flats, zonation is much more subtle. Whereas physical differences in such factors as water retention during

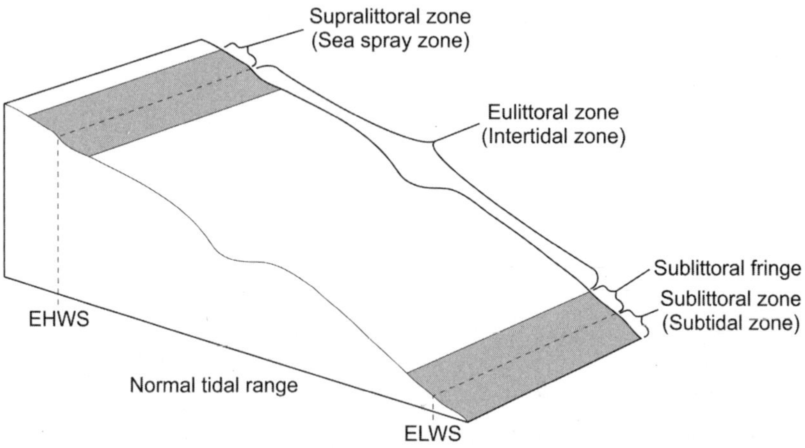

Figure 2.1 Commonly accepted zones on all coasts. EHWS = Extreme high-water mark during spring tides; ELWS = Extreme low-water mark during spring tides. *(Illustration by Jeff Dixon.)*

low tide can be easily observed, much of the invertebrate life is out of sight, buried in the bottom materials, making study of the zonation of life difficult. Special collection techniques and laboratory analysis are often required to identify organisms and detect differences in the animal community at various levels of a sandy beach.

Marine ecologists identify three broad belts of coastal habitat stacked one above the other. They are the supralittoral, eulittoral, and sublittoral zones (see Figure 2.1), although other names are frequently applied. "Littoral" means shore. The uppermost or supralittoral zone (sometimes also called the supralittoral fringe and the sea spray zone) marks an area never submerged below seawater but affected by a mist of salt spray rising from the waves crashing below. It runs from the highest reach of sea spray down to the uppermost reach of high tides. Life in this zone is affected by the ocean, but is not, strictly speaking, part of it. Lower on the shore is the eulittoral zone, more commonly called the intertidal zone because it lies between the extreme high-water-level spring tides (EHWS) and the extreme low-water-level spring tides (ELWS). Thus, at high tide, the area is flooded by the sea, and at low tide it lies exposed to the air. The lowest coastal zone, the sublittoral or subtidal zone, is always under water, but it is still influenced by wave action. Also called the nearshore, it extends from ELWS to the outer edge of the coast.

The vertical zonation of algae evident along coasts is related to the wavelengths of light that their various pigments can absorb (see Chapter 1). Chlorophyll, the pigment utilized by terrestrial plants for photosynthesis, occurs in the green seaweeds. Since green seaweeds absorb light primarily in the red (but also blue) wavelengths, they are restricted to the shallow depths of the upper eulittoral zone, for red light does not reach into deeper water. In red algae, chlorophyll is masked by pigments that absorb waves in the green and orange parts of the light spectrum.

They can use most of the wavelengths of visible light and can live at all depths in the coastal environment, although they tend to concentrate in the low-eulittoral and upper-sublittoral zones. Brown algae contain both chlorophyll and fucxanthin pigments. The latter absorbs the short wavelengths of blue-green light, and brown algae typically occupy habitat in the mid- and lower-eulittoral zones and down to depths of 30–50 ft (10–15 m) in the upper-sublittoral zone. Factors other than sunlight determine the vertical ranges of animals.

Latitude. Latitude affects yearly temperature patterns. In the coastal zone, the most important distinction is between polar latitudes, where sea ice is a factor, and nonpolar latitudes, where it is not. On the arctic shores of North America, Greenland, and Eurasia and on the coasts of Antarctica, pack ice—ice floes blown ashore and piled one on top of another—and fast ice can scrape the land and seabed clean of life, although some organisms do live in sea ice and annual algae may bloom in summer's open waters. Equatorward of the limits of sea ice, terrestrial vegetation lines the shore. The nature of the plant cover varies according to whether the region is tropical or temperate. Salt marshes are mostly temperate in distribution, whereas mangroves are for the most part restricted to tropical coasts. In the sublittoral zone and farther offshore (see Chapter 3), coral reefs are restricted to warm tropical waters and kelp forests to cold, temperate waters. Boundary currents may extend the latitudinal limits of some of these communities toward the Equator (in the case of cold currents) or toward the poles (in the case of warm currents).

Coasts: Environments of Constant Change

Waves create change in the coastal environment at time intervals measured at less than a minute. Tides commonly result in significant changes in water level every six hours. Seasons, whether evidenced by changes in temperature or rainfall, alter coasts every few months. Long-term change over centuries or millennia also occurs and is important in determining the nature of coastlines as well as the types of organisms that inhabit them. During the Pleistocene ice ages, some northern coasts were depressed well below sea level by the weight of overlying ice. When the northern ice sheets melted some 10,000 years ago, the coasts began to rebound. Some are still rising relative to modern sea level. In other places, broad areas of continental shelf were exposed when water that evaporated from the sea was held in the great ice sheets and sea level dropped. As dry land, the shelves were shaped by stream action; later, when the ice melted, they were flooded by rising sea levels. Today, warming of the oceans, associated with global climate change, is expanding seawater and causing a renewed rise in sea level that has already submerged the coasts of some Pacific and Caribbean islands. Even more than the melting ice cap of Greenland, continued warming-induced expansion threatens coasts around the globe, including the sites of many of the world's largest cities.

People have inhabited coasts, perhaps from the earliest beginnings of the human line. We have long exploited the living resources of the Coast Biome for food and have used sheltered harbors as hubs of commerce. Coastal vegetation has been altered or destroyed outright; estuaries and other inlets have been clogged with sediments; waters have been polluted. Because sediments and dissolved chemicals are carried into the oceans by rivers, human use of the land at great distances from the sea has affected the coast, usually negatively. However, positive actions are taking place, including the conservation of habitats and species in coastal marine reserves and national parks, the creation of artificial reefs, and the restoration of such coastal ecosystems as salt marsh and mangrove forests.

Rocky Coasts

Rocky coasts are areas where the sea is still eroding the solid bedrock foundation of continents and islands. Sea cliffs, headlands, and wave-cut terraces are common landforms, and they—as well as the life that lives on them—must bear the brunt of pounding waves and the abrasive sediments held in them. Water moving across the rock surface and its inhabitants creates three forces. *Drag* pushes objects in the direction of flow; its power increases as the area of an object increases. The force of *acceleration* increases with the volume of an object. *Lift* acts at a 90° angle to the direction of flow and can pry an object off the rock. Together, these three forces tend to limit the size of organisms on wave-swept shores, since larger forms are more easily dislodged by moving water than smaller ones.

Many forms of marine life have evolved ways other than small size to cling to the rocks and prevent being swept away. Sea squirts or tunicates, for example, produce a biological adhesive that sticks to wet surfaces. (It works somewhat like a sticky note: it is strong enough to hold them in place when necessary, but weak enough to let them be pealed off without being torn apart.) The mucus that snails lay down acts both as adhesive and as lubricant. Mussels tie themselves to rock with byssal threads, ropes of protein produced by the muscular foot of the mollusc. Crabs merely squeeze into crevices. The physics of flow is such that the wetted rocks are coated with a thin layer of slow-moving water called the boundary layer. Organisms that can stay in this layer are protected from the full force of the waves. Hence, encrusting coralline algae, sponges, and tunicates, and flat animals such as sea stars and chitons can thrive in rocky coastal habitats. Attached or sessile forms can create a habitat for mobile invertebrates by trapping sediments. As a thin layer of fine particles develops between the shells or other structures, it becomes home to polychaetes, gastropods, and crustaceans.

Hard surface shores are coated with a film of micro-organisms as are the shells of larger organisms and the fronds of algae. This microbial film consists of bacteria, cyanobacteria, diatoms, and protozoans and is an important food source for motile grazing invertebrates.

Attached or semiattached organisms on rocky shores depend on the waves to bring them oxygen and food in the form of dissolved nutrients, plankton, or organic debris and to carry away their wastes. Exposed coasts are dominated by filter-feeding animals that consume phytoplankton and other particles suspended in the turbulent ocean water and maintain a higher total biomass than sheltered coasts, where filter feeders are less prominent. Waves and currents are also essential for the dispersal of each species to new sites, either as floating larvae or as rafting adults.

Zonation

Vertical zonation, recognized by the presence of key species in characteristic assemblages, is visible and universal on rocky coasts (see Figure 2.2). The width of the bands can vary greatly from just a few inches to many feet: on sheltered coasts where wave action is weak, the bands are narrow; on exposed coasts where wave action is strong, the zones are wide. The actual organisms present may change

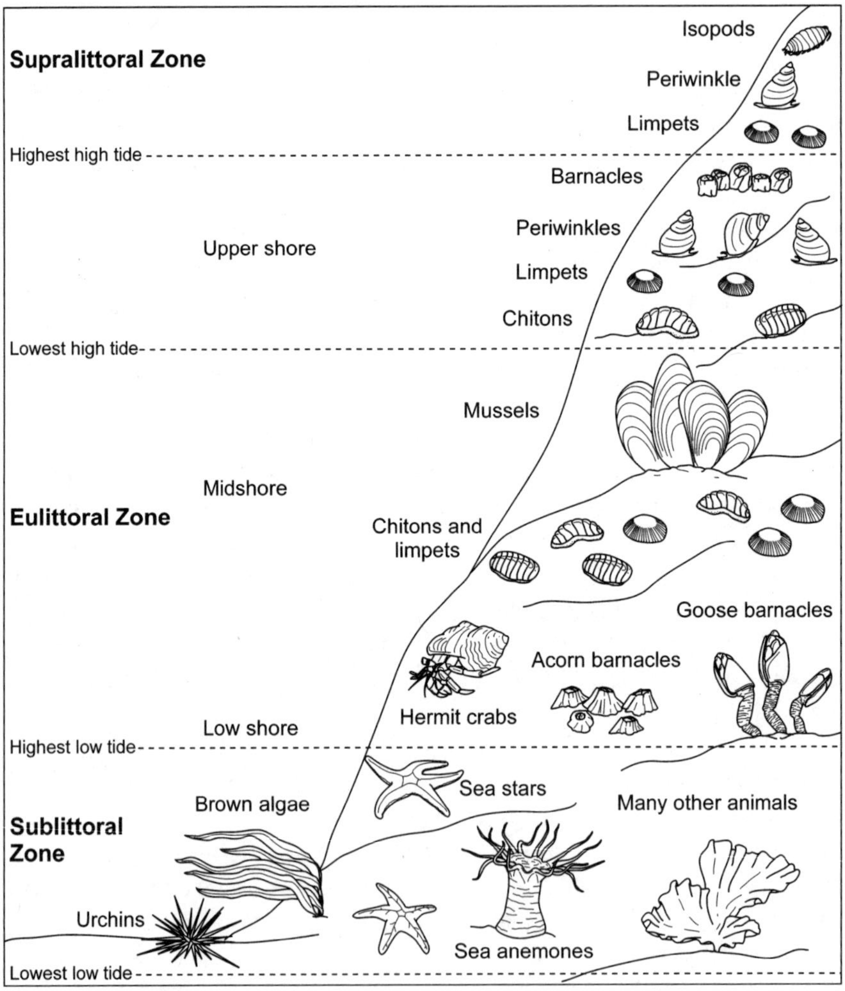

Figure 2.2 The vertical zonation of life on rocky coasts is similar around the world. *(Illustration by Jeff Dixon.)*

from one part of the world to the next, but similarity among the zones of widely separated regions is evident in terms of plant and animal morphology and community structure.

Supralittoral or sea spray zone. Rocks here are wetted by waves only during storms, but salt spray from breaking waves is a regular feature. The zone's upper limit is determined by the reach of salt spray; the lower boundary occurs where the rocks are submerged by the tide or by constant and strong wave action. Only a relatively few species occupy this zone, the top of which is essentially a land-based community of flowering plants tolerant of salt, lichens, and mosses. Black lichens and cyanobacteria occupy the lower part of the zone, known as the supralittoral fringe, and impart a distinct black line just above the high-tide mark to rocky coasts around the world. Depending on the latitude, other lichens may also be conspicuous as gray, blue-green, or orange belts.

Cyanobacteria are less important elements of this zone in polar areas and more important—to the point of being the only primary producers present—in tropical and subtropical regions. Many genera occur; and they also may grow in distinct bands, but their taxonomy is still too poorly known to be able to tell for sure. If splash from the surf is sufficient to keep the lowest part of the sea spray zone moist all or most of the time, some perennial seaweeds (red, brown, and green algae)—true marine species—may grow here also, but they are much more characteristic of the eulittoral (intertidal) and sublittoral (nearshore) zones. Those that do grow in this zone include the edible foliose red algae (*Porphyra*) known in Japan as *nori* and around the world as the seaweed that wraps *sushi.*

Rabbits and rodents inhabit the upper part of the supralittoral zone and attract foxes and other terrestrial predators. Seabirds such as fulmars and kittiwakes, puffins and murres nest in huge colonies on steep rocky coasts where their eggs and nestlings cling precariously to narrow ledges but are safe from predators. The most common and characteristic invertebrate residents of the lichen and cyanobacteria belt are periwinkles. Isopods are also common. The former are grazers, the latter eat detritus. Visiting the lower zone to scavenge or hunt are graspid crabs such as the Sally Lightfoot crab and hermit crabs, insects, birds, and small mammals.

Eulittoral or intertidal zone. Although displaying great complexity in environmental conditions and community structure, the intertidal region of coasts usually sorts itself into a few distinct bands commonly known, respectively, as the upper-shore, mid-shore, and low-shore zones. Typically in temperate regions, the upper shore is the barnacle zone. It also contains a limited number of species of upright perennial brown algae with an understory of small foliose red algae. A surface layer of crustose red algae and sometimes lichens is usual. Sometimes annual algae also occur.

In the tropics, cyanobacteria are especially abundant in this zone, their diversity increasing where wave action is strong. On the polar coasts of Arctic and Antarctic regions, this uppermost zone is generally scoured clean of life by ice. Perennial

Barnacles Settle In

Like many sessile invertebrates, barnacle life history is characterized by several stages. They start out as microscopic free-floating larvae called *nauplii* (singular = nauplius), part of the plankton riding the ocean currents. Nauplii change into second-stage larvae, tiny transparent *cypris*, which swim upward in the water column. Contact with a hard surface stimulates the cypris to crawl about looking for suitable attachment sites, apparently initially indicated by the presence of diatoms. If after closer inspection they find members of their own kind already there and other good signs, such as space, abundant prey, and few predators, the cypris attach themselves headfirst to the surface by means of a basal cement secreted by glands on their antennae. Settlement—the taking up of permanent residence—is completed by metamorphosis into the adult form and the production of the calcareous plates that will form a suit of armor around their bodies (see Figure 2.3).

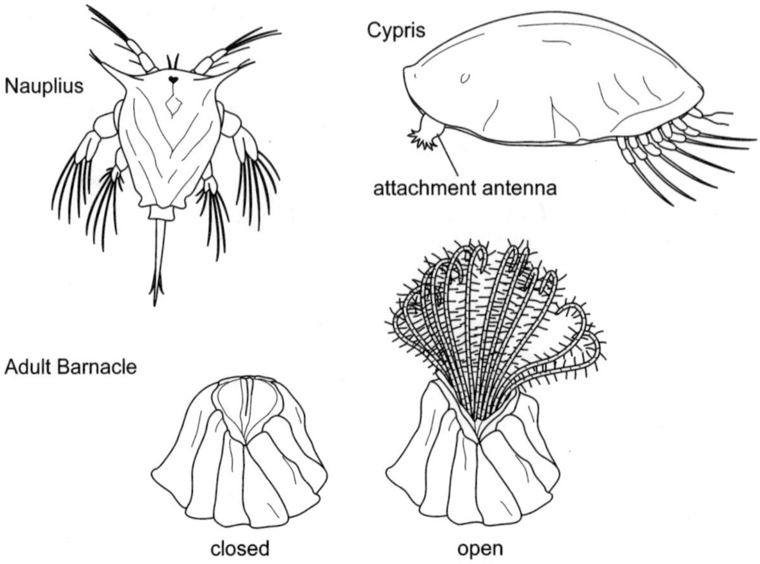

Figure 2.3 The life stages of a barnacle: The nauplius or first-stage larva is a microscopic member of the plankton. The cypris is just barely visible to the naked eye. This is the form that attaches to a hard surface. The adult barnacle when closed at low tide and when open and filtering food particles from coastal waters at high tide. *(Illustration by Jeff Dixon.)*

crustose red algae may survive in protected crevices. In the summer, diatoms and ephemeral green algae may temporarily occupy the upper shore.

The animals of the upper shore on exposed coasts are primarily filter-feeding sessile organisms that consume plankton and other particles suspended in seawater. Barnacles are widespread and dominant on the upper shore of exposed shores, although mussels are common and become dominant in severely exposed situations. Barnacles are permanently attached animals and may cover the surface to such a degree that other sessile or almost-sessile animals are excluded. Competition for space extends to mussels and to algae. Barnacles thrive in this part of the eulittoral where exposure to air is the longest in part because their shells protect them from dessication as well as predators. Their very presence seems to attract larvae of the same or related species so recruitment of new individuals is ensured.

Figure 2.4 Dark barnacles and light-colored limpets on a South African shore. The circular patches on the rock are scars left by grazing limpets. *(Photo by author.)*

The most common motile animal associated with barnacles is the limpet, a grazer that feeds on encrusted red algae and the biofilm of cyanobacteria. Limpets are able to clamp down on rock surfaces to make a waterproof seal and can lift the shell to promote evaporation if they need to cool off. They have fixed locations to which they return from feeding forays. Limpets of the genus *Patella* have rows of strong, horny teeth (the radula) capable of excavating the rock itself at their home sites and leaving visible scars on the rock surface (see Figure 2.4). Whelks are commonly among their main predators.

The mid-shore and low-shore zones may be seen as separate habitats or may be combined into a single zone depending on the location and the researcher. Either way, they possess higher species diversities than the upper shore. As is true for all coastal communities, the actual species present vary with latitude, ocean basin, and the degree of exposure of the coast to wave action. There can also be significant differences between what inhabits vertical and undercut rock surfaces and what may be found on more horizontal rock platforms.

Green, red, and brown algae all can occur in these lower intertidal zones. Mussels are significant members of the fauna on exposed coasts in temperate seas. Most widespread is *Mytilus edulis*, a species that occurs in both the Northern and

Tidepools

Tidepools always fascinate beachcombers during low tide. They are isolated bodies of water, part of the intertidal zone but not exactly representative of its submerged phase since they lack the effects of wave action and currents. Each tidepool is unique in its physical regime. Since they vary in area, depth, and volume, they respond differently to exposure under low-tide conditions. Small pools, especially, are vulnerable to changes in temperature and salinity that depend in large part on the weather of any given day. The temperature patterns will be more like those on land than in the ocean. High temperatures will increase evaporation rates, which can increase salinity and produce stratification of the water column. If the pool is in the upper-shore area and not flooded at high tide for several days in a row, the water may also become stratified by freezing temperatures or by the addition of freshwater from rains. Biological processes in the pool alter oxygen levels and pH. Nonetheless, the species composition of tidepools is similar to that on exposed intertidal surfaces, although there may be differences in relative abundance. Some zonation may be noticeable between high- and low-shore pools.

Southern Hemispheres. Mussels clump together in beds that provide habitat for a number of other species. The mussel matrix—the combination of shells and byssal attachments—decreases wave action, temperature, and sunlight; increases relative humidity; and traps sediments and detritus. A diverse association of macro-organisms takes advantage of these conditions. The epibiota lives on the shells or bores into them and may consist of encrusting coralline algae and ephemeral algae, sessile invertebrates such as barnacles, tube-building polychaetes, hydroids, and anemones. Limpets and chitons may visit the mussel bed to graze the algae.

Other motile animals finding food in the mid- and low-shore zones include various detritivores such as isopods, amphipods, and shrimps. An infauna dwells in the trapped inorganic and organic detritus. The mussels are not just a passive substrate for other organisms, but play an active role in maintaining the community. They filter huge amounts of particulate matter from the water column and release inorganic nutrients back into it. They are themselves a rich food source for a variety of predators, including sea stars, crabs, lobsters, fishes, and birds.

Sublittoral zone. The lowest part of the coast is only exposed during spring low tides. It is usually marked by the presence of large brown algae of the order Laminariales, the kelps. In kelp beds or the so-called kelp forests of cold temperate waters, red algae grow among the holdfasts as an understory below a canopy of laminarians floating up to 100 ft (30 m) above the seabed. Associated with kelp beds is a rich array of invertebrates, including herbivorous sea urchins and abalone. Sea urchins usually cluster in sedentary groups and feed on drift algae—the stipes and fronds of seaweeds that have broken off and float free, yet retain the ability to photosynthesize. Left as beach wrack on the shore at the high-tide mark, dead drift algae is an important energy source for intertidal and terrestrial detritivores. Under normal conditions the urchins apparently have no effect on the intact adult kelp population. For unknown reasons, however, urchins will sometimes form moving lines or "fronts" that consume huge amounts of attached kelp, decimating the beds and creating urchin barrens. Urchin numbers may be kept in check by predators such as sea stars, lobsters, fishes, and sea otters. Kelps are features of cooler waters. In warmer waters, a dense coating of tunicates and red algae replaces them.

Regional Expressions: Northern Hemisphere Temperate Waters

Many of the same genera are represented on rocky shores throughout the temperate Northern Hemisphere. The origins of many lie in the northeastern Pacific. Invasions from the Pacific into the North Atlantic during the mid-Pliocene were such that 83 percent of intertidal molluscs occurring on cold-temperate rocky shores of eastern North America are themselves invaders or have evolved from invaders from the Pacific. The contribution of new forms was much greater on the American side of the North Atlantic than the European side, although a number of genera and even species do occur on the coasts of both continents. Among the species found in both the northwest and northeast Atlantic are the periwinkles *Littorina saxatilus* and *L. obtusata*. Genera common to both sides include *Tectura* (limpets), *Nucella* (dog whelks), *Mytilus* (mussels), *Balanus* and *Semibalanus* (barnacles), *Strongylocentrus* (sea urchins), and *Chondrus* (red algae). These taxa, along with kelps, are among the more common and conspicuous elements of rocky coast communities everywhere in the North Atlantic.

Most of the better-studied rocky coasts are in the cold temperate regions of the Atlantic and Pacific oceans.

The two regions described below highlight both the diversity of species and the similarity in repeated community patterns of coasts separated from each other by a continent. (See Southern Hemisphere examples for comparison.)

Pioneering Studies

Early research on coastal communities led not only to a better understanding of specific coastal ecosystems but also to the development of some key concepts in modern ecology.

T. A. and A. Stephenson's landmark 1949 paper "The Universal Features of Zonation Between Tidemarks on Rocky Coasts," though purely descriptive, established the basic division of life zones still in use. Joseph H. Connell's experimental studies (1961) of barnacles on the rocky coasts of Scotland revealed the roles of interspecific competition and predation in community structure and became the basis of future field studies along aquatic and terrestrial environmental gradients. A few years later Robert T. Paine's work (1966) showed that predation and herbivory can actually increase the number of species occupying a given site. This led to the concept of a "keystone species"—a species that effects ecological relationships within a community to a degree way out of proportion to its abundance.

Salt marsh ecology also played an early and integral part in the development of ecological theory. The pioneering study of energy flow in the Sapelo, Georgia, salt marsh by John M. Teal (1962) helped set the stage for much of the research in ecosystem functioning conducted during the latter part of the twentieth century.

Northwest Atlantic rocky coasts: a cold temperate biota. The northeast coast of North America, including the Gulf of Maine and Atlantic coasts of Nova Scotia and Newfoundland, Canada, is bathed in the cold temperate waters of the Labrador Current. Coastal upwelling also contributes cool water in the northeastern part of the Gulf of Maine and along the southwestern shores of Nova Scotia. This is a coast of granitic headlands and sandstone beaches uplifted by crustal rebound at the end of the Pleistocene. Overall species diversity is low in comparison with the northeast Atlantic or the northeast Pacific, despite the fact that there is considerable regional variation in temperature, tidal range, wave exposure, nutrient inputs, and ice scour.

Rocks of the supralittoral or splash zone are home to cyanobacteria from several genera and ephemeral macroalgae, both red and green. Black lichens form a distinct dark band at the base of the zone. Periwinkles are the dominant grazers.

On semiexposed coasts, the eulittoral or intertidal zone has three clearly distinguished belts. Uppermost is a barnacle zone densely populated by the acorn barnacle. The dogwhelk is its chief predator. The mid-shore is generally a brown algal zone. In sheltered areas the dominant fucoid is *Ascophyllum nodosum*; on semiexposed shores it is joined or replaced by *Fucus vesciculosis*. Brown algae disappear with increasing exposure; the edible mussel occupies most space on severely exposed sites. On semiexposed coasts brown algae must compete for space with barnacles and mussels. They are most successful where predation by whelks and other animals creates open patches among the sessile molluscs. Brown algae will be out-competed in this zone by ephemeral red algae and green algae, both the leafy sea lettuce and the more grass-like green string lettuce, if they are not held in check by grazers. Herbivores include amphipods, snails, and limpets.

The lowest part of the eulittoral is a red algal zone occupied by two edible foliose "mosses" that are harvested for use as emulsifiers and thickeners in the food and pharmaceutical industries. Carrageen moss dominates on vertical surfaces, whereas Irish moss is the most abundant red alga on horizontal ones. Heavy grazing of ephemeral algae by an invasive species, the common periwinkle, lets Irish moss flourish. Predators of mussels, including sea stars, shore crabs, lobsters, and sea ducks such as Common Eider, reduce or eliminate mussel beds that would also compete for space. Other grazers of algae in the lower eulittoral are chitons and sea urchins. Their predators include whelks, crabs, and sea stars. Algae are essentially absent from the most exposed sites, where, instead, mussels are found in large numbers. Strong surf keeps most of their predators away.

The sublittoral zone has kelps as dominants. Among them are horsetail kelp, sugar kelp, and sea colander. Irish moss dominates the understory, but red fern—a filamentous red alga—is also prevalent and may form its own belt at the bottom of the zone. Crustose coralline algae of several genera cover the seabed. Grazers in the kelp beds include limpets, periwinkles, and sea urchins. Snails graze on sea colander, filamentous red algae, and diatom films, while isopods concentrate on the coralline ground layer. Sea urchins can be dominant elements in the sublittoral zone, responsible for what some scientists call two alternative states of the community. When sea urchins are rare, the kelps and other macroalgae are abundant; when urchin numbers are high, the kelps are overgrazed and coralline algae dominate.

In the kelp beds, a red algae understory is habitat for motile invertebrates such as shrimps, amphipods, isopods, and juvenile crabs. Sessile invertebrates attach to the fronds of algae. Kelps may host colonies of hydroids, and red algae can have a coating of hydroids, tunicates, and the spat of mussels.

Predators of this zone include lobsters, the Jonah crab, green crabs, sea stars, and fishes such as winter flounder, haddock, eelpout, and wrasse. Sea ducks such as Red-breasted Mergansers, Common Goldeneye, and Old Squaw consume both invertebrates and small fish.

A Most Successful Invader

During the middle of the nineteenth century the common periwinkle greatly expanded its distribution and numbers along American coasts in the North Atlantic and became the most abundant rocky coast herbivore in the region. It is not native to the northwest Atlantic and is generally assumed to have been transported from Europe by early settlers of Nova Scotia. Some question lingers, however, as to just when it arrived. While the mid-1800s seem a logical time for invasion, some evidence suggests it may have been on North American coasts in small numbers since the days of the Vikings, or that it may even have crossed the ocean from Europe in the late Pleistocene.

Northeast Pacific rocky coasts: a warm temperate biota. Three faunal provinces or distinct assemblages of animals are recognized along the west coast of North America. North of Point Conception, California, is a cold-temperate region under the influence of the Alaska and California currents. Fogs produced over these two cold currents tend to reduce the dryness of low-tide conditions, especially in spring and summer. Species-rich Monterey Bay with its magnificent kelp forest and charismatic sea otters lies in this province. Once the California Current is deflected away from the coast (at approximately Point Conception), coastal waters are warmer and central California, a region from approximately Santa Cruz south to the U.S.-Mexico border has warm-temperate marine communities. Off the Baja California peninsula, the ocean environment is considered tropical, even though seasonal upwelling of cool waters is experienced. The description that follows focuses on Central California as an example of the Northern Hemisphere's warm-temperate, exposed rocky coast environment. This habitat is scattered in patches at headlands on the mainland and along the coasts of the Channel Islands. This is a region of mediterranean climate with subtropical temperature patterns and an annual precipitation pattern of dry summers and wet winters.

The supralittoral fringe or spray zone is usually barren, although in places a film of cyanobacteria covers the rocks. During the wetter parts of the year—winter and spring—ephemeral green algae (sea lettuces) and red algae are present, as are mats of benthic diatoms. The few animals in this zone are mostly limpets, periwinkles, and isopods.

The upper-shore zone of the eulittoral is commonly covered with dense populations of barnacles. Tufts of red turfweed and another red algal "moss" grow with rockweed, a brown alga. Grazers include a small periwinkle, turban snail, and several limpets.

Mid-shore on moderate to fully exposed coasts is the domain of filter-feeding mussels and gooseneck barnacles. On more sheltered sites, they will be joined by herbivorous chitons. Whelks are important predators in the zone. Where space allows, the iridescent blade red alga grows.

The low shore is covered by a dense growth of surfgrass, kelps, and numerous red algae. Surfgrass is a true flowering plant with roots, stems, and leaves. Like other seagrasses, it serves as an important nursery area for marine invertebrates and fishes.

The most visible and noteworthy aspect of the sublittoral or subtidal zone are the large kelps whose blades reach up to and float on the surface of the water. This kelp forest extends seaward onto the continental shelf and is described in Chapter 3.

Regional Expressions: Southern Hemisphere Temperate Waters

Rocky coasts of the Southern Hemisphere display much the same zonation patterns as described above for the Northern Hemisphere shores. However, separated from the northern coasts by vast tropical seas, the coasts of southern Africa and southern South America possess different sets of organisms. The examples selected for description are coastal situations most comparable to those already described for the east and west coasts of North America.

Southern Africa. The southern tip of Africa has three coastal environments. The west coast, from the Cape of Good Hope north along the Skeleton Coast of Namibia, faces the South Atlantic and the cold Benguela Current with its sea surface temperatures (SST) of 48°–59° F (9°–15° C). Upwelling creates nutrient-rich waters. The east coast, from Cape Agulhas to latitude 26° S, faces the Indian Ocean and is influenced by the strong Agulhas Current, which brings warm waters south from the tropics. It has a subtropical marine environment with average SST ranging from 72°–81°F (22°–27° C). Regular wind-generated upwelling brings cool water (54°–59°F or 12°–15° C) and nutrients up from the bottom along the Agulhas Bank, which runs from Port Elizabeth, South Africa, to Cape Agulhas. Between Cape Agulhas and the Cape of Good Hope, the South Coast is a mixing area of the Benguela and Agulhas currents. This warm-temperate region experiences ocean temperatures of 70°–79° F (21°–26° C). The west coast has relatively few species, but each tends to occur in great abundance; the east coast has high species diversity, but each species tends to occur in low numbers; and the south coast is characterized by a high degree of endemism among its animals.

The west-coast environment is most comparable to the northeast Pacific, since both are affected by the cold eastern boundary currents of their respective ocean basins and strong wave action. The rocks of the splash zone or supralittoral zone have mossy patches of red algae and clumps of foliose red algae. A periwinkle is the dominant grazer, but other snails from the eulittoral zone also occur. Limpets are present as well. In the upper eulittoral or intertidal zone, limpets are the most abundant animal seen. The barnacle cover is sparse and composed of the same three kinds found on the east and south coasts. Uppermost in the zone is a belt of high-growing foliose red algae. With increasing depth the algal cover becomes more diverse. Green sea lettuce is prominent in the mid-shore. Toward the lower mid-shore green algae are joined by and then replaced by different red algae and finally brown algae, all of which continue into the lowest parts of the intertidal zone. In the low-shore region, rocks are encrusted with red algae and with the sandy tubes of colonial polychaetes. Other animals in the lowest parts of the zone include blue-black mussels, limpets of the genus *Scutellaria*, and anemones. Just above the low-tide mark, the ribbed mussel is abundant. African Black Oystercatchers specialize on limpets, while Kelp Gulls select snails at low tide. The giant clingfish pries limpets from the rock when the intertidal zone is flooded.

The sublittoral or subtidal zone on the west coast is occupied by a kelp forest. The dominant giant bamboo kelp is a key part of both the three-dimensional structure of the community and its food chain. Pieces broken off by strong waves form masses of drift that collect on beaches as a wrack line and, on rocky shores, are consumed by isopods. (See Chapter 3 for a discussion of this kelp forest's role in the marine environment above the continental shelf.) Some unique ecological connections between land and sea exist along the west coast of southern Africa. The Cape clawless otter lives on land, but in this region a distinct population feeds in the shallow coastal waters, where it hunts bottom-dwelling fish, rock crab, octopus, and rock lobster. At the Cape of Good Hope, chacma baboons forage among rocks at low tide and in the kelp wrack on the beach for mussels, limpets, lobsters, rock crabs, and the egg cases of sharks, from which they extract egg yolk and embryonic sharks.

The great populations of cormorants and Cape Gannets that roost and nest on offshore islands deposit huge quantities of nitrogen-rich guano on the rocks. This runs off in rain and high surf to fertilize the rock platforms edging the island and stimulates the growth of phytoplankton. The zooplankters that then feed on these floating microalgae are food for the sardines and pilchards that are consumed by the seabirds. Before the guano was mined for fertilizer in the mid-1800s, African Penguins burrowed into the thick deposits to lay their eggs (see Plate IIIa). Now the dwindling penguin populations are more apt to place their nests between boulders or shrubs or in burrows dug in sand.

Chile. Rocky coasts are common between 18° and 42° S latitude along the west coast of South America. Here the cold eastern boundary current of the South Pacific, the Humboldt Current, and upwelling bring cold-temperate conditions well into the tropics. The supralittoral zone in the northern (low latitude) parts of the region are under intense sunlight and support only patches of dark red encrusting algae. The upper eulittoral is, as is almost always the case on rocky shores, a barnacle zone. Two species dominate. The mid-shore zone typically has a wide band of mussels, as well as bands or patches of green-red algae. The low shore contains several different algal and faunal assemblages depending on slope. Horizontal surfaces support red algae. These are grazed by chitons in the higher parts of the zone and keyhole limpets in the lower reaches. Shaded vertical surfaces sport velvety mounds of a fleshy green alga. Chief grazers are small limpets. Fishes are important grazers and predators at high tide throughout the intertidal zone, at the base of which is a band of kelp-like brown algae that extends into the sublittoral. American Oystercatchers take limpets and snails at low tide.

In the deeper water of the sublittoral, the kelps are joined by red algae, and grazers include the black sea urchin, a large chiton, and the black snail. Marine otters are among the predators feeding on crustaceans, molluscs, and fishes. The Humboldt Penguin breeds on offshore islands, as do guano-producing cormorants and pelicans. These birds consume fish and cycle the nutrients of the sea onto the land at their roosts and nesting sites. In some locations, Southern sea lions also haul out on the shore.

Along the coasts of southern Chile (42°–55° S), south of Chilöe, the climate is cool and humid—not unlike that of the Pacific Northwest of the United States. The coast is indented with fjords, and south of 48° S some are still fed by glaciers from the Andes. On sheltered shores and offshore islands, lichens form several vegetational bands in the supralittoral. The upper eulittoral is a narrow band about 10 in (30 cm) wide with a cover of red algae and the free-living, filamentous brown alga. Below it is a barnacle and mussel zone without macroalgae that may be 20 in (50 cm) wide. The primary predator is a large whelk, but sea stars are also present. The low shore has a band of pink calcareous crusting algae grazed by limpets. The base of the eulittoral is marked by the presence of the kelp-like *Lessonia vadosa*. During high tide, the eulittoral zone is visited by a number of fishes, including the Chilean comb-tooth blenny, which gnaws green and red algae from the rocks. The common Chilean clingfish is an amphibious omnivore throughout the zone. Its modified pectoral fins act as a suction disk and allow it to attach to rocks in the surf zone. Able to breathe air, this large clingfish can remain out of water for hours at a time if it stays moist under rocks or seaweed. It consumes both limpets and macroalgae. Carnivorous fishes such as triplefins and a different clingfish, eat amphipods, crabs, polycheates, and snails.

The subtidal zone is conspicuous as a 150–300 ft (50–100 m) wide true kelp forest with a floating canopy of giant kelp. Marine otters and southern sea lions feed in these southern waters. Magellanic Penguins replace the Humboldts that occur closer to the Equator (see also Chapter 3).

Tropical coasts. The intensity of sunlight in the tropics—where solar radiation strikes Earth at angles close to 90° all year—together with the high temperatures and high evaporation rates at low tide eliminate most seaweeds from the spray and upper-intertidal zones. The supralittoral zone also has no foliose lichens such as encountered in temperate latitudes. Instead, a thin layer of crustose lichens and cyanobacteria coat the rock surfaces. When wetted by spray or rainwater, periwinkles graze in the zone. At night, when humidity is higher, hermit crabs arrive from the land to scavenge and grapsid crabs come up from the intertidal zone to hunt. The intertidal zone has a film of cyanobacteria accompanied by filamentous green algae. Both provide food for limpets, chitons, snails, isopods, and amphipods. Herbivorous fish enter the zone during high tide; grapsid crabs with uniquely spoon-shaped claws come at low tide to scrape algae off the rocks. Only below the mean low-tide level does coastal life become diverse. This is particularly true on coral reefs (see Chapter 3).

Antarctic rocky shores. Antarctica and its offshore islands have their coasts bulldozed clean by ice to depths greater than 45 ft (15 m), preventing the growth of perennial macroalgae and sessile animals. However, at depths below the scouring effect of ice such organisms may abound. In summer, ice-free areas occur on the Antarctic Peninsula, Adelie Land, and islands such as the South Shetlands; and these exhibit the same zonation pattern seen elsewhere in the world, although considerable variation exists from place to place depending on the amounts of ice and snow present. Many of the species occurring on Antarctic rocky coasts are endemic to the region. The supralittoral fringe is marked by black lichens. The upper eulittoral (intertidal) has a felt-like cover of annual diatoms and filamentous green algae. In the lower eulittoral, annual red and green algae dominate. The base of the eulittoral zone is marked by a belt of black marine lichen that continues to grow on rocks some 30 ft (9 m) below the mean low-water level in the sublittoral zone. In addition to the lichen, a number of red algae occur in the sublittoral zone, including the encrusting corallines.

Animals tend to concentrate in the lower-eulittoral and sublittoral zones. Antarctic limpets dominate and graze on the diatom felt and encrusting algae during high water. Also occurring are dense clusters of small bivalves, a chiton, gastropods, several amphipods, an isopod, nemertine or ribbon worms, and flatworms (turbellarians). The less the impact of ice, the greater the variety of organisms.

Under fast ice, as in McMurdo Sound, life is also abundant. On hard substrates macroalgae and attached suspension-feeders again demonstrate a clear zonation. In shallow water an iridescent blade red alga is abundant; it is replaced in dominance at intermediate depths by another red alga, *Phyllophora antarctica*, and brown macroalgae. Below 80 ft (25 m) the very large Antarctic kelp with its 3 ft (1 m) wide blades is most conspicuous. Animal life occurs in three distinct zones. From 0–50 ft (0–15 m) is a bare zone much of the year, but when it is freed of ice sea urchins, sea stars, ribbon worms, a large isopod, and notothenid fish such as emerald rockfish enter the zone to feed on polychaetes, amphipods, and molluscs. At intermediate depths of 80–150 ft (15–33 m), cnidarians such as sea anemones, soft corals, tunicates, and hydroids dominate. A sharp divide exists between the cnidarian zone and the sponge zone below it. Extending down to depths of nearly 600 ft (180 m), a sponge zone is made up of a diverse array of sponge species that resembles the variety of forms hard corals assume in tropical reefs. There are staghorns, fans, bushes, and "volcano" sponges. Like coral reefs, they serve as refuge for motile species and attachment sites for sessile anemones, hydroids, bryozoans, and a number of different molluscs. The bivalve *Limatula hodgonsii* is especially abundant. Sea stars and a nudibranch are the principal predators of sponges.

Soft-Sediment Coasts

Physical Environment

Loose particles of various sizes accumulate along coasts where deposition is the primary geomorphic process. These materials range in size from pebbles to coarse sands to fine sands to silts and clays (mud). They move in from other areas on currents and by wave action. The size at any particular beach depends on the velocity of longshore currents, strength of wave action, and the types of particles available for transport. On exposed shores, where wave action is strong, pebble beaches form. In the shelter of enclosed bays and estuaries, mudflats occur. Most common are quartz sands and volcanic (basaltic) sands that originated on land and carbonate sands formed from marine deposits of both biological and geological origin. In the eulittoral or intertidal zone, a gradient of particle sizes occurs in which coarser materials occupy areas high on the shore and finer particles concentrate at low-tide levels.

Soft-sediment coastal environments differ in several significant ways from those of rocky shores (see Table 2.1). They are three-dimensional; that is, zonation occurs as horizontal or surface bands influenced by elevation and tidal range and as vertical layers varying according to depth below the surface of substrate. Organisms live not just on the beach (the epibiota) but within the beach (the infauna). Furthermore, soft-sediment shores are habitats characterized by instability. The small particles are continually moved about by the swash and backwash of waves. In many instances, the organisms living on and in the sand and mud move the substrate particles around themselves as they dig, burrow, and feed in a process known as bioturbation. Even the biological aspect of the environment is always changing since the fauna of sandy beaches is highly mobile. Attached forms so characteristic of rocky shores are virtually absent.

The entire beach may disappear and reappear. Sand is moved along a beach by wind, waves, and currents. If the supply is blocked, as by a groin, or if erosion is accelerated by storm action, the beach can vanish altogether. In the mid-latitudes, it is common for beaches to become greatly reduced in size during winter as a result of increased storm activity, but come spring and summer broad sandy beaches form once again.

Geomorphologists refer to two extremes defining the dynamics of soft-sediment shore environments. At one end of the spectrum are dissipative beaches, where gentle slopes and strong wave action create a wide surf zone in which wave energy is dispersed and thereby reduced. Fine sands (<200 μm) are deposited. Such gently sloping shores often have high tidal ranges. Incoming and outgoing tides pump water through the spaces between sand grains and renew oxygen supplies and remove wastes. The intertidal or eulittoral zone of such beaches usually supports a varied infauna.

At the opposite end of the spectrum are reflective beaches, which bounce waves off the shore at their full strength. Slopes on such beaches may be as steep as 25° and particle sizes will range from coarse sands to pebbles and cobbles that compose so-called shingle beaches. The incoming swash has more impact than tides in pumping water through the sediments. Because of large particle size, water is not easily held in interstitial spaces so the surface layer dries out rapidly during low water conditions.

Ecologists may recognize four kinds of soft-sediment shores as more or less distinct habitat types:

- Shingle or pebble beaches are those with the largest particles. The slope is steep and wave action strong.
- Open sand beaches are semiexposed and affected by wave action. They have moderate slopes and behind them are wind-blown dunes. These beaches have a smooth profile often altered by storms and are composed of coarse to fine sands.
- Protected sand beaches receive little impact from wave action. They have low-angle slopes and are composed of fine and very fine sand.
- Lastly, protected mudflats at the head of inlets and on the landward sides of barrier islands are areas where wave action is slight, allowing the smallest particles to settle out. Organic detritus and fine sediments are deposited on gentle slopes. These become locations where salt marshes and, in the tropics, mangroves may develop.

Particle size strongly influences a key control of the distribution of life in soft-sediment areas, the rate of infiltration of water. Rates are highest in coarse beach deposits, leaving the upper levels dry at low tide and allowing repeated flushing of wastes and renewal of nutrients and oxygen. Deposits of fine particles become and stay saturated and stagnant. Water may be held between particles (that is, interstitial water) in upper levels or replaced from below by capillary action. This gives rise to vertical stratification in sand beaches at low tide. The surface zone will become dry due to evaporation and the gravitational descent of water to deeper parts of the deposit. Below the surface zone is the zone of retention, where water is lost by gravity but then replaced by capillary action. This zone provides the best conditions for organisms living in the beach: adequate water, oxygen, food, and substrate stability. Below it lies a zone of resurgence into which gravity pulls water from above. The deepest level is a zone of permanent saturation, stagnant and deficient in oxygen (see Figure 2.5).

The moisture conditions of the vertical zones are repeated across the surface of the shore. The highest part of the beach has dry sand, lower intertidal areas are zones of retention, and the subtidal area has a permanently saturated substrate. The horizontal zonation of soft-sediment coasts can be described in terms of supralittoral (spray zone), eulitttoral (intertidal), and sublittoral (subtidal), just as rocky coasts are, but the zones are not as readily evident and shift with tides, seasons, and storms. And since sandy shore species are mobile, some animals change their location on the beach with every tide.

Yet another classification scheme for zonation takes into account beach dynamics, and identifies a Dune Zone above the level of spring high tides and a Beach Zone from the drift or wrack line to the extreme low-water mark. The beach

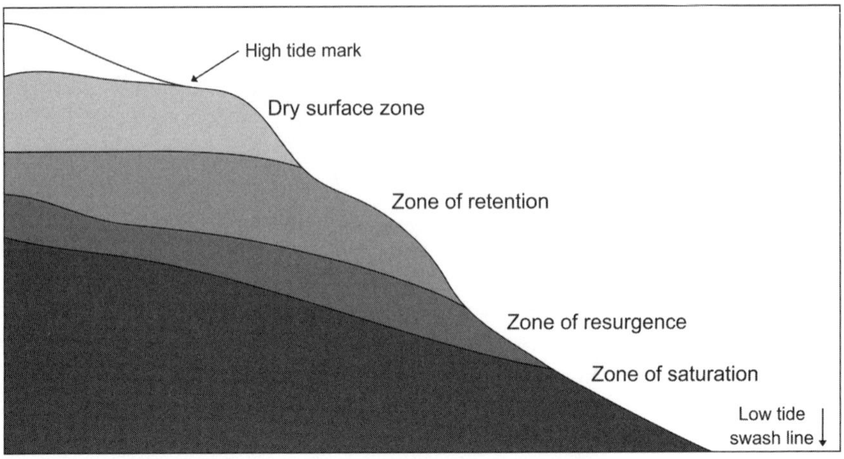

Figure 2.5 Vertical zonation on sandy beaches. *(Illustration by Jeff Dixon. Adapted from Knox 2001.)*

is sectioned into a backshore zone that is covered only during spring high tides or storms and a foreshore that extends from the highest reach of wave swash to the low-water mark. The Nearshore Zone, the counterpart of the sublittoral, extends from the low-tide level out to the depth at which wave action no longer erodes the seabed. It can be subdivided into an Inner Turbulent Zone (that is, a surf zone) where waves break and an Outer Turbulent Zone where orbiting water particles are still circular or nearly so and stable (see Figure 2.6).

Life on Soft-Sediment Coasts

Primary producers. Photosynthesis on soft-sediment coasts is done almost exclusively by a microflora of bacteria, cyanobacteria, diatoms, and autotrophic flagellates. Macroalgae are absent unless there are bits of hard material such as shells and stones buried beneath the sediments to which they can attach. Some microorganisms adhere to sand grains, but others live free in the interstices between grains. Sunlight sufficient for photosynthesis penetrates only 0.2 in (5 mm) into the sand, but motile members of the microflora undergo daily vertical migrations, coming to the surface to reach sunlight during daytime low tides and then descending into the sand when the water level rises and at night. In the surf zone on beaches exposed to strong wave action, there may be large enough numbers of diatoms in the phytoplankton to form visible patches in the water. Microorganisms and small macroalgae also occur as epiphytes, growing on hard surfaces such as stones and shells, on the stems of marsh grasses, the leaves of seagrasses, the root of mangroves, or the fronds of macroalgae.

Consumers. The interstitial fauna must be adapted to high rates of water flow through the spaces between sand grains, to the dryness of low tide, and to the ever-

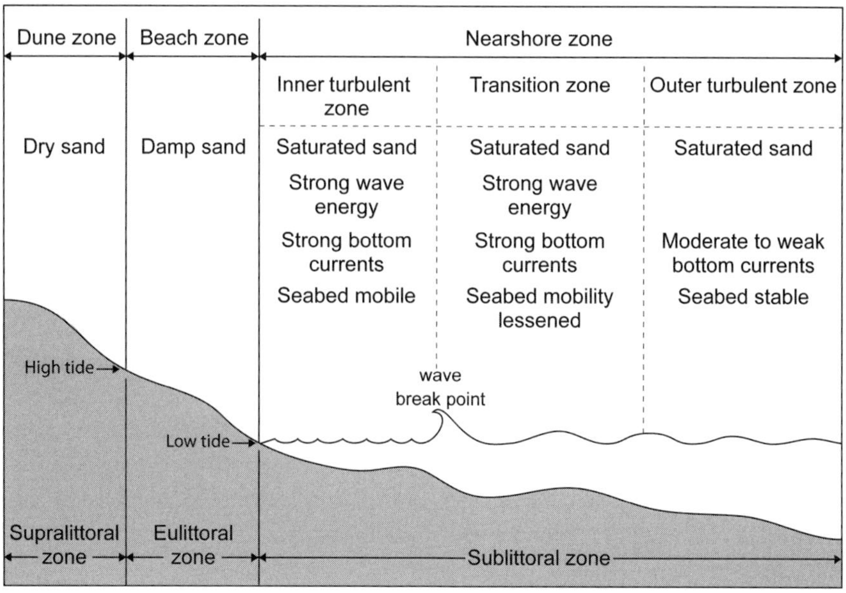

Figure 2.6 Horizontal zonation on sandy beaches. *(Illustration by Jeff Dixon. Adapted from Knox 2001.)*

shifting nature of the sediments among which they live. In the zone of retention, oxygen is not limiting, but at lower levels and in finer deposits, the environment is depleted of oxygen (anoxic) everywhere except in a shallow surface layer and in and around the tubes and burrows of macro-organisms. Without the flushing of detritus that occurs in coarser-grained deposits, fine muds and silts can become rich in organic matter, the food of detritivores. Most animals are very small (members of the meiofauna) but are important links in detritus food chains, because they either graze on decomposers (bacteria and fungi) or themselves consume and break down organic detritus. Some live in the beach sands only while they are larvae; as adults they become part of the benthic macroinvertebrate fauna. Others, such as rotifers, certain copepods, ostracods, tubellarians, nematodes, and many other taxa, are permanent residents. Some are nonselective filter-feeders, others are specialized predators, and yet others are omnivores. The mucus that some of these organisms excrete actually supports the growth of the bacteria and speeds the decomposition of organic matter. In so doing it provides more food for the consumers of bacteria.

The macrofauna of exposed sandy beaches is dominated by polychaete or bristle worms, crustaceans, echinoderms, and molluscs. Cnidarians—soft corals and anthozoans, in particular—can also be important. Fishes, both herbivores and carnivores, are significant components of the beach community during high water. Polycheates burrow into the sediment or construct tubes that protrude above the surface. Among them are filter-feeders, deposit-feeders, and selective predators.

Crustaceans include isopods, amphipods, crabs, and ghost shrimp, and they may burrow, swim, or crawl across the surface. Some build tubes. Crustaceans utilize all feeding strategies, even parasitism and scavenging. Echinoderms are represented by sea stars, brittle stars, sand dollars, sea urchins, and sea cucumbers. All live on or very near the surface of the substrate. The molluscs include deposit-feeding gastropods and carnivorous nudibranchs and octopi, as well as suspension- and deposit-feeding bivalve clams.

In general, invertebrates fall into one of three functional groups on the shore. Bioturbators destabilize the substrate such that muds and finer sands are resuspended in the water column, moved around on the beach, or eroded away. They do this by digging, burrowing, or deposit-feeding. Other invertebrates are sediment stabilizers; their activities bind grains of sand together. They may build tubes and other structures on or in the sediment that serve to reduce the resuspension of fine particles and promote deposition instead. Fecal pellets, often produced in great amounts and expelled onto the surface, can stick particles together to form a crust that resists disturbance. Finally, some organisms irrigate the sediments. Their tubes and burrows modify the subsurface environment by letting water circulate through it, oxygenating the immediate surroundings and removing wastes.

On sandy shores all invertebrates need ways to keep themselves from being washed away by waves and tides. Burrowing into the sediment is the most effective and widespread means. Crustaceans can use their jointed legs to dig, but they don't all do it the same way. Mole crabs quickly back into their holes, but most others burrow in sideways. The soldier crab acts like a corkscrew and twists itself into the sand. Isopods go in head first.

Soft-bodied worms and molluscs must depend on different mechanisms. Typically they inflate some part of the body to make an anchor and then draw the rest down to it, repeating the process as necessary to reach a suitable depth. The lugworm goes in head first, inflates its pharynx; and then pulls the other segments down. A bivalve will use its muscular foot to accomplish the same thing.

Animals of the meiofauna, smaller than grains of sand (0.5–100 μm), are often long and thin. They can wriggle among and adhere to the sand grains. Nematodes and copepods are most abundant among the meiofauna that spend their lives below the surface but require no true burrows.

In addition to active burrowers, some animals avail themselves of the bodies or constructions of others. Hydroids attach to the shells of bivalves such as surf clams and become hitchhikers. When their hosts are buried below the sand, they stretch their bodies into the water to feed. A number of animals simply occupy burrows excavated by others. For example, the U-shaped burrow of a ghost shrimp (*Callianassa californiensis*) may be inhabited by five different species at the same time. The most common "freeloaders" are a polychaete scale worm (*Hesperonoë adventor*), a pea crab (*Scleroplax granulata*), and a fish, the goby *Clevelandia*. The small clam *Cryptomya* hides in the mud near the shrimp's burrow so that it can insert its siphon into the oxygenated water within.

Scavengers and predators are common on sandy beaches, where suspension-feeders are abundant but buried below the surface and stranded sealife makes for nutrient-rich though unpredictable sources of food. Most carnivores are highly opportunistic surface dwellers. They either sit in ambush or dig and probe into the sediments for prey. Beach tiger beetle (*Cincincela dorsalis*), an endangered species in the Chesapeake Bay area, is an ambusher in its larval stage but an active hunter as an adult. On tropical and subtropical shores, ghost crabs are prevalent. They actively pursue their prey, but will also scavenge the dead ones washed up on the sand. Shorebirds such as sandpipers, plovers, and oystercatchers are the most conspicuous vertebrates hunting on the beach. From September through April, they may occur by the thousands on their wintering grounds in both hemispheres. Most breed during the Northern Hemisphere summer high in the Arctic and migrate in huge flocks along distinct flyways, stopping off periodically at traditional staging posts to feed. The sandpipers and oystercatchers hunt by feel. They walk along probing the sand with their long bills. Plovers are visual hunters. They stand still scanning the beach for movement then quickly peck at any prey they have spotted with their short bills.

The species composition of sandy shore communities varies with latitude, but is rather similar within broad latitudinal belts. This means that opposite sides of an ocean the same distance from the Equator display a certain sameness in organisms; greater differences arise among tropical, temperate, and polar regions of a given ocean basin. Although most phyla and families occur everywhere, different phyla will dominate at different latitudes.

Regional Expressions: Sandy Beaches

Temperate areas. The intertidal zone of a sandy beach in temperate regions often seems empty of life, and the upper parts especially do contain many fewer species than the subtidal zone. However, the animals are often below the surface and highly mobile, so their presence is difficult to detect with standard sampling techniques, and the fauna is not as well known as that of rocky shores. Even so, some zonation can be recognized by even the casual observer.

The supralittoral fringe may contain salt-tolerant land plants such as saltworts, glassworts, and salt marsh grasses. On beaches without salt marsh or mangrove, air-breathing crustaceans such as beach fleas (amphipods) are prevalent. Air-breathing crabs and isopods can also occur in considerable numbers.

The intertidal zone generally lacks macroalgae. Animals occupy the zone of retention, where it remains damp at low tide, but oxygen and nutrient supplies are regularly refreshed by water infiltrating the sands. This infauna includes various marine isopods and amphipods, burrowing polychaetes and calianassid shrimps, and swash-riding mole crabs and burrowing surf clams (see Figure 2.7).

On the east coast of the United States, they may be preyed upon by the ghost crab, itself a burrowing animal. In finer-grained sediments in more sheltered

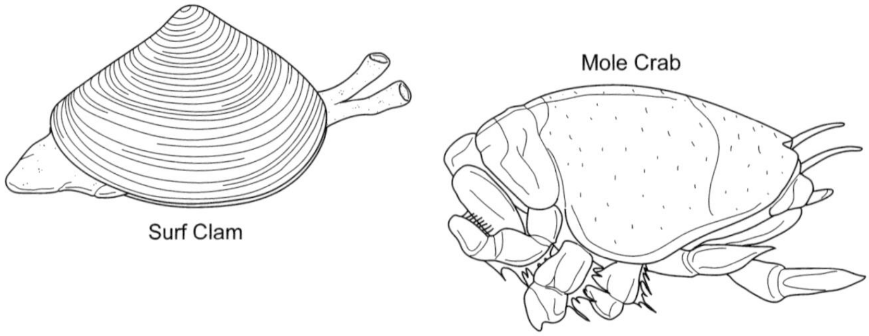

Figure 2.7 Invertebrate surfers: a surf clam, and a mole crab. *(Illustration by Jeff Dixon. Adapted from Lippson and Lippson 1984.)*

settings, deposit-feeders are varied and abundant. Some, such as the lugworm, a polychaete, is a major bioturbator of worldwide distribution. It forms U-shaped burrows and ejects fecal pellets onto the surface in piles of looping castings that are familiar to many beachcombers. Deposit-feeding shrimps are also worldwide in occurrence. Bivalves are suspension-feeders and are represented by the small clam *Tellina modesta* on the west coast of the United States and the large hard-shelled clam or Northern quahog (*Mercenaria mercenaria*) along the east coast. Elsewhere cockles (*Cardium* and *Cerastoderma*) may occur in huge numbers.

Among echinoderms found along sheltered, fine-sediment shores are the globally occurring heart urchins and sand dollars. Snails that can drill through the shells of bivalves are common predators, as are a great variety of shorebrds.

Many of the species of the low shore continue into the sublittoral zone. Mysid or opossum shrimps, sea cucumbers, and more amphipods join them to make this the most diverse zone. In sheltered locations in the subtidal zone, seagrass meadows flourish.

Tropical regions. In the tropics, beaches composed of quartz sands are similar to temperate shores in their habitat zonation and (at the generic level) community composition. Species diversity, however, is considerably lower. In monsoon climates, the coastal habitats and organisms face major changes in salinity on yearly basis. The heavy rains of the summer monsoon lower salinity; evaporation during the dry season can raise salinity. High amounts of rainfall and associated

Surfing

Surf clams (*Donax* spp.) and mole crabs (*Emerita* spp.) are the surfers of the invertebrate world. They employ different mechanisms for moving in the waves. The surf clam uses its extended foot and two siphons as a surfboard. It then floats on the incoming wave until the wave's energy is dissipated, at which point it quickly burrows into the sand of the surf zone to begin filter-feeding.

The mole crab tucks in its legs and, like a small barrel, lets the waves roll it up the beach. At the end of its ride, it burrows into the sand to hold its position and await the next wave of the rising tide. In a reverse manner, this suspension-feeder uses the waves of the ebbing tide to surf back to the lower shore, so as not to be caught exposed at low tide.

runoff can also reduce salinity periodically in areas where the wet season extends throughout the year. In dry tropical climate regions, the coast is subject to high temperatures, high evaporation rates, and sporadic precipitation, all of which can stress beach organisms. Another factor lowering species richness in the tropics is the common occurrence of carbonate sediments, which typically are fine grained or compacted. As a result, water does not infiltrate easily and the habitat becomes anoxic and able to harbor few species. Foraminiferans and an epifauna dominate under such conditions. Tropical snails, such as horn shells or ceriths, mostly feed on detritus or the film of diatoms. On the upper shore, ghost crabs and isopods are common.

Polar regions. In polar regions both the intertidal zones and shallow seabed of the subtidal zone are scoured by ice. In the Arctic, the subtidal seabed is further disturbed by the bottom-feeding behavior of fish, seals, walruses, and whales. At depths from sea level down to 30 ft (10 m) live larvae of midges and scavenging isopods and amphipods. From 30 ft to about 95 ft (30 m) below sea level an increase in the number of species occurs due to the presence of kelps and phytoplankton. Herbivores include opossum shrimp, amphipods, isopods, krill, and bottom-dwelling fishes. Suspension-feeding clams and soft corals are also common. Predators include crabs and walruses, which feed heavily on clams.

The waters off Antarctica have no large fishes, skates, rays, sharks, or bottom-feeding mammals to disturb the soft sediments, although "beached" icebergs blown by the wind may dig furrows into the seabed. The few sublittoral benthic communities studied are dominated by the tube-building crustaceans and burrowing polychaetes.

Muddy Shores

At low tide, visible films of diatoms, cyanobacteria, and flagellates such as euglena color the mudflats brown, green, or golden-brown. These organisms, of worldwide occurrence, make up a group of sediment-dwelling photosynthetic cells known as the epipelon. They migrate 0.04–0.08 in (1–2 mm) to the surface at low tide to reach sunlight and then move back into the mud about an hour before the rising tide covers the mudflat. If attachment sites for macroalgae are present, green filamentous algae of the genus *Enteromorpha* occur.

Among the surface dwellers (epifauna) of muddy shores are permanent residents such as crabs and snails. In warmer climates, fiddler crabs are active at low tide. In northern Europe, the shore crab is active when the flats are submerged. In other parts of the world, typical crabs include the omnivorous blue crab of eastern North and South America and the mud crab found throughout the Indo-Pacific region. Small mud snails may occur in large numbers. They eat detritus, but also scavenge dead carcasses beached on the shore.

The most abundant and widespread animals are members of the infauna. A meiofauna composed largely of copepods, nematodes, and flatworms (turbellarians) coexists with a macrofauna of bivalves, crustaceans, worms of several phyla, burrowing anemones, and burrowing brittlestars. The muds are often deficient in oxygen due to both the fine particle size that keeps the substrate saturated and the amount of organic material decaying within it. Animals of the infauna have various adaptations that help them survive in anaerobic conditions. Many have ways to set up currents that move oxygenated water into their burrows at high tide. The oxygen is stored for use during low tide, at which time they may also reduce their oxygen demands by reducing their activity. Cockles and some other mudflat dwellers are able to breathe air at low tide.

At high tide, mudflats are visited by a number of fish predators, including mullets and flounders. At low tide, shorebirds such as egrets and herons probe the mud for prey.

Estuaries

Estuaries are the interface between freshwater and marine biomes. Defined as semienclosed areas where freshwater streams meet the salty sea, estuaries are highly variable physical environments that demand special tolerances or adaptations of the organisms living in them. Nonetheless, highly productive communities usually develop.

Almost all estuaries are tidal. The shape and shallowness of nearly enclosed inlets alters the normal symmetry and height or amplitude of a tide wave in the open sea. Rising and high tides are faster and last for shorter periods of time than ebbing and low tides. Friction against the sides and bottom of an estuary slows the lower layer of water, so the incoming tide runs faster at the surface, propelling the wave ever higher and steeper. When the tidal range is exceptionally high and the estuary constricts toward its head, the energy of the wave is concentrated by the converging sides and shallowing bottom of the inlet to increase greatly the amplitude of the tide wave. In the Bay of Fundy, the height on the inflowing tide increases as the wave moves up the inlet. At the mouth it is about 15 ft (5 m) high. By the time the Bay forks into Chignecto Bay and the Minas Channel, the tidal swell can be nearly 30 ft (9 m) high, and near the head of each branch, water rises some 50 ft (15–16 m) against the shores at high tide.

Tidal Bores

When tides are highly asymmetrical as a result of the great tidal range, a wall of water called a tidal bore forms at the front edge of the incoming tide. Perhaps only 100 rivers in the world have tidal bores, and sometimes bores only develop during the highest of high tides. The flooding tide rushes up the Severn estuary in England and forms a bore about 3 ft (1 m) high, which is higher than those in many places, but not extraordinary. The world's greatest occurs on China's Qiantang River, which flows past Hangzhou and empties into the East China Sea. Ahead of the highest spring tide of the year, the bore may be close to 30 ft (9 m) high and rush upstream at 25 mph (40 kph). Other times of year, it ranges from 5–15 ft (1.5–5 m) high. The funnel-shaped Amazon estuary also forms an impressive tidal bore more than 15 ft (5 m) high. The bore travels upstream at speeds of 20 mph (30 kph) or greater, and its effects are still felt in tributary rivers 180 mi (300 km) inland. The *pororoca*, as the phenomenon is known locally, can be ridden like the surf, in some places in Brazil for more than 30 minutes and over many miles. Tidal bores erode the shores of estuaries and stir up bottom sediments, limiting the benthic fauna.

Tidal range has more widespread influences than the rare but spectacular tidal bores. It helps determine both the amount and the location of sediment deposits. In microtidal estuaries, the tidal range in less than 6 ft (2 m), so river flow is the prevailing means of moving sediments about. Such estuaries are often bar-built and their waters highly stratified with a distinct salt wedge. Deltas commonly form at the mouth of the river. Mesotidal estuaries have tidal ranges between 6 and 25 ft (2–4 m). Sediments are primarily moved by waves and tidal currents. Sandbars are frequent, and the strong tidal influence produces deltaic deposits on both the landward side (flood deltas) and seaward side (ebb deltas) of bars. Saltmarshes drained by a network of tidal creeks occur at the head of these estuaries. Macrotidal estuaries have a tidal range in excess of 25 ft (4 m), and tidal currents determine the distribution of sediments. They usually have wide mouths and are funnel-shaped. Fine-grained sediments are typically deposited only along the shores, usually near the head, and become mudflats vegetated with fringing salt marshes or fringing mangrove. Linear sandbars oriented parallel to the tidal currents form and reform in the mouth of these usually well-mixed estuaries.

As landscape features, all estuaries are relatively young geologically speaking and have short life spans. In these respects, they resemble most lake ecosystems. In the higher and temperate latitudes, almost all estuaries probably came into being some 6,000 years ago with the rise of sea level at the end of the Pleistocene Epoch. Less is understood about the history of tropical estuaries, but it is likely that most also postdate the Pleistocene. One way to categorize estuaries is according to their topography and method of formation (see Figure 2.8). Six general types are recognized:

- **Drowned valleys** occur on broad coastal plains and are the result of stream-cut valleys carved across continental shelves when they were exposed during the drop in sea level accompanying Pleistocene glaciation (see Figure 2.8a). They were flooded by rising sea levels when the great ice sheets melted early in the Holocene. This type of estuary, also known as ria, is generally restricted to and typical of temperate regions. The Chesapeake Bay is a classic example.
- **Funnel-shaped coastal plain estuaries** form where rivers flow across flat, low-lying land before reaching the ocean (see Figure 2.8b). The estuary consists of the lower reaches of the river. The mouth is very broad and the river width tapers upstream. The rising tide enters the mouth and, depending on the volume of river discharge, may turn the river water brackish. River-borne sediments are laid down as the velocity of the flow decreases in contact with the open sea, so bars and islands form in the river mouth. The lower Amazon River is a classic example of such an estuary, as is the Rio de la Plata estuary, also on the Atlantic coast of South America.
- **Bar-built estuaries** are created when spits or bars block the entrance to a bay or inlet and limit the inflow of seawater so that a brackish lagoon forms as freshwater stream runoff dilutes the entrapped saltwater (see Figure 2.8c). At least seasonally and often daily at high tide, the estuary is connected to the sea. Spits and baymouth bars are attached to the land, the products of longshore drift, whereas sandbars and barrier

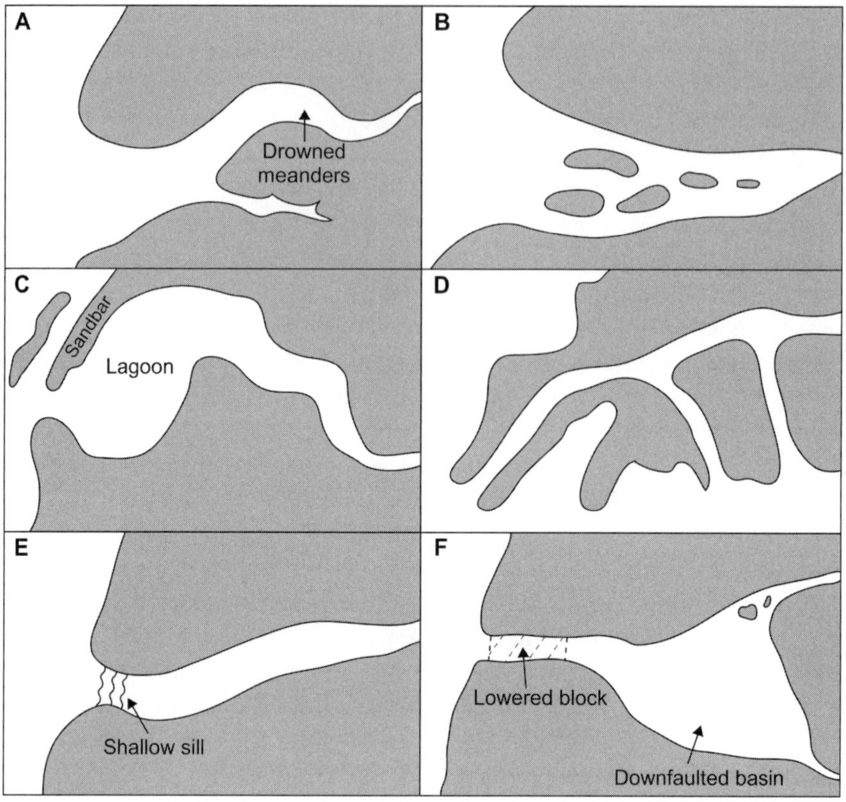

Figure 2.8 Estuaries are classified according to their shapes and the ways they were formed: (a) drowned valley, (b) funnel-shaped coastal plain estuary, (c) bar-built estuary, (d) delta-front estuary, (e) fjord, and (f) tectonic estuary. *(Illustration by Jeff Dixon. Adapted from Kaiser et al. 2005.)*

islands form offshore, apparently the result of past or present wave action on shallow continental shelf deposits. The lagoons are usually quite shallow and amass deep deposits of sediments. Albemarle South, North Carolina, is an example, as is Galveston Bay and other lagoons behind the barrier islands off Texas's Gulf Coast. The world's largest coastal lagoon, Lagoa dos Patos, lies south of Porto Alegre in southeastern Brazil.

- **Delta-front estuaries** occur where rivers build a delta that restricts the tidal inflow of saltwater (see Figure 2.8d). The lower Mississippi River is a prime example of this type of estuary.
- **Fjords** are features of high latitude coasts in regions once covered by continental or alpine glaciers (see Figure 2.8e). They are flooded U-shaped valleys carved by moving ice into solid rock. As such, they commonly have steep sides, bottoms well below sea level, and shallow sills at their entrances. The sill prevents the inflow of deep ocean waters and limits circulation of water within the fjord to an upper layer at levels above the height of the sill. The floors have relatively thin deposits of sediments deposited,

and these as well as the deeper waters are generally deficient in oxygen due to infrequent mixing with aerated surface waters. Benthic organisms therefore are few and overall productivity low. Fjords are characteristic of the coasts of Norway, southern Alaska and British Columbia, southern Chile, and South Island, New Zealand.

- **Tectonic estuaries** are produced by downfaulting or other types of subsidence near the mouth of a river (see Figure 2.8f). San Francisco Bay, just west of the San Andreas fault system, is a textbook example of a tectonic estuary. Tectonic movement lowered a coastal block enough for ocean water to enter through the Golden Gate and flood an interior, downfaulted basin.

Estuaries are common along Atlantic and Gulf coasts of the United States, where the continental shelf is wide and gently sloping. They account for 80–90 percent of the coastline. On the west coast, however, the shelf is narrow and rivers cut through mountain ranges close to the coast; estuaries are rare, accounting for only 10–20 percent of the coastline.

The chemical environment of an estuary is largely determined by the relationships between the freshwater flow entering at the head of the inlet and the tidal intrusion of seawater at its mouth, although climate is also important. Since tides are involved, significant and rapid changes in salinity, temperature, and turbidity occur on a daily basis, as well as seasonally. Tidal range together with the slope of the estuary floor determine how far upstream the tidal effects and brackish water extend. The amount of precipitation and its seasonality, if any, coupled with evaporation rates also plays a major role. Salinity normally grades from 0 in the river to 35 (the salinity of seawater) at the mouth of the estuary. In the dry or the wet and dry tropics and subtropics, however, high evaporation rates can cause the salinity of a lagoon to become greater than that of the open sea. This condition creates so-called negative estuaries, such as Laguna Madre, Texas, or Laguna San Ignacio in Baja California—the bay famous as a calving ground of gray whales, or the Spencer Gulf in South Australia.

At any given point in an estuary, salinity varies with tidal ebbs and flows; the greatest differences are experienced mid-estuary. Since freshwater is lighter than brackish and salty water, the river's discharge will float on top of a layer of saltwater for some or all of the length of the estuary. The low-salinity surface layer moves downstream toward the mouth, while a deeper, more saline layer moves upstream toward the head of the estuary. The degree to which these two layers mix provides another means of distinguishing among estuarine systems:

- **Salt-wedge estuaries** are highly stratified (see Figure 2.9a), and the vertical profile of the salinity gradient is steep. Saltwater mixes into the outgoing freshwater flow, but there is little downward movement of the surface freshwater lens and mixing of the two layers is minimal. Phytoplankters are held in the surface layer near the light, but their nutrient supply is cut off as there is no force to carry settled particles upward. Particles that settle out of upper layer are carried upstream in the lower layer and tend to accumulate at the tip of the wedge of deeper saltwater. The position of the tip of salt wedge changes according to the flow of the river. With less than average river flow, the salt wedge

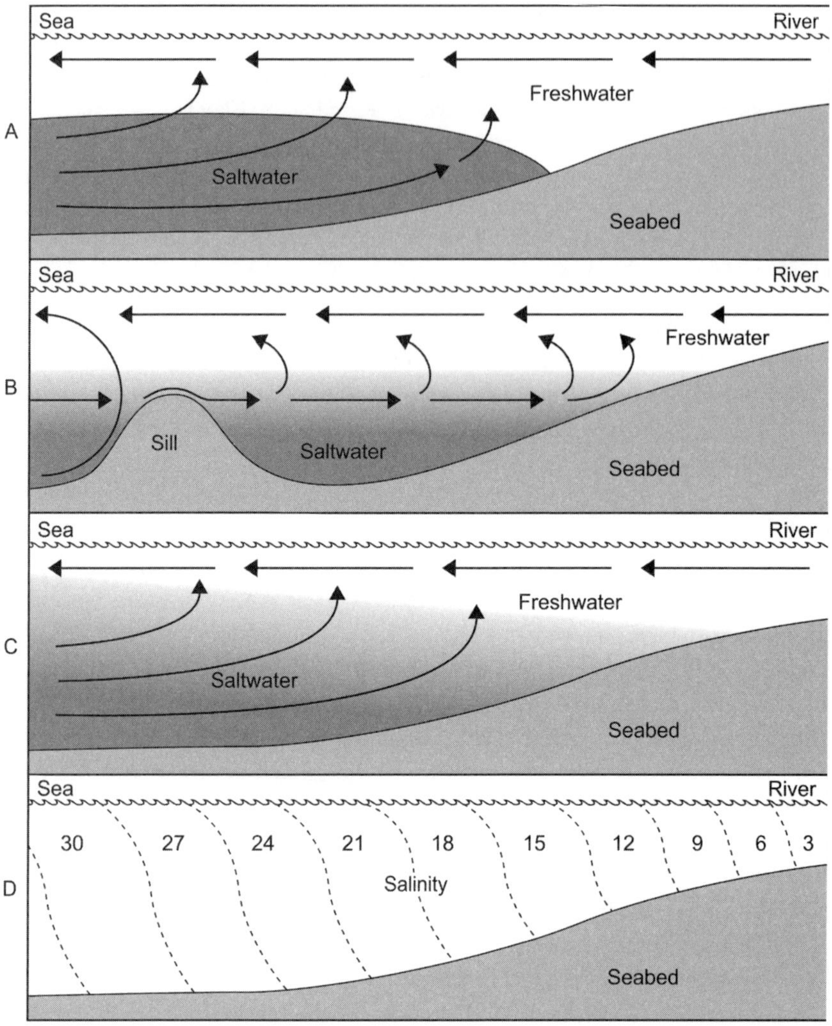

Figure 2.9 Estuaries vary according to where and by how much the water column is mixed: (a) salt-wedge estuary, (b) fjord, (c) partially mixed estuary, and (d) well-mixed estuary. *(Illustration by Jeff Dixon. Adapted from Knox 2001.)*

moves farther inland and deposition of sediments is the rule. With greater-than-average river flow, the wedge is displaced downstream and erosion of sandbars may occur. The Mississippi River estuary is a good example, as are the Rhone and Ebro rivers which enter the Mediterranean Sea. The tip of the Mississippi's salt wedge can move back and forth 100–200 mi (160–320 km) each year. Among other salt wedge estuaries are the Amazon River, Brazil; St. Lawrence River, Canada; and the Pearl River, China.

Fjords are also stratified estuarine systems, but the pattern differs from the classic salt-wedge type. A deep layer of saline water is trapped in the estuary behind the same sill that prevents deep seawater from entering. Mixing occurs only within the water shallower than the sill (see Figure 2.9b). Aerated water can only replace deep water during storms, so most of the time the lower layer is anoxic.

- **Partially mixed estuaries** have less-steep salinity gradients than a fully stratified system. Mixing is enough to affect salinity: the salinity of the upper layer increases downstream, while the salinity of the lower layer decreases upstream. The turbulence that occurs at the boundary between outgoing freshwater and incoming saltwater is sufficient to resuspend sediments and bring them into the euphotic surface layer (see Figure 2.9c). Phytoplankton productivity is high and so the productivity of the system as a whole is high. The rich Chesapeake Bay is a partially mixed estuary as are the smaller estuaries, such as that of the James River, that feed into it. Other famous estuaries that are partially mixed are San Francisco Bay, the Thames River in the United Kingdom, and the Yangtze River (Chang Jiang) in China.
- **Well-mixed or completely mixed estuaries** are not stratified; at any given point salinity is essentially the same at the surface as at depth (see Figure 2.9d). Salinity only varies longitudinally according to distance downstream from the head. Strong tidal currents dominate and scour the bottom. When they reverse during each tidal cycle, they can cause high turbidity and keep phytoplankton populations relatively low because of the reduction of sunlight able to penetrate the sediment-laden waters. Phytoplankton reflects the fairly simple longitudinal salinity pattern. Few freshwater types live in Coos Bay, Oregon, for example. Nanoflagellates and other species restricted to this estuary populate the upper reaches, while dinoflagellates are more numerous than diatoms in the middle reaches. At the lower end, conditions are more like the open sea; diatoms dominate in winter and spring and dinoflagellates have a summer bloom. Other nonstratified or well-mixed estuaries include Delaware Bay; the Severn estuary, United Kingdom; and the Ganges River estuary, India.

Rotation of the Earth, or the Coriolis Force, causes moving water to be deflected to the right of its intended path in the Northern Hemisphere. In stratified and partially mixed estuaries in the Northern Hemisphere, the surface waters moving downstream are pushed to the right-hand side of the estuary, forming a thicker lens of fresh or low-salinity water on that side. The seawater flowing into an estuary is similarly deflected so that it piles up on the left-hand side. The result is a bank-to-bank change in salinity across an estuary and high-salinity water occurring farther upstream on the left side than the right. In completely mixed estuaries, lower-salinity water occurs at all depths on the right-hand side.

The shift and separation of the positions of outgoing and incoming waters also set up a surface circulation pattern within the estuary that is counterclockwise in the Northern Hemisphere. This circulation means that, though tides rise and fall, water does not move in a straight line in and out of an estuary. Instead it circulates upstream of the mouth. This reality means that estuaries trap and concentrate rather than flush out sediments and plankton and pollutants. A single water molecule may have a resident time in an estuary measured in weeks, even though the tide goes in and out twice a day. Nevertheless, water does leave, and a plume of surface water leaving an estuary is often visible well into the open sea because of its sediment load. In the Northern Hemisphere, the plume tends to hug the coast and circulate in a counterclockwise direction around an ocean basin. The opposite is true in the Southern Hemisphere, where moving fluids are deflected to the left.

Sediments that originate on the land enter an estuary as the suspended load of the rivers. Marine sediments are carried in on tidal currents. Both may occur in such large amounts that most estuaries are brownish even when not polluted. The ability of moving water to carry particles in suspension depends on the velocity of the flow. Slower water can hold fewer particles than can fast-moving water; only the smallest particles remain in suspension. As the river water and tidal currents meet, their respective velocities diminish and each deposits successively finer and finer materials. The finest muds and silts are laid down in the middle of the estuary, and this is where the vast mudflats typical along the banks of most estuaries tend to occur. The higher-velocity rising tide can carry a greater suspended load than slower ebbing waters, so that all sediments brought into the estuary are not flushed out each tidal cycle And since the volume of tidal water is generally much greater than that of river water, most of the finest materials are marine in origin. A lengthwise gradient of sediments in which coarse-grained particles grade into fine-grained particles between the head and mid-estuary point becomes established and is mirrored with a coarse- to fine-grained zonation from mouth to mid-estuary. The sediment profile in turn influences which plant and animal communities develop at different positions along the estuary.

Life in Estuaries

Most benthic and pelagic organisms in estuaries are of marine origin. The exception occurs in soft-sediment intertidal habitats where flowering plants with terrestrial origins become rooted and establish some of the most important communities associated with estuaries, those of seagrass beds, salt marsh, and mangrove. In these places, a mix of marine and terrestrial species reflects the habitat's role as interface between land and sea. Each of these communities receives detailed treatment later in this chapter.

A wealth of phytoplankters may be in the water and interstitial bacteria, fungi, and algae may be in the sediments. These form the first steps in grazing and detritus food chains.

Detritus food chains dominate energy flow and nutrient cycling in estuarine systems. Benthic communities are mainly deposit-feeding polychaetes and snails and suspension-feeding polychaetes and molluscs. Oysters and mussels may cluster in dense aggregations called reefs. Bivalve reefs are ecosystems in and of themselves. The bivalve shells are attachment sites for other organisms, and they trap sediments to create habitat for an infauna. An oyster reef studied in North Inlet, North Carolina, consisted of oysters (*Crassotrea virginica*), mussels (*Brachydontes exustus*), six other molluscs, 18 polychaetes, nine arthropods, nematodes, and nemertrean worms. Bivalves filter particles out of the water and expel their wastes into the water, thereby playing major roles in nutrient cycles. They probably control phytoplankton populations by removing so many from the water. They also affect water quality by ingesting huge amounts of suspended sediments and converting them to fecal pellets that settle to the bottom and are consumed by deposit-feeders.

Predators of benthic organisms include crabs, lobsters, shrimps, and flatfishes such as flounders. Intertidal flats are visited at low tide by shorebirds. Each species has a different bill length and specializes in capturing invertebrates buried at different depths in the exposed sediments. Common on North America shores are Long-billed Dowitchers, Whimbrels, godwits, oystercatchers, and several short-billed plovers. Gulls master the shellfish by dropping them on hard surfaces such as shingle beaches and roadways to break them open. Tidal flats in estuaries host tens of thousands of nonresident shorebirds that stopover during their long migrations between Arctic breeding grounds and tropical, even equatorial, wintering grounds.

Among the nekton, invertebrates such as swimming shrimps and crabs form important links in the food web. Krill, for example, are food for fish, seabirds, and marine mammals. A large number of fish species inhabit estuaries during at least part of their life cycles. In temperate areas, the most important are eels, herring-like fish family (Clupeidae), anchovies, saltwater catfish, killifish, basses, drums, croakers, salmon, and flounders (family Pleuronectidae). Also found are silversides, blennies, sculpins, surfperch, and majarras. Even greater diversity occurs in tropical estuaries, where once again herring-like fish, saltwater catfish, drums, croakers, and anchovies are most abundant. Also common are flounders from several families, lizard fish, mullets, threadfins, gobies, rays, puffers, majarras, grunts, and cichlids. Boreal estuaries are least diverse; they usually support salmon and trout, smelt and capelin, sticklebacks, sandlance, and sculpins. In Antarctic waters the family Galaxioidei dominates.

Few fish are exclusively estuarine; among those that are estuarine are killifish and some gobies. Most species spend only part of their life cycle in an estuary. Different ones are migrating in and out at different times of year. Part-time residents can be divided into three main groups. Most are saltwater spawners. They release their eggs or larvae offshore, and the larvae drift into estuaries as part of the plankton borne by the tide. In the nursery areas, the larvae grow into juveniles that become demersal and feed on the bountiful supply of benthic organisms in

Toxic Blooms

Some algae are notorious because of their toxic or noxious blooms. When their populations reach peak numbers, the water may become discolored with reddish, brownish, or yellowish stains marking the presence of so many cells. Those that produce toxins are primarily dinoflagellates such as *Protogonyaulax catanella*, *P. tamarensis*, and *Pyroclimium bahamense*. When shellfish ingest these algae, the toxins become magnified in their tissue. People who consume the shellfish can become ill and even die from paralytic shellfish poisoning. Mackerel also eat dinoflagellates, and humpback whales in Cape Cod Bay are known to have been poisoned by eating mackerel on at least one occasion. The dinoflagellate *Pfisteria piscidia* was associated with fish kills in North Carolina.

Diatom blooms are more apt to cause nuisances such as scum washed up on beaches or the stench of hydrogen sulfide that is given off when vast numbers of cells go unconsumed and decay under anaerobic conditions. However, the diatom *Pseudonitzschia multiseries* was implicated in amnesic shellfish poisoning in mussels in Prince Edward Island and in die-offs of pelicans and cormorants near Monterey Bay.

Shad Runs and Early Environmental Laws

In Colonial Virginia, the spring spawning runs of anadramous fishes were vital parts of a household's annual economic cycle. Fish fed the family and some were also exported. Sturgeon and striped bass were taken at this time of year, but most important were the herrings. Alewives arrived in late February/early March to be followed by American shad in late March and the glut or May herring in April and May. The first environmental law was enacted in 1680 to prohibit a method of fishing known as gigging in the lower Rappahannock River estuary. Gigging involves spearing a fish with a pronged but barbless pole that resembles a small pitchfork, grabbing hold of the catch, and dispensing of it with a whack to the head. In the process, many fatally injured fish escaped, and by summer the stench of rotting carcasses became unbearable.

By the late 1700s, after the Piedmont had been settled and forests cleared and converted to farmland, dams and the siltation of spawning beds had greatly reduced fish populations. In 1759, mill owners on the Rapidan River, a major tributary of the Rappahannock River, were required to install 10 ft openings in their dams to let fish pass. Through the next decade, similar laws were enacted in many Piedmont counties. These "fish slopes" were to remain open from March through May each year and were the forerunners of modern fish ladders that enable migrating salmon to by-pass even very large dams.

sublittoral sediments, on intertidal mudflats, or in the tidal creeks meandering through salt marshes. Estuaries often support enormous numbers of fish younger than one year old. Some, such as mullets, stay to grow into adults. Atlantic menhaden, an important prey species for striped bass, bluefish, sharks, and even marine mammals, has a somewhat different life history pattern. Menhaden spawn offshore near the entrances of estuaries along the east coast of North America in late fall and winter. One to three months later, the larvae enter the estuaries when they are 0.4–1.3 in (15–20 mm) long. Menhaden larvae capture individual zooplankters, but once in the estuary, they metamorphose into filter-feeders depending mostly on the phytoplankton. Between August and November, the young-of-the-year form dense schools and leave the estuary. Juveniles and adults live in the ocean waters over the continental shelf, migrating north in summer and south in winter. Fish are not the only saltwater spawners. Blue crab females release larvae offshore that become part of the plankton. After several molts, they settle to the bottom and are washed into the estuary on the tide. They grow to adults and mate in the estuary, the next generation of gravid females leaving once again to release their larvae.

Some fish are estuarine spawners. The winter flounder of eastern Canada and the northeastern United States is a good example. It moves into estuaries during the winter months and early spring to lay its eggs on the bottom. Juveniles spend their first year in the estuary and then return to the sea.

Finally, some fishes spend part of their life cycle in freshwater and part in the estuary. Anadromous species such as salmon, sturgeons, lampreys, striped bass, and shads spawn in freshwater. Although they spend little time in estuaries, they make up seasonal fisheries highly valued by both sportsmen and commercial fishermen. Not surprisingly many now occur in historically low numbers, and populations and waterways are managed to conserve them. Upstream spawning runs of alewife, blueback herring, hickory shad, and American shad are still annual spring spectacles in clean, undammed rivers all along the east coast of the United States. The fertilized eggs and larvae of shads drift downstream and develop into juveniles in estuarine nurseries. Many stay two to four years and then move offshore. Adults return to the sea soon after spawning. Pacific salmon are another classic example of an anadramous fish, but they are somewhat unusual. They only make the spawning run once. They pass through estuaries on their way from the open sea to lay their eggs in oxygen-rich waters of streams and then die, often far removed from the coast.

Catadramous fish do the opposite. Best known are eels. Both the American eel and the European eel spend most of their lives in freshwater streams but reproduce in the Sargasso Sea near the center of the North Atlantic gyre off the North American continental shelf. The two species spawn in separate areas and then die. The planktonic larvae of American eels drift northwest to the east coast of North America and European eel larve drift eastward to Europe for about a year. They arrive at their respective destinations as juveniles (known as elvers); most move up freshwater streams, where they may remain for 20 years.

In temperate regions most fish that divide their lives between freshwater and saltwater are anadramous; in the tropics most are catadramous. Eels have a somewhat different pattern: they move from temperate streams to a subtropical sea to spawn.

Estuaries have long attracted human settlement and today, as in the past, they are preferred locations for port facilities and other transportation nodes, industries, agricultural production, and commercial and subsistence fishing. Large urban centers grew on many shores as a result. The impacts on estuaries of all these human activities have largely been negative. Accelerated erosion of uplands cleared for farming increased sedimentation and filled in estuaries and, since ancient history, rendered ports unusable as they became stranded miles from open water. Extreme sedimentation suffocates benthic organisms and wipes out shellfish reefs. Untreated sewage flowing into the water causes eutrophication, an increase in nutrients that stimulates algal blooms and results in massive die-offs that deplete the water of oxygen as the algal cells decay. Fish kills can result. Industrial effluents contaminate the water with organic compounds such as DDT and PCBs and heavy metals such as zinc, cadmium, lead, and mercury. These compounds enter the food chain, accumulating in deposit-feeders and suspension-feeders and then poisoning their predators, including humans. Waterways heavily used by freighters, warships, and even recreational vessels are subject to oil spills and antifouling poisons applied to hulls to free them of barnacles and other sessile organisms. Destructive physical alteration of estuaries happens with the dredging of shipping channels, "reclamation" of tidal flats, salt marshes, and mangroves for agricultural land, resorts, marinas, residences, and industries, and—increasingly—conversion to aquaculture ponds. Other near-universal problems include invasions of nonnative organisms and changes related to rising sea levels and climate change. The value of estuaries and, in particular, the special habitats that serve as nursery areas and act as a defense against wave-driven erosion of the coast is well known. Throughout the world a growing emphasis is being placed on balancing the ecological needs of our natural heritage (conservation) with the economic needs for their use (development) in what is known as integrated coastal zone management.

Salt Marshes

Salt marshes occupy sheltered intertidal areas in estuaries, lagoons, and on the lee sides of barrier islands on the upper shore above mudflats. Worldwide in distribution, they are especially common in the temperate regions of the globe, since mangroves often occupy similar sites in many parts of the tropics. Perennial grasses, especially cordgrasses, are the most abundant plants in the marsh, but they may be accompanied or even replaced by forbs such as sea asters and sea lavenders or succulent subshrubs such as pickleweeds and glassworts.

The grasses and other plants are of terrestrial origin. Occurring in areas regularly flooded by the tide, these land plants display various adaptations to withstand high concentrations of salt—that is, they are halophytes. Most have the ability to exclude salt uptake at the roots, secrete excess salt through special glands, or accumulate and store salt in leaves that then can be shed. The problem they encounter living in seawater is that there can be a higher concentration of salt in their environment than in their cells. Without some means of overcoming this unfavorable gradient, osmosis would pull water out of the cells and cause the plant to wilt and die; and sodium and chloride ions would move into the cells until their concentrations were lethal. Succulence is a common defense against high salt concentrations in halophytes: the high amount of water in the cells dilutes the salt solution. Still, higher-than-normal (for land plants) amounts of salt do accumulate in their tissues, so other means of preventing a toxic buildup are necessary. They may exclude the uptake of sodium and chloride by their roots with membranes of exceptionally low permeability to those ions. They may also have a means of pumping excess ions out of the roots. Halophytes may maintain an osmotic pressure in balance with their surroundings by increasing the concentration of certain amino acids in their cells rather than allowing toxic salts to create the equilibrium. Some cordgrasses and other plants have specialized cells or glands that secrete salt onto the leaf surfaces. High concentrations of salt in the leaves of halophytes actually helps them survive by drawing water up from their roots. Water is generally hard to come by in the tissues of halophytes because of internal osmotic pressure gradients. Waxy cuticles cover the leaves, and stomata are deeply sunk to reduce transpiration and conserve the internal water supplies. Many relatives of salt marsh plants are found in deserts, where a similar tolerance of high salt concentrations is often required.

Salt marsh grasses trap fine sediments in their tangle of stems, roots, and rhizomes, and slowly build up the surface level of the marsh. Since grasses are not uniformly distributed, some areas build up as hummocks and others without grasses become depressions. As the uneven surface develops, water draining with the

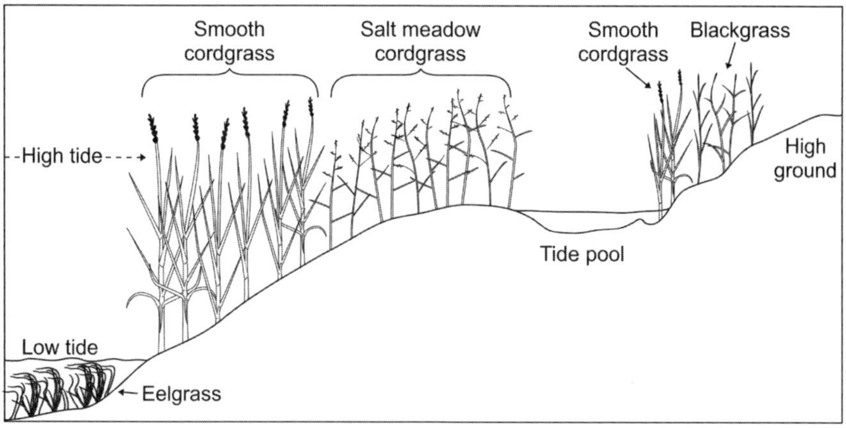

Figure 2.10 Zonation in a northeastern saltmarsh in the United States. *(Illustration by Jeff Dixon. Adapted from Knox 2001.)*

ebbing tides seeks the low areas and becomes channelized in a growing system of creeks. Continued rising of the marsh surface causes the creeks to cut deeper, so that channel bottoms may become 3 ft (1 m) lower than the rest of the marsh. A branching network of tidal creeks drains a mature marsh when the tide is going out and distributes water through the marsh when the tide rises (see Plate IIIb). Open water lagoons and unvegetated salt pans may be scattered throughout a marsh. With the large amounts of mud and silt carried in tidal waters, the creeks often develop natural levees, raised ridges along their banks. Thus a variety of microhabitats—hummocks, depressions, pans, creeks, levees, and lagoons—occur in a mature marsh that encourage occupation by a variety of organisms. Plants and animals live in distinct zones running from the high-water mark down to the low according to their salt tolerance (see Figure 2.10). The saltiest parts of the intertidal zone tend to be mid-shore, an area generally occupied by succulent halophytes.

In the upper marsh, precipitation and runoff dilute salts and flush them from the sediments. At lower levels, exposed to the air for only short periods of time, evaporation rates are lower and the ebbing tide removes excess salts. However, the saturated soils of the low marsh, stabilized by grass roots and members of the infauna such as mussels, are low in oxygen. Plants of the low shore have fine (adventitious) roots near the soil surface that can capture oxygen and transfer it to the deeper root system that anchors the plant in place. Special tissue with large gas-filled chambers known as aerenchyma acts as an air duct to move the oxygen downward. Some of this oxygen leaks from the roots oxygenating the substrate. Nonetheless, decay of the huge volume of dead plant matter that accumulates on the marsh floor each year still depletes oxygen in the bottom sediments and decay by anaerobic bacteria becomes the norm. As a by-product of the biological process of decay, these bacteria produce hydrogen sulfide, which can be toxic to many organisms if not washed out by the tide. Hydrogen sulfide gas gives mudflats at the seaward margin of the marsh the stench of rotting eggs at low tide.

Salt marshes are among the world's most productive plant communities, yet there are relatively few herbivores. A well-known study conducted on Sapelo Island, Georgia, revealed that less than 4 percent of the primary production of salt marsh grasses entered the grazing food chain. (This is probably not representative of all salt marshes.) Sucking insects such as aphids, planthoppers, and grasshoppers are common, although vertebrates such as geese and muskrat can be important grazers. In addition, many salt marshes have had a long history of use as pasture for domestic cattle, sheep, and horses. Salt hay is still harvested for forage in some parts of the world.

With so little of the biomass consumed as living tissue, most of the energy fixed by plants flows through detritus food webs either in the marsh itself or in adjoining mudflats and estuaries into which organic debris is transported from the marsh. Dead leaves of grasses still standing in the marsh support fungi. The fungi as well as the dead plant material itself are food for marsh periwinkles and amphipods. These invertebrates shred the dead grass. Small fragments drop to the floor of the marsh, where they become food for deposit-feeders such as fiddler crabs and snails and filter-feeders such as ribbed mussels and oysters. Other common detritivores include grapsid crabs, annelid worms, and nematodes. Carnivores in the marsh's detritus food web include mud crabs, fish such as killifish, birds such as rails, herons, and egrets, and mammals such as raccoons.

The salt marsh fauna consists of estuarine or marine mudflat species that extend their ranges up the creeks and into the mud between marsh plants. A number of terrestrial animals such as songbirds, otter, raccoons, and foxes extend their range seaward into the marsh. However, a number of animals are salt marsh specialists. Living on and among the grasses are sap-sucking insects such as aphids and nectar- and pollen-feeding butterflies as well as male horseflies (*Tabanus*), deer flies (*Chrysops*), and mosquitoes (*Aedes*)—the females, however, are blood-suckers. Some of the invertebrate detritivores are also salt marsh specialists, including the pulmonate snails, some beetles, some mussels, and several crustaceans. Spiders are common and conspicuous predators of the smaller insects. In the eastern United States, the wealth of invertebrates attracts nesting songbirds such Seaside Sparrows, Savannah Sparrows, Song Sparrows (see Figure 2.11), and Long-billed Marsh Wrens, while a host of waterfowl including Black Ducks, Green-winged Teal, Hooded Mergansers, and Canada Geese feed in the creeks. Marsh Hawks (Northern Harriers), Ringed-billed Gulls, and Short-eared Owls prey on the birds, their eggs, and the numerous small rodents that inhabit the upper marsh.

Animals face major challenges from exposure to rapidly changing salinity levels and periodic flooding, both consequences of the tidal environment in which they live. Rising and falling tides threaten motile creatures with being swept away. Being submerged at high tide precludes breathing air, while being exposed at low tide requires the ability to breathe air. Burrowing is a common response among

Adaptations among Saltmarsh Song Sparrow Populations

The North American Song Sparrow has many subspecies, some of which are endemic to isolated salt marshes on different parts of the continent. A few subspecies are physiologically adapted to drinking saltwater, while in other populations, birds obtain moisture from their food or from dew and fog condensed on marsh plants. They build their nests off the ground and time egg-laying in early spring, a few weeks before inland subspecies, to avoid the highest spring tides of summer.

Figure 2.11 Song Sparrow. Some subspecies are well-adapted to life in the salt marsh. *(Photo © Jemini Joseph/Shutterstock.)*

marsh invertebrates, but some simply stay above water level all day by moving up and down the leaves and stems of marsh plants. Among the epifauna are pulmonate snails, such as the common coffee bean snail on the Atlantic coast of North America, that lack gills and instead have a mantle cavity that acts as a lung, letting them breathe air. Periwinkles also breathe air but use greatly reduced gills on the left side of the mantle cavity. The marsh periwinkle of the eastern United States is seldom submerged, since it climbs higher on cordgrass stems as the tide rises, presumably to escape being preyed upon by blue crabs.

Fiddler crabs feed on the tidal flats during daytime low tides and retreat to their burrows, plugging them with mud to preserve a pocket of air, when the tide comes in. Other crabs respond differently. *Eurytium limosum* and *Sesmara reticulatum* feed at high tide and retreat to burrows at low tide. They occupy the low marsh at low tide. *Sesmara cinereum* does not use a burrow at all, but climbs above the water at high tide.

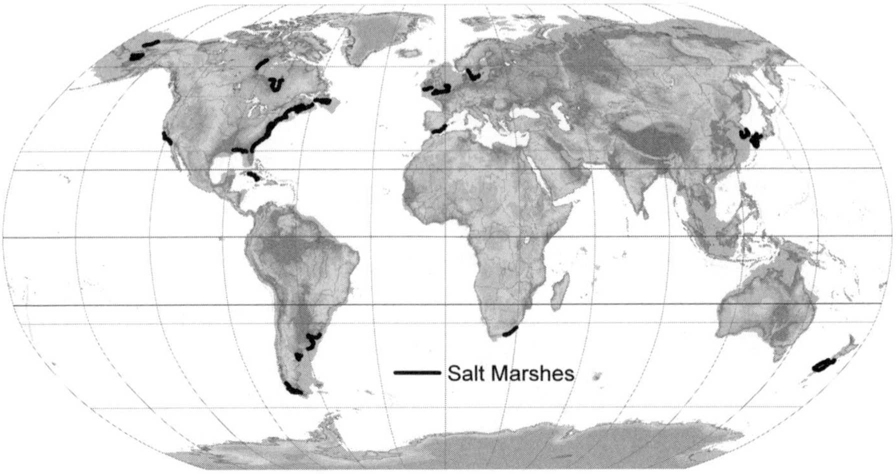

Figure 2.12 World distribution of salt marshes. *(Map by Bernd Kuennecke.)*

Regional Expressions: Salt Marshes

Salt marshes are widespread (see Figure 2.12), developing above the Arctic Circle and also being found well into the tropics, where they generally occur as patches of grassland within mangrove stands. Species composition and patterns of zonation vary according to latitude and according to which continent they fringe. Characteristics of salt marsh in selected regions are provided below.

Arctic salt marshes. Arctic salt marshes have few plant species. They are dominated by the grass *Puccinella phryganodes* and sedges of the genus *Carex*.

North American salt marshes. In the United States, salt marshes are the main type of intertidal habitat along the Atlantic and Gulf coasts, but are rare and spottily distributed on the west coast. The west coast has long been tectonically active and continues to undergo active mountain-building, so few coastal lowlands exist on which salt marshes can develop. Along the Arctic Ocean and Bering Sea coasts, fast ice for up to nine months of the year prevents the establishment of marsh grasses; and farther south along the Gulf of Alaska to Puget Sound, recent glaciers have dug out deep fjords without lowland flats. South of Puget Sound as far as northern California, the continental shelf is narrow and too precipitous for the conditions suitable for salt marsh to have developed. Only in flooded coastal river valleys such as San Francisco Bay or where bay-mouth spits trap river-borne sediments, as in southern California, do the deep fine-grained sediments needed by salt marshes plants and animals accumulate.

Atlantic and Gulf Coast salt marshes. In the north, around the Bay of Fundy, the marsh consists largely of the grass *Puccinella americana* and the reed *Juncus balticus*.

At the upper margins salt marsh merges with bogs. Farther south, along the coasts of the northeastern United States, the high marsh is often occupied by marsh elder and blackgrass. Along southern Atlantic and Gulf coasts, salt-marsh ox-eye is abundant in the high marsh. Mid-marsh areas are dominated by salt marsh cordgrass, and the vast areas of low marsh are dominated by single-species stands of smooth cordgrass. Indeed, smooth cordgrass is the dominant species between the mean sea level and the mean high-water level from Canada to Florida. The more extreme habitat of the mid-shore is dominated by successive bands of Virginia pickleweed, salt grass, and black needlerush. Smooth cordgrass again dominates the low marsh but in two distinct size classes. Higher on the shore, the cordgrass is short; lower on the shore, tall stands occur.

The more common animals are those noted above in the general description. Coffee bean snails are most abundant above the high-tide mark. Fiddler crabs of several species are associated with the low marsh and feed on tidal flats during low tide. Most other invertebrates are associated with tidal creeks, lagoons, and pans. Clapper Rails living in tall cordgrass at the edge of creeks feed on square-backed marsh crab; those living among medium-height grasses on gently sloping levees capture fiddler crabs; while those living in the short grass on the lowest parts of the marsh concentrate on periwinkles. In the brackish water swamps from South Carolina to the Gulf Coast, the King Rail is present where giant cutgrass dominates. It feeds on fiddler crabs.

Rails are secretive and rarely seen, but Virginia Rails and the Sora are relatively abundant salt marsh birds. Shorebirds such as Willets are associated with the tall grass of the high marsh. Common herons of the east coast include widespread species such as the Great Blue Heron, Little Blue Heron, and the Black-crowned Night Heron. White egrets—Common Egret and Snowy Egret—are perhaps the most visible animals; they feed along the edges of creeks and lagoons. Snow Geese are winter visitors that feed on the roots and rhizomes of cordgrass. Common rodents of the marsh are meadow mice, meadow jumping mice, white-footed mice, harvest mice, and muskrats. Larger mammals visiting the high marsh include opossum, whitetail deer, mink, otter, and raccoons.

West Coast salt marshes. Along the shores of Alaska and British Columbia there are no well-integrated salt marsh communities. Instead a mosaic of single-species stands of sedges and grasses develops. The salt marsh grass *Pucinella phryganodes* is the first invader soon joined by the perennial tundra grass *Dupontia fischeri*. They begin building the marsh substrate. Other plants that may come into the marshes include several sedges, tufted hair grass, and red chimo daisy.

The coasts of Washington and Oregon are generally covered by macroalgae such as the green algae gutweed and sea lettuce or the brown alga, *Fucus distichus*, or, even an intertidal moss. In those rare situations where low sandy areas form behind bay-mouth spits, the low marsh vegetation consists of Virginia glasswort or three-square bulrush, and the higher marsh contains the wiry saltgrass, the

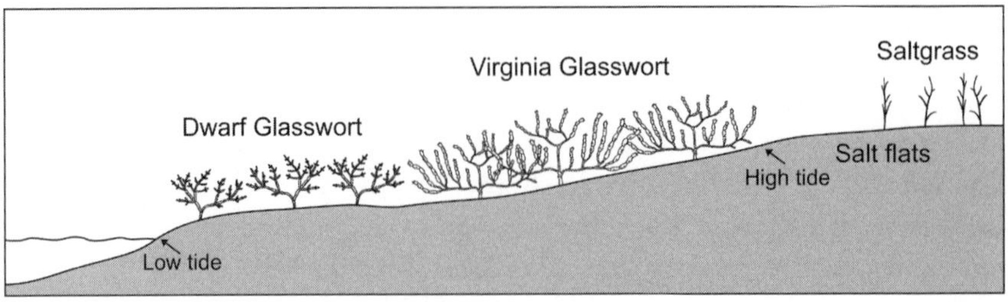

Figure 2.13 Zonation in southern California salt marshes. *(Illustration by Jeff Dixon. Adapted from Lenihan and Micheli 2001.)*

fleshy-leaved yellow-flowered aster known sometimes as Salty Susan, and goose-tongue.

In southern California, where evaporation in the dry summer months is great and salt content correspondingly high, a simple community of succulent subshrubs develops on sandy substrates (see Figure 2.13). The low shore is covered with dwarf glasswort. This gives way to stands of Virginia glasswort in the upper marsh. Above the extreme high-water mark, there may be salt flats with only cyanobacteria growing on them or stands of saltgrass. More zones develop on muddy shores such as those surrounding Newport Bay. The low shore is dominated by California cordgrass. Above this, Virginia glasswort grows with the cordgrass. Near the mean high-water mark, a more diverse community of halophytes including Virginia glasswort, dwarf glasswort, saltwort, alkali seaheath, and seaside arrowgrass develops. The highest part of the marsh, above the extreme high-water mark, is vegetated with yet another glasswort, a perennial shoregrass, and a saltbush. Many of these halophytes may be covered by a leafless orange parasite, dodder. Higher up the shore are barren salt flats.

Scattered salt marshes continue to be found into Baja California, where California cordgrass dominates the low shore, Virginia glasswort the mid-shore, and shoregrass the upper marsh. Above the high-tide level, succulent-leaved halophytes including Palmer's seaheath, desert-thorn, and saltbush grow until they encounter the true fog desert of the peninsula. Between 27° and 24° 30′ N latitude, salt marsh transitions into mangrove on Baja's Pacific Coast.

California's salt marsh fauna is similar to that elsewhere in the temperate zone at the generic level. Several common reptiles, including the side-blotched lizard, the southern Alligator lizard, and the western fence lizard reflect the desert-like nature of the environment. The small, rarely seen Black Rail inhabits glasswort marshes along with Clapper Rails, Savannah Sparrows, and Song Sparrows. The small patches of salt marsh habitat that characterize the west coast of North America are extremely important stopover spots for migratory shorebirds and waterfowl on the Pacific Flyway. More than 100 bird species are known to visit on their way to and from breeding grounds on the Arctic tundra. Among them are Western and

Least Sandpipers, Dowitchers, Willet, and Killdeer. A number of surface-feeding or dabbler ducks such as Pintail, Green-winged Teal, Northern Shoveler, and American Wigeon also depend on these resting and feeding areas, as do American Coots. Unlike the east coast, geese are uncommon. Among small mammals living in the marshes are California meadow mouse, deer mouse, western harvest mouse, and ornate shrew. Desert cottontails and the brush rabbit are common, as is the black-tailed jackrabbit. The much larger herbivore, the mule deer, also feeds in salt marsh. Mammals hunting in the marsh include long-tailed weasels, striped skunks, gray foxes, and coyotes.

European salt marshes. On the coasts of northern and western Europe, salt marshes are rare features and usually found at the head of estuaries. Commonly salt marsh grass, annual glassworts, and black-grass rush are the dominant plants. Variations occur. In the Baltic Sea area, bulrushes are early invaders of soft sediments, later to be joined by chaffy sedge, toad rush, and another sedge. On sandy substrates in Scandanavia, grasses dominate. Salt marsh grass grows in association with red fescue and creeping bentgrass, and the marshes are heavily grazed by livestock. In contrast, marshes of the North Sea, where the substrate is mud and clays, have few grasses and instead are typically vegetated with forbs. Sharing dominance are sea pink, sea lavender, sea plantain, sand spurry, and arrowgrass.

In the Mediterranean region, where the climate is similar to Southern California's with its dry summers and wet, mild winters, salt marshes usually are covered by halophytic subshrubs and perennial forbs. Especially prevalent are glassworts and sea lavenders. In mature marshes, spiny rush commonly dominates.

Temperate South American salt marshes. Salt marshes have limited occurrence on the Atlantic side of the South American continent since abrupt cliffs form much of the eastern edge of the landmass and below them are extensive sandy beaches and dune fields exposed to the sea. Areas of sheltered inlets with soft-sediment substrates are uncommon. On the west coast, salt marsh is even rarer, being restricted to small inlets in central and southern Chile.

The largest marshes occur in Argentina south of the Rio de la Plata on the muddy estuary of the Salado River in Samborombón Bay and around Bahía Blanca and Bahía San Blas at the southeastern edge of the pampas. The low marsh is an essentially single-species stand of Brazilian cordgrass. Mid-shore a different cordgrass grows in a more complex community with saltgrass, sea club-rush, and spiny rush. The upper marsh is a zone of halophytic shrubs with glassworts, pickelweeds, and a Patagonian member of the goosefoot family.

Other marshes occur in coastal lagoons and tidal inlets in Uruguay and in the La Plata estuary south of Buenos Aires, Argentina. In these marshes, sedges and grasses abound in a narrow outer or lower marsh that is submerged in fresh or brackish water each day. In Uruguay's largest marsh on the lower Santa Lucia River west of Montevideo common sedges include California bulrush, three-square bulrush, and a reed. Common plants in Rio de la Plata marshes are a grass, seashore paspalum, totora reed, and common spikerush. In both instances, the upper marsh has more the saline conditions and is covered with halophytic glassworts, saltbush, sea purslane, and the forb *apio Cimarron*.

South of 44° S latitude lies the coast of Patagonia and the eastern edge of the cold Patagonian steppe. A high sea cliff extends most of the way to the entrance of the Strait of Magellan, and only where it is dissected by rivers do salt marshes occur. These small marshes are shrublands of low-growing, salt-tolerant plants such glasswort, pickleweed, and saltbush joined by the scaly-leaved succulent "mata verde," marsh rosemary, and sea heath.

Tropical South American salt marshes. In the tropics of South America, salt marshes develop in one of three environments. First, South American cordgrasses, especially Brazilian cordgrass, are invaders of recently formed mudflats in estuaries or in the tidal channels surrounding mangrove stands from the Guianas to southern Brazil. The fate of the cordgrass is to be replaced by mangrove. The grasses trap enough fine sediment to capture and anchor the floating seedlings of the mangroves, which grow to shade out the sun-loving grasses. The second habitat type that harbors salt marsh plants are saline soils within a mangrove woodland or on the landward edge of the mangrove community. This is the most usual place to find a salt marsh in the tropics. The areas are only flooded by spring high tides. Especially in areas with long dry seasons, high evaporation and strong capillary action act together to concentrate salts at the surface. In Brazil, plants of these inland marshes include the Brazilian cordgrass along with other grasses such as seashore dropseed and seashore paspalum, the alkali bulrush, and succulents such as sea purslane, saltwort, and beach bloodleaf. The third habitat that supports salt marsh is cutover mangrove in Guanabara Bay, Brazil, near Rio de Janeiro. In other parts of tropical South America, regrowth in cleared mangrove areas usually begins with the golden leather fern.

South African salt marshes. Only southernmost Africa (poleward of about 33° S latitude) lies in the temperate zone beyond the range of mangroves and thus this is the only region of Africa where salt marsh occurs to any extent. On the soft-sediment shores of the Indian Ocean a zonation of vegetation comparable to that in temperate parts of the Northern Hemisphere exists. The low shore is a zone of small cordgrass and red algae below which, in the subtidal zone, is a seagrass meadow of Cape eelgrass. Halophytic shrubs occupy the mid-shore, where pickleweed forms a seaward belt. Above it is a belt of sea lavender. The upper shore will be occupied by other shrubby pickleweeds if it is muddy and seashore dropseed if it is sandy. Animal life in the cordgrass community of the lowshore is dominated by the mud prawn. Also occurring are three burrowing, deposit-feeding salt marsh crabs. Two kinds of barnacle can be very abundant low on the cordgrass stems. The mangrove snail may occur in the pickleweed zones.

Mangrove (or Mangal)

Mangrove is a term applied to both an ecological category of plant and the habitat in which such plants grow. About 75 percent of the world's coasts that lie between 25° N and 25° S (see Figure 2.14) are vegetated by mangroves: any of approximately 70 species of salt-tolerant, mostly evergreen woody plants. These shrubs and trees form forests or swamps—also called mangal—on saline, waterlogged soils in the intertidal zone from the highest level of spring high tides down close to mean sea level.

Mangrove habitat occurs in three general forms. Riverine mangroves occupy the deltas of rivers in the brackish waters of tropical estuaries where the tidal range is slight. Fringing mangroves are pioneers on the intertidal flats of more exposed coasts, where they experience significant tidal ranges and wave-action. When the tide is in, their roots are submerged in seawater (see Figure 2.15). Basin mangroves develop on the landward side of fringing mangroves, where tidal and wave action are much reduced. Exposed to the effects of both rainfall and high evaporation rates, they must be able to withstand both low and high soil salinities.

Mangrove Geography

Mangroves are a taxonomically diverse group of plants. Similar adaptations to salinity evolved in at least 19 different plant families. Two families are particularly well represented around the world, the black mangroves (Avicenniaceae) with eight species in a single genus (*Avicennia*), and the red mangroves (Rhizophoraceae), with four genera (*Rhizophora, Bruguiera, Ceriops,* and Kandelia). The genus *Rhizophora* has eight species. In Australia and Southeast Asia, the family Sonneratiaceae, with five species, is important. Also of note are white mangroves of the genus *Laguncularia* (family Combretaceae) and one genus of palm, *Nypa* (family Palmae). While two genera (*Avicennia* and *Rhizophora*) are found throughout the tropics, most other mangroves are confined either to the Old World or to the New World plus West Africa. Old World (Indo-Pacific) species number 40–50, whereas only 10 species are known from the Americas and West Africa.

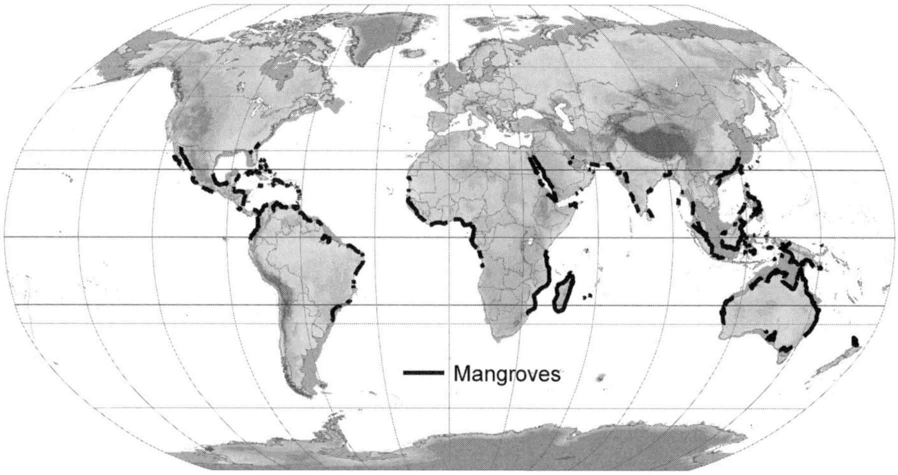

Figure 2.14 World distribution of mangroves. *(Map by Bernd Kuennecke.)*

Figure 2.15 Mangroves' aerial roots are exposed at low tide at Cape Tribulation, Australia. *(Photo © Daniel Gustavsson/Shutterstock.)*

Mangroves grow in both wet and dry tropical environments and, as a result, vegetation structure ranges from a low shrubland in desert areas to towering forests with tree heights greater than 120 ft (40 m) at the mouths of rivers in regions of tropical rainforest. Whatever the growthform of dominant plants, the key adaptations allow survival in a saline and often waterlogged substrate. Some type of aerial root or pneumatophore is characteristic (see Figure 2.16). Within the roots are air-filled passages opening to the outside through pores or lenticels. The form of the aerial roots varies from genus to genus. The red mangroves (*Rhizophora* spp.) have prop roots, some of which extend from high on the trunk above the high-water mark and arch down to the ground. They form an impenetrable mass that captures sediments and blunts the force of the waves and helps expand the mangal habitat seaward. Black mangroves (*Avicennia* spp.) have thin vertical pencil-like pneumatophores rising from roots. They are completely covered at high tide. *Bruguiera* roots resemble cypress knees, while the cannonball mangrove (*Xylocarpus granatum*) that ranges from East Africa to Southeast Asia has laterally flattened, ribbon-like roots that snake across the mud surface.

The aerial roots carry oxygen from the atmosphere to the roots. Some oxygen then leaks into the sediments to help aerate the upper layer of mud and create the soil conditions necessary for mangrove growth. The woody plants deal with the high salt content in much the same way as salt marsh grasses. *Rhizophora*,

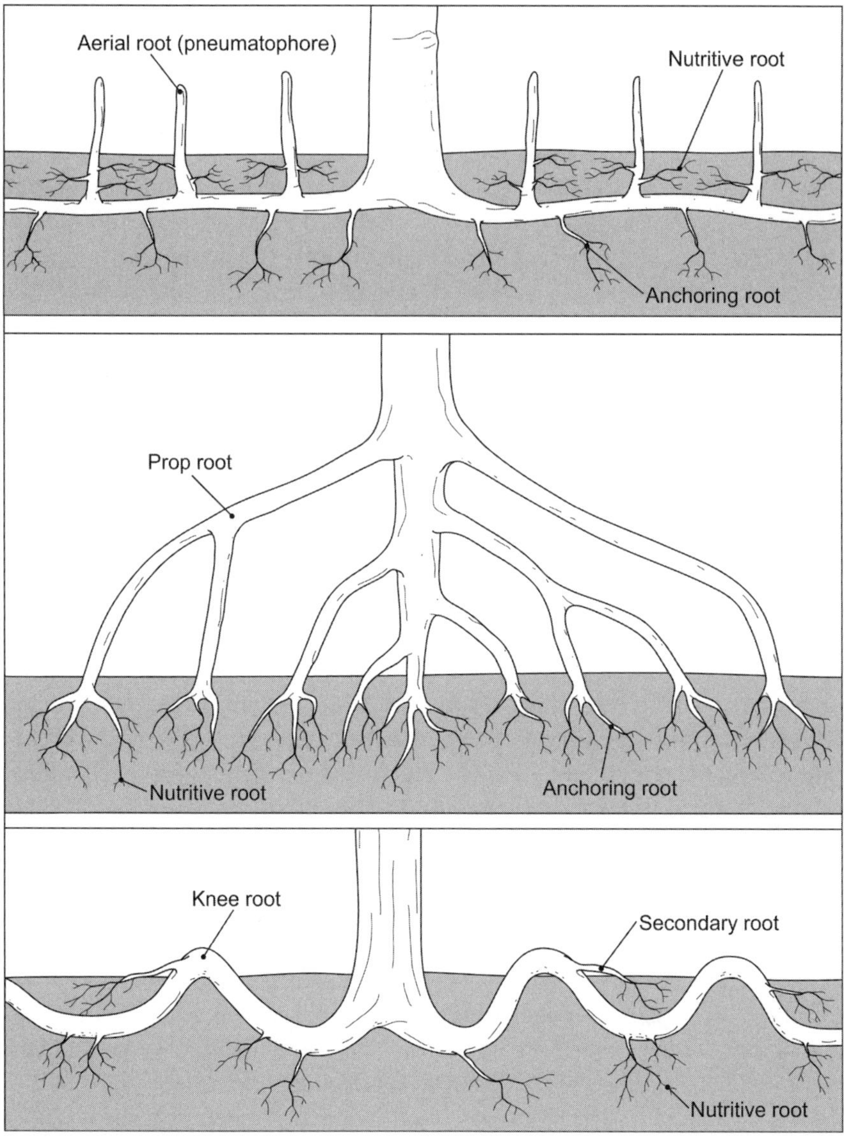

Figure 2.16 Different types of aerial roots found in mangrove plants. *(Illustration by Jeff Dixon. Adapted from Little 2000.)*

Bruguiera, and *Sonneratia* mangroves prevent the uptake of sodium and chlorine by their roots. *Avicennia* and a few other genera allow salts to enter the roots and move up the stems, but have salt glands in their leaves to secrete the excess. Still others accumulate salt in the leaves or bark and then get rid of it by shedding these tissues. All keep the osmotic pressure in the cell sap of their leaves high enough to be able to draw water up from the roots.

Many mangrove species exhibit vivipary or cryptovivipary reproductive strategies in which the embryo develops while the fruit is still on the tree. In true vivipary, the growing embryo breaks through the fruit wall, whereas in cryptovivipary the embryo only penetrates the seed coat. The former is characteristic of species of *Rhizophora*, *Bruguiera*, *Ceriops,* and *Kandelia*; the latter mode is typical in the genera *Avicennia*, *Aegiceras*, and the palm, *Nypa*. The resulting seedling or capsule in both cases resembles a long bean pod and seems to be an adaptation for dispersal rather than a response to the intertidal environment. The seedlings drop from the trees into the water, where they can float for weeks until they are carried to favorable new sites. Once they touch ground, they quickly take root and grow.

Plants other than trees and shrubs grow in mangrove swamps and forests. Epiphytes such as orchids and ferns cluster on the branches, as do bromeliads in the Neotropics. None of these groups are as diverse, however, as in upland forests, and their presence may be limited by salt spray. Semiparasitic mistletoes also grow on branches in the canopy. On the leaves as well as on the stems and aerial roots are algae and cyanobacteria. Terrestrial ferns such as the golden leather fern invade cutover areas in the Neotropics, or small salt marshes may develop on similarly disturbed sites.

Zonation of the vegetation parallel to the coast is apparent in all mangal. Many times each belt is occupied by only one or two mangrove species. A typical pattern in the Americas is to have three zones, as in Puerto Rico, where red mangroves occupy the seaward edge of the stand. Black mangroves grow just inland of the red mangrove in areas where inundation is less frequent. White mangrove and button mangrove form the landward margin. In the Indo-Pacific region five zones between mean sea level and the high beach, where waves impact only during the most extreme high tides, are more common.

Several microhabitats within the mangrove are well suited to animals. The leafy canopy hosts birds and mammals—most of them temporary visitors—and a multitude of insects, especially mosquitoes and midges. Ants and termites and orb-weaving spiders are also abundant. Holes in branches where water collects allow mosquito and midge larvae to mature. The trunks and aerial roots are attachment sites for sessile barnacles and oysters as well as feeding grounds for periwinkles and some tree-living crabs. The soil surface is the domain of hermit crabs, snails, and mudskippers, while an infauna consisting of nereid polychaete worms, snails, crabs, and—in the Indo-Pacific—mudlobsters inhabits the soil itself. These invertebrates continually rework the substrate to create a topography of mounds and burrows and aerate the substrate, enhancing growing conditions for the mangroves themselves. Permanent and semipermanent pools attract small crabs and are also home to a variety of insect larvae. Finally, the creeks draining the mangrove harbor crocodiles and fish.

Animal zonation is evident and appears to be related more to the structure of the vegetation than to tidal conditions. The vertical component of zonation from ground level to canopy is much stronger than the horizontal one inland from the

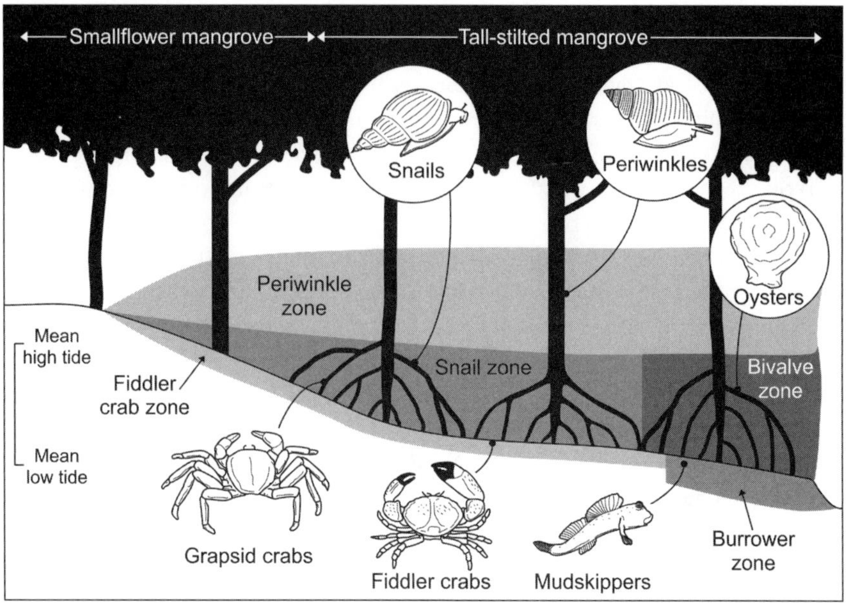

Figure 2.17 Vertical zonation of animal life in a mangrove stand in Malaysia. *(Illustration by Jeff Dixon. Adapted from Little 2000.)*

coast. Figure 2.17 gives a general picture of local distribution patterns within a wet-tropics mangrove swamp in Malaysia. The *Rhizophora* zone, flooded by most high tides, is the main place that animal distribution seems determined by tidal heights. Burrowing invertebrates of several phyla are abundant in these muds that are exposed for only short periods of time at low tide. Above them, attached to the prop roots of the red mangroves as high up as the high tide reaches, is a concentration of oysters and barnacles.

The rest of the mangal inland from this fringe is divided only vertically. Fiddler crabs and grapsid crabs dominate the surface muds and create their own runs through the tangle of roots. *Sesarma* and other mud-dwelling grapsid crabs are the major consumers of the detritus falling from the mangroves above, and a few species even climb up to consume living leaves. Crabs also bring decomposing leaves into their burrows thereby preventing the loss of up to 30 percent of the production of the mangroves, which might otherwise be swept out of the ecosystem on the tide.

Above the mud, on the aerial roots of mangroves is a snail zone. These gastropods mostly graze epiphytic algae and cyanobacteria. At heights submerged only at the highest spring tides, is the periwinkle zone. Different periwinkles sort themselves out spatially and ecologically, some grazing on algae and fungi on living leaves, for example, while others forage on the bark of branches or trunk or on the marine fungi decomposing leaves and wood. The uppermost level of the mangrove

Mudskippers

Mudskippers (*Periophthalmus* and other genera) are air-breathing fish with prominent eyes on the tops of their heads. Amphibious, they live in burrows but emerge at low tide to walk along the surface at low tide on modified pelvic and anal fins. One species actually climbs into the mangrove by means of a sucker formed from fused pelvic fins. They become dehydrated if they stay out of the water too long, so they must return to their water-filled, anoxic burrows, where they also deposit their eggs. Mudskippers have a unique way of oxygenating their underground home. They carry mouthfuls of air down into the burrow, which is constructed so as to trap a large of bubble air when they expel it. They may make several trips before the tide returns in order to have enough air for themselves and their developing eggs, which are attached to the top of the air chamber. Most mudskippers are omnivores.

is the canopy. The leaves of mangroves are unpalatable to most animals, both invertebrates and vertebrates, but the leaves, flowers, and fruits of epiphytes and lianas may provide nourishment for insects and other terrestrial organisms. The proboscis monkey of Borneo is one of a very few mammals that actually consumes living mangrove leaves (see Plate IV). Its obvious pot-belly is a result of large, compartmented stomach filled with bacteria that digest cellulose and neutralize toxins in mangrove leaves.

Large colonies of seabirds may nest and roost in mangrove, but they gain their food from the sea. Wading birds likewise nest and roost in the canopy but find food on the tidal flats. Small birds are attracted to the wealth of insects in the canopy and invertebrates on the forest floor when it is exposed at low tide.

Regional Expressions

Neotropical mangroves. Four trees make up most mangrove in the Americas and also occur in West Africa. These are the red mangrove, black mangrove, white mangrove, and buttonwood mangrove. The black mangrove is the most cold-tolerant of New World mangroves and so is the only species found at the poleward extremes of mangrove distribution, where it assumes a shrubby growthform. On the Atlantic coast of North America, black mangrove reaches its northern limit at San Augustine, Florida (29° 52′ N), but it occurs at even higher latitudes in Bermuda (32° 20′ N). The northern limit of red mangrove is at Cedar Key, Florida (29° N). In the Southern Hemisphere, both reach their southern limits at Florianopolis, Brazil (27° 30′ S), but other mangroves extend as far south as the mouth of the Arananguá River (29° S). On the Pacific coast of the Americas, the northern limit of black mangrove is near Puerto Lobos, Sonora (30° 15′ N), close to the head of the Gulf of California; but on the cool and foggy Pacific coast of Baja California, it is at Ballena Bay (27° N). The southern limit is barely across the Equator near the Ecuador/Peru border (3° 40′ S). An extremely arid climate and proximity of the cold Humboldt Current offshore probably inhibit the growth of mangroves. The tropical Pacific coast of South America generally lacks quiet bays and lagoons or river deltas built of fine sediments, the habitats conducive to the establishment of mangroves.

Pacific coast. The greatest species richness in Neotropical mangroves occurs on the Pacific coasts of Costa Rica, Panama, and northwest Colombia, where several red mangroves, and two black mangroves grow. An endemic mangrove, *Pelliciera rhizoporae*, in the tea family (Theaceae), possesses fluted buttresses and occurs only on the Pacific coast of Central America and northwestern Colombia and on the Galapagos Islands.

The large number of sheltered bays and, in Costa Rica, the many streams flowing out of the Talamanca Mountains, provide the conditions needed for mangrove development. A relatively short dry season from January to April ensures more than adequate freshwater from rainfall. Indeed, mangroves often are mixed with plants more indicative of freshwater wetlands such as the buttress-rooted dragonwood tree and prickley-pole, a spiny-stemmed palm. Freshwater raphia palm swamps are often nearby.

There is little ground cover except in shaded areas, where there may be a dense cover of saltworts or mangrove lilies. Lianas such as mangrove rubber vine are widely occurring, as are some leguminous shrubs on the landward fringe. Epiphytes are also fairly common and include bromeliads and orchids. The most common orchid is the large magenta-flowered "flute-player's schomburgkia." It has a strange association with ants that carry organic debris into its hollow pseudobulbs and live there. The accumulation of dead insects and plant material is decomposed by bacteria and fungi and then absorbed by the orchid. Experiments show that orchids produce more flowers when they are inhabited by ants. However, some ants also tend mealybugs, which feed on orchid leaves to the detriment of the host plant.

Animal life is relatively diverse. Among the more conspicuous reptiles are American crocodile, spectacled caiman, green iguana, the running-on-water basilisk (or Jesus Christ) lizard, and the boa constrictor. The Mangrove Hummingbird and the Yellow-billed Cotinga are rare endemic birds. The hummingbird seeks nectar in the flowers of *Pelliciera rhizophorae*, the only mangrove pollinated by a vertebrate. Roseate Spoonbill, Mangrove Black Hawk, Muscovy Duck, Boat-billed Heron, Mangrove Cuckoo, and the Mangrove Warbler are other largely Neotropical birds associated with mangrove. So, too, are a couple of rails, While Ibis, Black-necked Stilt, Amazon Kingfisher, and many others.

White-tailed deer browse the leaves of some mangroves. Crab-eating raccoons eat crabs and molluscs procured from both mangrove stems and bottom muds. Among other strictly Neotropical mammals inhabiting or visiting mangrove are a rodent, the paca; two monkeys—the mantled howler monkey, and the white-throated capuchin; two anteaters—the pygmy anteater and the Mexican anteater; and the Central American otter.

Pacific Coast mangroves are under threat from high sedimentation resulting from forest removal from steep mountain slopes. Agricultural development is a major problem not only because of clearing of the mangrove but also because of the runoff from fields that carries pesticides and fertilizers into these coastal wetlands. Charcoal production using mangrove wood has been destructive, as has stripping the bark from larger red mangroves for the production of tanning chemicals. The largest protected swath of mangrove on the Pacific Coast is the Térraba-Sierpe Mangrove Reserve in Costa Rica. It covers about 85 mi^2 (220 km^2) and is considered a wetland of international significance.

Caribbean mangroves. Mangrove occurs along the Caribbean coast of Central America and the fringes of the many cayes (keys) and islands of the region. On the mainland, mangrove extends the full length of Belize south into Guatemala's Bahía de Annatique. It plays an important role in preventing coastal erosion by the many tropical storms spawned in the Caribbean. This is an area of relatively high precipitation, ranging from 55 in (1,400 mm) in the north to 155 in (4,000 mm) in the south. All four mangroves common to the Neotropical region as a whole are encountered along this coast, where they form major wintering grounds for many North American migratory birds and habitat for numerous Neotropical animals. Five sea turtles—green (*Chelonia mydas*), hawksbill (*Eremochelys imbricata*), loggerhead (*Caretta caretta*), leatherback (*Dermochelys coriacea*), and Kemp's ridley (*Lepidochelys kempi*)—use the area, as do two crocodiles (*Crocodylus acutus* and *C. moreletti*). A unique habitat on the edge of tropical rainforest, Belize's coastal mangroves are today threatened by deforestation, overfishing, urban expansion, the dumping of trash, industrial discharges, and oil spills.

On islands and cayes off the coast is a separate system of mangroves associated with Belize's 135 mi (220 km) long barrier reef and two coral atolls. Red mangrove is especially common, with black mangrove, white mangrove, and coconut palms prevalent in some places. Intertidal areas are dominated by red, white, and buttonwood mangrove, while permanently flooded areas have nearly pure stands of black mangrove. Reef mangroves are nesting sites for White Egrets, Anhingas, Neotropical Cormorants, Boat-billed Herons, and White Ibises. Brown Boobies nest on Man-O-War Caye.

Much reef mangrove is protected—at least on paper—within the Belize Barrier Reef Reserve, a World Heritage Site. It is nonetheless threatened by illegal bird hunting and egg collecting by local people and poorly managed ecotourists, who trample vegetation, disturb nesting birds, and improperly dispose of wastes.

Another major area of mangrove in the Neotropics is the Greater Antilles, the four large islands (Cuba, Hispaniola, Puerto Rico, and Jamaica) that form the northern border of the Caribbean. Complex mangrove landscapes have developed in response to environmentally diverse conditions, as have a number of endemic plants and animals. Coastal fringe mangroves are scrubby stands of red mangrove backed by black mangrove and white mangrove. Buttonwood mangrove forms the landward edge. Lush stands of tall mangrove up to 80 ft (25 m) high develop at the mouths of larger rivers, which are rather rare features in the Greater Antilles. Mangroves, seagrass beds, and coral reefs often comprise a single functional unit or ecosystem, and it is difficult to separate the flora and fauna of one from the others. Endemic animals include the Cuban crocodile, Cuban Green-Woodpecker, Jamaican Tody, and subspecies of the Mangrove Warbler and Clapper Rail. Endemic anole lizards are also found. Mangroves are also habitat for the endangered West Indian manatee.

Local people harvest or degrade mangrove resources for construction timbers, firewood, and charcoal-making. Shrimp, lobster, and oysters are exported to the world market. More than three-fourths of Puerto Rico's mangroves were destroyed in the 1970s as part of control projects aimed at malaria-carrying mosquitoes and for urban development. Today, mangrove restoration and preservation programs are planned or under way in most countries.

The Lesser Antilles are yet another mangrove region in the Caribbean. These small islands form a double chain arcing south from Sombrero and Anguilla to Grenada. Low-elevation, flat limestone islands form the outer chain at the edge of the Atlantic Ocean; higher, volcanic islands occur as an inner chain. Ocean currents carrying freshwater north from the Amazon and Orinoco rivers of South America pass the southernmost islands and decrease the salinity of their coastal waters, producing conditions favorable to the development of mangroves. Fringing mangrove is the rule, although riverine communities do develop at the mouths of rivers. Mangroves also occur in basins or depressions formed at the mouth rivers blocked by barrier spits, as in St. Lucia. In such areas, mangroves grow in swamps with dragonwood tree or in saltmarsh and freshwater marshes. Many others are part of a landscape composed of mangrove, seagrass meadow, and coral reef.

Many of the same reptiles associated with mangrove in Belize or in the Greater Antilles also occur in the Lesser Antilles, including sea turtles, green iguana, anole lizards, boa constrictors, and caiman. Among frequently seen birds are Spotted Sandpiper, Great Blue Heron, Cattle Egret, and Belted Kingfisher—all birds familiar to North Americans. Neotropical species such as the Lesser Antillean Pewee, West Indian Whistling Duck, and Lesser Antillean Bullfinch join them. These mangroves are also important habitat for the West Indian manatee.

Local people extract timber from mangrove forests and depend on them as nursery areas supporting their fisheries. Deforestation is a problem, especially on Guadeloupe, Martinique, and St. Lucia. The expansion of tourism, with its related development issues, is a threat on all islands. A growing concern is the apparent increase in the frequency and strength of tropical storms. Hurricanes flattened entire mangrove stands in Martinique in the recent past.

Atlantic mangroves: Brazil. The vast amounts of clay and other fine sediment carried by the Amazon River form myriad islands and mudflats at the river's mouth and along the Atlantic coast as far north as Cabo Caciporé and south as Bahía de São Marcos. In the lower Amazon itself, flat land and a high tidal range (16–23 ft; 5–7 m) permit mangrove habitat to extend upstream some 28 mi (45 km). Freshwater is abundant in this region of humid tropical climate; indeed, so much so that competition from freshwater plants tends to limit mangrove. Red mangrove is the most common species; and close to the coast it attains heights near 80 ft (25 m). Two black mangroves are prominent on the coast north of the river's mouth, where they may stand 150 ft (45 m) tall. Four other mangroves occur in riverine areas. Much of this mangrove forest is intact, since—with the notable exception of the city of Belem—human population density is low. Inaccessibility protects the trees from large-scale use as firewood, charcoal, construction timbers, and tanning acids.

Southeast of the Amazon River, on both sides of Bahía de São Marcos in the State of Maranhão, lies Brazil's largest and most complex mangrove system, which reputedly contains the greatest aboveground mangrove forest biomass in the world. The bay west of the island of São Luis contains hundreds of islands and mudflats that are colonized and stabilized by mangroves. Mangroves also edge the coast and extend up the rivers and estuaries entering it. Here, the trees may grow to heights of 150 ft (45 m). The same species found at the mouth of the Amazon occur here, too. The abundance of freshwater from rainfall that can be in excess of 150 in (4,000 mm) a year and the many streams entering the bay promotes the development of mangrove, but also means that mangrove is frequently associated with palms and freshwater aquatic plants. Eastward along the shores of Bahía de São Marcos and the rest of Maranhão, the dry season becomes longer and salinities rise. Mangroves become less and less well developed as a consequence.

Maranhão's mangroves are extremely important habitat for shorebirds and are major breeding and feeding areas for wading birds such as herons, Roseate Spoonbill, and endangered birds such as the Scarlet Ibis and Wattled Jacana. Other endangered animals associated with these mangroves are several sea turtles that breed in the area, the West Indian manatee, and the uniquely South American river dolphin or tucuxi. Still largely protected by inaccessibility and low numbers of human residents, Maranhão's mangroves are nonetheless threatened by overexploitation of its crabs and shrimp by local fishermen, the extraction of trees for domestic uses, conversion to rice paddies, and mercury contamination resulting from gold-mining operations in the vicinity.

Isolated patches of mangrove continue to be found in southern Brazil from the State of Rio de Janeiro to Florianopolis in the State of Santa Catarina. Only three kinds occur, but not always occur together.

Although significant nursery and refuge areas for diverse juvenile crustaceans, molluscs, and fish, the real importance of these southern mangroves is as stopover points for long-distance migratory birds, including shorebirds such as Semi-palmated Plovers, White-rumped Sandpipers, Lesser Yellowlegs, and Greater Yellowlegs. The Scarlet Ibis, once believed extirpated from most of its South American range, reappeared in Cubatão in the early 1980s, an encouraging sign that mangroves can be restored in this the most densely settled part of Brazil. Likewise, Orange-winged Parrots are benefiting from the protection of mangrove on the São Paulo and Paraná rivers.

Indo-Pacific mangroves. The enormous region of the Indo-Pacific encompasses the Indian Ocean coasts of East Africa, the Indian subcontinent, Southeast Asia, and northern Australasia. The diversity of mangroves here is the highest in the world, but species are not uniformly distributed. Mangrove vegetation is highly fragmented because of the few sites favorable for establishment, the insular nature of much of the region, and a long history of human impact. Several subregions can be distinguished; six are highlighted below.

East African mangroves. Mangroves grow along the East African coast from Somalia south through Mozambique. Five species are common. Another species, *Xylocarpus benadivensis*, is endemic to the region. Much of the area is under the influence of monsoons. The southeast monsoon that blows from April through October brings more rain, stronger winds, and stronger wave action than the northeast monsoon, which is typical the rest of the year. South of Malindi, Kenya (3° 14′ S), the climate changes to humid tropical. Warm ocean currents arriving from the east divide near the Tanzania-Mozambique border to flow north and south along the East African coast. The northern limit of mangrove is met along the dry coast of Somalia where wind-driven upwelling creates a cold current part of the year. Fringing mangroves occur only where groundwater discharges lower salinity; the most extensive stands are riverine, such as those at the mouths of the Rufiji River in Tanzania and the Zambezi River in Mozambique. Some riverine mangroves extend far inland along tidal rivers. Mangrove forests between Mozambique's Beira and Save rivers line the banks upriver for 30 mi (50 km), with treetops some 100 ft (30 m) above the ground. Species composition varies with salinity, depth of water table, and the soil's ability to retain moisture and its pH and oxygen content. Sandy soils are colonized by blackwood, while muddy soils along streams are preferred by red mangrove. Wetter areas support orange mangrove, drier areas yellow mangrove. The landward edge of mangrove stands consists of Indian mangrove and cannonball mangrove. In fringing mangroves along open coasts, the main pioneer species is mangrove apple. Orange mangrove may grow as the landward edge of the stand.

East African mangroves are important habitat for Nile crocodiles, hippopotamus, Sykes monkey, and otter. Endangered green sea turtles and olive ridleys visit the mangrove and dig nests near the mouths of some of the larger rivers. The large forest on the Rufiji River delta is an important stopping over point for migrating wetland birds such as Curlew Sandpipers, Roseate Tern, and Caspian Tern.

Mangroves may be found in association with seagrass meadows, coral reefs, and dune forests and are thus part of larger system that functions as refuge and nursery area for a variety of marine species. In addition to providing habitat for sea turtles, the mangroves of Mozambique are important refuge for what may be the last viable population of dugong in East Africa. Waters off the Zambezi delta and its mangroves harbor a major prawn fishery, humpback whale nursery, and sizeable populations of large sharks and porpoises. Today, mangrove is being converted to rice paddies, salt-evaporating pans, and aquaculture and being encroached on by urban development. Mangrove trees are still cut for firewood and construction timber, the latter exported to the Middle East.

Man-Eating Tigers of the Sundarbans

The Sundarban mangroves, somewhat surprisingly, are critical habitat for the Bengal tiger, the Indo-Pacific's largest terrestrial predator. A uniquely adapted population, tigers of the mangrove swim from island to island hunting chital deer, barking deer, wild pig, and macaques. The tigers also have a reputation for attacking and eating humans. They are the only population of man-eating tigers in South Asia today and thrive in the dense tangle of mangrove trunks and pneumatophores in swamps frequently visited by fishermen and honey collectors.

Sundarban mangrove. The world's largest mangrove ecosystem, the Sundarban mangroves, occupies some 3,860 mi^2 (10,000 km^2) on the huge delta that is the meeting place of the Ganges, Brahmaputra, and Meghna rivers in Bangladesh and West Bengal State, India. Here, the summer monsoon brings heavy rains and frequent cyclones from June through September, and total annual rainfall can be in excess of 135 in (3,500 mm). Summer temperatures may rise above 118° F (48° C). The dominant mangrove tree in this maze of river channels and islands is the valuable timber tree sundri, from which the region's forest apparently derives its name. Sundri has no pneumatophores, but it does possess buttresses. Nor does it exhibit vivipary, as most mangrove trees do. Many other mangroves occur, including gewa, cedar mangrove, cannonball mangrove, keora, gorn, orange mangrove, red mangrove, and the nipa palm.

Reptilian predators also swim in the rivers and include two saltwater crocodiles, a gavial, and the water monitor lizard. The waterways are home to the Gangetic freshwater dolphin as well. The mangrove forests themselves host a large number of crabs and shrimps among their roots and the tree-climbing mudskipper. Some 170 kinds of birds have been reported, including a globally threatened large stork, the Lesser Adjutant, and the secretive, grebe-like Masked Finfoot. This vast area is an important wintering ground for migratory birds, including shorebirds, gulls, and terns.

The entire ecosystem is considered endangered as a consequence of human pressures. Almost half of the forest has been cut for firewood or to make charcoal. The timber industry also has been removing trees in unsustainable ways, just as the shrimp growout industry has been removing shrimp fry at unsustainable levels. Conversion of mangrove to shrimp aquaculture ponds is an expanding problem. Human activities far removed from the coast also have major negative impacts on the mangrove ecosystem. Most dire are the consequences of clearcutting forests on the slopes of the Himalayas. Subsequent accelerated erosion of the uplands contributes huge amounts of silt to the rivers, which then deposit it in the low-moving waters of the delta and suffocate the juvenile marine life in the mangrove nursery. Upstream in the Ganges, diversion of water for irrigation during the dry season has raised critical salinity levels in coastal waters.

Myanmar mangroves. The mangrove forests on the multichanneled delta of the Irrawaddy River in Myanmar (formerly Burma) are perhaps the most degraded in the Indo-Pacific. Only small fragments remain. Among the many mangrove species are three red mangroves, keora, cedar mangrove, cannonball mangrove, a black mangrove, smallfower mangrove, other orange mangroves, sundri, and two palms—nipa palm and, on drier sites, the mangrove date palm. With the apparent extirpation of the tiger from the area, ungulates such as sambar, hog deer, mouse deer, barking deer, and tapir are common in protected forest reserves, as are wild boar. A small population of wild Asian elephants visits the mangroves during the dry summer and drinks saltwater.

Resident and migrant birds are abundant and varied. Residents include the Oriental Darter, Little Cormorant, Reef Heron, Ruddy Shelduck, Bronze-winged Jacana, several shorebirds, and the Lesser Black-backed Gull. The Edible-nest Swiftlet uses limestone caves nearby for nesting.

In streams at the southern end of the delta is refuge for the last population of crocodiles in the area and a few small populations of river terrapin.

The Irrawaddy is the fifth most heavily silted river in the world (behind the Yellow River in China, the Ganges in India, the Amazon in Brazil, and the Mississippi in the United States). Sedimentation rates are increasing as a result of deforestation and poor agricultural practices in its watershed. It is estimated that, if the situation does not improve, all mangroves will be gone by 2050.

Indochinese mangroves. Fringing mangroves occur in areas of near-daily flooding by tidal or brackish water along the coasts of Thailand, Cambodia, and Vietnam. Much of the coast, however, is naturally without mangroves since most is exposed and rocky, and major river deltas and estuaries are rare. The largest extent of mangrove was in the Mekong River delta in southern Vietnam, but it was destroyed by napalm and the defoliant known as Agent Orange during the Vietnam War. Efforts are currently under way to restore these forests.

Indochina's mangroves are among the most diverse and contain 60 percent of all mangrove species recorded throughout South Asia, Southeast Asia, and Indonesia. On the edge of open coasts, the typical pioneer is baen. Inland in more protected sites with less frequent tidal flooding is a belt of tall-stilted mangrove and smallflower mangrove. Still further inland on higher ground where water is brackish, the mangrove community is dominated by black mangrove, mangrove apple, nipa palm, and mangrove date palm.

It is critical habitat for some rare and endangered waterbirds, including the Lesser Adjutant, Storm's Stork, White-winged Wood Duck, and Spot-billed Pelican. It also supports rare reptiles, including the water monitor lizard, the false gavial, and a saltwater crocodile.

Sunda Shelf mangroves. The Sunda Shelf is the continental shelf that extends south from Indochina and on which lie the islands of Sumatra and Borneo. On the east coast of Sumatra and southern shores of Borneo is another of the world's most biologically diverse mangrove ecosystems. One of five mangrove species (black mangarove, red mangrove, mangrove apple, orange mangrove, and nipa palm) may be dominant in different parts of this highly varied region. Most stands display a strong zonation of species. The outer edge of the forests is usually made up of black mangrove or mangrove apple. Landward, the next belt will be dominated by red or orange mangrove trees. The farther inland one goes, the firmer are the soils and the greater the species diversity. Where the influence of freshwater is strong, nipa palms are prevalent.

Borneo's mangroves are noteworthy because they are home to the odd proboscis monkey (see Plate IV), one of only a few mammals restricted to mangrove habitat and able to digest mangrove leaves. They consume primarily young leaves and seeds from unripe fruits.

As is true in many parts of the Indo-Pacific region, the mangroves of the Sunda Shelf are being degraded through timbering, land clearance for agriculture, conversion to aquaculture, and urban development. Shrimp farming and cockle culture are growing industries. Many parts of the mangrove are being felled for commercial charcoal production and, increasingly, for the production of wood chips and pulp.

Australasian mangroves. Australasia includes Australia, Papua-New Guinea, New Caledonia, and New Zealand. The mangroves along the tropical coasts of this region are concentrated on the southern coast of New Guinea and the northeastern coast of Australia.

New Guinea. The greatest extent of mangrove on southern Papua-New Guinea's coast is at the mouths of the Purari, Kikori, Fly, Northwest, and Otakwa rivers, around Bintuni Bay and on the southern Vogelkop Peninsula. Most of this area has a humid tropical climate. Mangrove habitat originates with the establishment of one of the two black mangroves of the region, baen or blackwood, on sheltered shores, or mangrove apple on the banks of tidal streams. Tree roots trap fine sediments and build up the substrate, creating the conditions preferred by red mangrove, which invades, shades the sun-loving pioneers, and eventually replaces them. Succession continues with colonization by tall-stilted mangrove and smallflower mangrove. At some distance from the shore, orange mangrove finds suitable habitat and comes to dominate older communities in association with sundri and other mangrove species. Where freshwater is a major factor in the environment, nipa palm is abundant, often occurring in single-species stands. Lightning strikes are a significant part of the dynamics of mangrove forests in parts of New Guinea. Lightning may kill many canopy trees at a time. Apparently, it travels through the root system and destroys the cell membranes involved in regulating salt uptake. A gap some 165 ft (50 m) in diameter may be created in which a dense growth of golden leather fern and seedlings of tall-stilted mangrove and other trees develops. It may take 200–300 years for the canopy of the cleared patch to recover its mature height.

Australia. Thirty-nine kinds of mangrove are known from Australia. With the exception of one endemic species (*Avicennia integra*), all are also found on New Guinea or in Southeast Asia. The richest communities are on the shores of the Coral Sea in the humid tropical region of northeastern Queensland, where 35 species have been recorded. The number of mangroves decreases to the south until in the cooler climates of South Australia and Victoria only the grey mangrove survives. The height of the mangrove diminishes from north to south. In Queensland, closed-canopy forests dominated by red mangrove and orange mangrove have trees up to 130 ft (40 m) tall. Aridity increases southward in tropical Australia and the mangroves become open-canopied woodlands or low (3–15 ft; 1–5 m tall) open shrublands. In the subtropical parts of the range, open woodlands of grey mangrove may attain heights of 35 ft (10 m), but near their southern limit in Corner Inlet, Victoria (38° S latitude), they are less than 15 ft (5 m) high.

On the eastern coast of Australia a complex mosaic of microhabitats and hence plant communities forms as a result of the dynamics of sedimentation and erosion in an estuarine environment, but a general zonation pattern is still evident. Where salinity is high, the lowest part of the intertidal zone, just above mean sea level, has mangrove apple (*Sonneratia alba*) or grey mangrove growing on it. Mid-shore has a mixed stand of red mangroves and orange mangroves, and the upper shore has yellow mangrove and, once again, grey mangrove. Shores in low-salinity regions of an estuary have a different sequence of species. The lowest, fringing belt of mangrove contains either a mangrove apple (*Sonneratia caseolaris*) or nipa palm. Above that is a band dominated by cannonball mangrove, while the typical mangrove of the highest intertidal zone is looking-glass mangrove.

In Western Australia, where little rain falls, the mangrove community is relatively simple. Along the sweep of coast facing Indonesia across the Indian Ocean, there are only seven species of mangrove. Usually there is a seaward fringe of grey mangrove backed by a band of red mangrove and, higher on the coast, belts of yellow and grey mangroves. Large barren salt pans are conspicuous features of the high shore.

As is often the case in mangroves worldwide, decapod crustaceans such as ghost shrimps, hermit crabs, fiddler and ghost crabs, spider crabs, and mud crabs are the most abundant animals of the floor of the mangrove forest. Locally, however, snails in a variety of genera (for example, *Cerithium*, *Littoraria*, *Nerita*, and *Ellobium*) may be dominant on sediments as well as on living and dead plant matter. Insects may be represented by more species than any other group in decaying wood, but crabs, polychaetes, and ship worms (Teredinid bivalves) are also diverse.

Further Readings

Books

Knox, George A. 2001. *The Ecology of Seashores.* Boca Raton, FL: CRC Press.

Koehl, Mimi. 2006. *Wave-swept Shore: The Rigors of Life on a Rocky Coast.* Berkeley: University of California Press. Excellent photographs and discussion of Pacific Coast rocky shores and tidepools.

Lippson, Alice Jane, and Robert L. Lippson. 1984. *Life in the Chesapeake Bay.* Baltimore: Johns Hopkins University Press. Wonderful drawings of plants and animals of the soft-sediment shores and saltmarshes of Atlantic embayments from North Carolina north to Canada.

Videos

BBC. 2002. "Coasts." Programme 8, *Blue Planet: Seas of Life*. Available on DVD.
BBC. 2002. "Tidal Seas." Programme 7, *Blue Planet: Seas of Life*. Available on DVD.

Appendix

Biota of the Coast Biome

Rocky Shores: Northern Hemisphere Temperate Waters

Northwest Atlantic Rocky Coasts	
Spray or supralittoral zone	
Primary producers	
Cyanobacteria	*Calothrix* spp., *Lyngba* spp., *Rivularia* spp.
Black lichen	*Verrucaria maura*
Red algae	*Bangia* spp., *Hildenbrandia* spp., *Porphyra* spp.
Green algae	*Blidingia* spp., *Ulothrix* spp.
Herbivores	
Periwinkle	*Littorina saxatilus*
Intertidal or eulittoral zone	
Primary producers	
Brown algae	*Fucus vesiculosis, Ascophyllum nodosum*
Carrageen moss	*Mastocarpus stellatus*
Irish moss	*Chondrius crispus*
Sea lettuce	*Ulva lactua*
Green string sea lettuce	*Ulva intestinalis*
Detritus and plankton eaters (filter-feeders)	
Acorn barnacle	*Semibalanus balanoides*
Edible mussel	*Mytilus edulis*
Herbivores (grazers)	
Amphipods	*Hyale nilsonii*
Common periwinkle	*Littorina littorea*
Snail	*Lacuna vincta*
Limpet	*Acmaea testudinalis*

(*Continued*)

Chiton	*Tonicella ruber*
Sea urchin	*Strongylocentrotus droebachiensis*
Carnivores	
Dog whelk	*Nucella lapillus*
Shore crab	*Carcinus maena*
Rock crab	*Cancer irrorratus*
Lobster	*Homarus americanus*
Sea star	*Asterias vulgaris*
Common Eider	*Somateria mollissima*
Subtidal or sublittoral zone	
Primary producers	
Horsetail kelp	*Laminaria digitata*
Sugar kelp	*Laminaria saccharina*
Sea colander	*Agarum cribosum*
Irish moss	*Chondrus crispa*
Red fern	*Ptilota serrata*
Crustose red algae	*Lithothamnion, Clathromorphum,* and *Phymotolithon*
Herbivores	
Limpet	*Tectura* spp.
Periwinkle	*Littorina* spp.
Snail	*Lacuna vincta*
Isopod	*Idotea* spp.
Carnivores	
Jonah crab	*Cancer borealis*
Sea stars	*Asteria* spp.
Winter flounder	*Pseudopleuronectes americanus*
Haddock	*Melanogrammus aeglefinus*
Eelpout	*Macrozoarcus americanus*
Wrasse	*Tautogolabrus adsperus*
Red-breasted Merganser	*Mergus serrator*
Common Goldeneye	*Bucephala clangula*
Old Squaw	*Clangula hyemalis*

Northeast Pacific Rocky Coasts

Splash or supralittoral zone	
Primary producers	
Sea lettuces	*Ulva* spp.
Red algae	*Porphyra* spp., *Bangia vermicularis*
Herbivores	
Limpet	*Collisella digitalis*
Periwinkle	*Littorina keenae*
Isopods	*Ligia* spp.

Intertidal or eulittoral zone	
Primary produceers	
Red turfweed	*Endocladia muricat*a
Red algal "moss"	*Mastocarpus papillatus*
Iridescent blade red alga	*Iridaea flaccida*
Rockweed (brown alga)	*Pelvetia fastiga*
Surfgrass	*Phyllopadix* spp.
Kelps	*Laminaria setchelli* and others
Herbivores	
Periwinkle	*Littorina scutulata*
Turban snail	*Tegula funebralis*
Chitons	*Katharina emarginata*; *Nuttallina californica*
Carnivores	
Whelk	*Nucella emarginata*
Detritus feeders (filter-feeders)	
Barnacle	*Balanus glandula*
Gooseneck barnacle	*Pollicipes polymerus*
Mussel	*Mytilus californianus*
Subtidal or sublittoral zone	
Primary producers	
Giant kelp	*Macrocystis pyrifera*
Kelps	*Pterogophora californica*, *Laminaria* spp.
Herbivores	
Purple sea urchin	*Strongylocentrus purpuratus*
Red sea urchin	*Strongylocentrus franciscanus*
Abalone	*Haliotus* spp.
Carnivores	
Kellet's whelk	*Kelletia kelletii*
Knobby sea star	*Pisaster giganteus*
Spiny lobster	*Panulirus interruptus*
Sea cucumbers	*Parastichopus* spp.
Octopuses	*Octopus* spp.

Rocky Shores: Southern Hemisphere Temperate Waters

South Africa: West Coast

Splash or supralittoral zone	
Primary producers	
Moss-like red alga	*Bostrychia mixta*
Foliose red alga	*Porphyra capensis*

(*Continued*)

Herbivores	
Periwinkle	*Littorina africana*
Limpet	*Patella granularis*
Intertidal or eulittoral zone	
Primary producers	
Foliose red alga	*Porphyra capensis*
Red alga	*Aeodes orbitosa*
Crustose red algae	*Lithothamnion* spp.
Green sea lettuce	*Ulva lactuca*
Brown alga	*Spachnidium rugosum*
Brown alga	*Chordaeia capensis*
Herbivores	
Limpet	*Patella granularis*
Limpet	*Scutellaria argenvillei*
Limpet	*Scutellaria cochlear*
Detritivores	
Barnacle	*Chthamalus dentatus*
Barnacle	*Tetraclita serrate*
Barnacle	*Octomeris angulosa*
Polychaete	*Gunnarea capensis*
Blue-black mussel	*Chloromytilus meridinalis*
Ribbed mussel	*Aulacomya ater*
Sea anemones	*Bunodactis* spp.
Carnivores	
African Black Oystercatcher	*Haematopus moquini*
Kelp Gull	*Larus dominicanus*
Giant clingfish	*Chorisochismus denex*
Subtidal or sublittoral zone	
Primary producers	
Bamboo kelp	*Ecklonia maxima*
Split-fan kelp	*Laminaria pallida*
Herbivores	
Abalone	*Haliota midea*
Sea urchin	*Parechinus angulosus*
Snails	*Turbo* spp.
Hottentot	*Pachymetopon blochii*
Strepie	*Sarpa salpa*
Carnivores	
Rock lobster	*Jasus lalandii*
Dogfish sharks	Family Squalidae

Cape fur seal	*Arctocephalus pusillus*
Bank Cormorant	*Phalacrocorax capensis*
Cape Gannet	*Morus capensis*
African Penguin	*Spheniscus demersus*
Cape clawless otter	*Aonyx capensis*
Chacma baboon	*Papio ursinus*
Detritivores	
Isopod	*Ligia dilatata*
Sponges	*Polymastia mamillaris, Tethya* spp.
Tunicate	*Pyura stonolifera*
Sea cucumber	*Pentacta doliolum*
Sea cucumber	*Thyone aurea*
Barnacle	*Notomegabalanus algicola*

Central Chilean Coast (18°–42° S)

Spash or supralittoral zone	
Primary Producers	
Crustose red alga	*Hildenbrandia lecannelliere*
Intertidal or eulittoral zone	
Primary producers	
Green algae	*Ulva rigida* and *U. compressa*
Green alga (fleshy)	*Codium dimorphum*
Red alga (mid-shore)	*Mazzaella laminariodes*
Red algae (low-shore)	*Gelidium chilense, G. lingulatum*
Red alga (low-shore)	*Laurencia chilensese*
Red alga (low-shore)	*Corralina officianalis*
Kelp	*Durvillaea antarctica*
Brown alga	*Lessonia nigrescens*
Herbivores	
Chiton	*Chiton granosus*
Keyhole limpets	*Fissurella crassa* and *Fissurella limbata*
Small limpets	*Collisella ceciliana, Collisella zebrina*
Small limpet	*Siphonaria lessoni*
Carnivores	
American Oystercatcher	*Haematopus palliatus*
Detrivores	
Barnacle	*Chtalamus sabrosus*
Barnacle	*Jehlius cirratus*
Mussel	*Perumytilus purpuratus*

(*Continued*)

Subtidal or sublittoral zone

Primary producers

Kelp	*Durvillaea antarctica*
Brown alga	*Lessonia nigrescens*
Red alga	*Mesophyllum* sp.
Herbivores	
Black sea urchin	*Tetrapygus niger*
Chiton	*Acanthopleura echinata*
Black snail	*Tegula atra*
Carnivores	
Guanay Cormorant	*Phalacrocorax bouganvillii*
Peruvian Pelican	*Pelecanus thagus*
Humboldt Penguin	*Spheniscus humboldti*
Marine otter	*Lontra feline*
Southern sea lion	*Otaria byroni*

Southern Chilean Coast (42°–55° S)

Splash or supralittoral zone

Primary producers

Lichens

Intertidal or eulittoral zone

Primary producers

Red alga	*Bostrychia mixta*
Red alga	*Hildenbrandia lecannellieri*
Filamentous brown alga	*Pilayella littoralis*
Kelp-like brown alga	*Lessonia vadosa*
Herbivores	
Limpets	*Nacella magellanica, N. mytilum*
Chilean comb-tooth blenny	*Scartichthys viridis*
Carnivores	
Whelk	*Concholepas concholepas*
Sea star	*Heliaster helianthus*
Sea star	*Stichasater stratus*
Triplefins	*Tripterygion chilensis* and *T. cunnighami*
Clingfish	*Myxodes viridis*
Omnivore	
Chilean clingfish	*Sicyases sanguineus*

Subtidal or sublittoral zone	
Primary producers	
Giant kelp	*Macrocystis pyrifera*
Kelp-like brown alga	*Lessonia flavicans*
Fleshy red alga	*Epymenia falklandica*
Foliose red alga	*Gigartina skottsbergii*
Carnivores	
Magellanic Penguin	*Spheniscus magellanicus*
Marine otter	*Lontra feline*
Southern sea lion	*Otaria byroni*

Antarctic Coasts

Splash or supralittoral zone	
Primary producers	
Black lichens	*Verrucaria* spp.
Intertidal or eulittoral zone	
Primary producers	
Annual diatoms	
Filamentous green alga	*Urospora penicilliformis*
Filamentous green alga	*Ulothrix australis*
Annual green algae	*Chaetomorpha* spp.
Annual red alga	*Monostroma hariotti*
Annual red alga	*Leptosomia simplex*
Herbivores	
Antarctic limpet	*Nacella concinna*
Chiton	*Tonicina zschauii*
Gastropod	*Eatoniella* sp.
Gastropod	*Laevlitorina* sp.
Isopod	*Cymodocella tubicauda*
Carnivores	
Emerald rockfish	*Trematomus bernacchii*
Detritivores	
Bivalves	*Kidderia subquantrulatum* and others
Nemertine or Ribbon worms	Phylum Nemertinea
Flatworms	Phylum Platyhelminthes
Subtidal or sublittoral zone	
Primary producers	
Black lichen	*Verrucaria serpuloides*
Coralline alga	*Lithophyllum aequable*
Coralline alga	*Lithothamnion granuliferum*

(*Continued*)

Under ice	
Primary producers	
Iridescent blade red alga	*Iridaea cordata*
Red alga	*Phyllophora antarctica*
Brown alga	*Ascoseira mirabilis*
Brown alga	*Leptophyllum coulmanicum*
Brown alga	*Desmarestia* spp.
Brown alga (kelp)	*Himanothallus grandifolius*
Animals (0–50 ft)	
Sea urchin	*Sterechinus neumayeri*
Sea star	*Odonaster validus*
Ribbon worm	*Parborlasia corrugatus*
Isopod	*Glyptonotus antarcticus*
Animals (50–150 ft)	
Sea anemones	Phylum Cnidaria, order Actinaria
Soft corals	Phylum Cnidaria, order Alcyonacea
Tunicates	Subphylum Urochordata, class Ascidiacea
Hydroids	Phylum Cnidaria, order Hydroida
Animals (150 ft–600 ft)	
Sponges	Phylum Porifera
Sea anemones	Phylum Cnidaria, order Actinaria
Hydroids	Phylum Cnidaria, order Hydroida
Bryozoans	Phylum Bryozoa
Bivalve	*Limatula hodgonsii*
Sea stars	Phylum Echinodermata, class Asteroidea
Nudibranch	*Austrodoris mcmurdensis*

Sandy Coasts

Characteristic Species of Sandy Shores Worldwide

Supralittoral fringe or high-shore zone (see also salt marsh and mangrove)	
Salt-tolerant land plants	
Glassworts	*Salicornia* spp.
Salt marsh grasses	*Spartina* spp. and others
Mangroves	Many species in many genera and families
Animals	
Beach fleas or Scuds	Subphylum Crustacea, order Amphipoda
Isopods	Subphylum Crustacea, order Isopoda
Eulittoral or mid-shore zone	
Primary producers	
Cyanobacteria	
Diatoms	
Dinoflagellates	

Detritivores	
Lugworm	*Arenicola* spp.
Surf clams.	*Donax* spp.
Shrimps (deposit-feeding)	*Callianassa* spp.
Clams	*Tellina* spp., *Mercenaria* spp., and others
Cockles	*Cardium* spp. and *Cerastoderma* spp.
Heart urchin	*Echinocardium* spp.
Sand dollars	*Dendraster* spp. and *Mellita* spp.
Ghost crab	*Ocypode quadrata*
Sublittoral fringe or low-shore zone (see also seagrass meadows)	
Primary producers	
Phytoplankton	
Seagrasses	
Herbivores	
Opossum or Mysid shrimps	Phylum Mysidacea
Marine isopods	Subphylum Crustacea, order Isopoda
Marine amphipods	Subphylum Crustacea, order Amphipoda
Detritivores (in addition to those animals listed above for the mid-shore)	
Sea cucumbers	Phylum Holothuroidea
Soft-shelled clams	*Mya* spp.
Ribbon worms	Phylum Nemertinea
Polychaetes	Phylum Polychaeta

Sandy Coasts in Polar Regions

Subtidal or sublittoral zone: Arctic	
Primary producers	
Phytoplankton	
Kelps	
Herbivores	
Opossum or Mysid shrimps	Phylum Mysidacea
Marine isopods	Subphylum Crustacea, order Isopoda
Marine amphipods	Subphylum Crustacea, order Amphipoda
Demersal fishes	Superclass Osteichthyes
Detrivores	
Clams	*Hiatella* spp. and *Mya* spp
Soft corals	Phylum Cnidaria, order Alcyonacea
Carnivores	
Crabs	Phylum Arthropoda, order Decapoda
Rays	Phylum Chordata, order Rajiformes
Demersal fishes	Superclass Osteichthyes

(*Continued*)

Walrus	*Odobenus rosmarus*
Seals	
Subtidal or sublittoral zone: Antarctic	
Detrivores	
Tube-building crustacean	*Ampelisca baureri*
Tube-building crustacean	*Gammaropsis* sp.
Burrowing polychaete	*Aspitobranchus* sp.

Muddy Shores

Some Characteristic Species of Muddy Shores Worldwide

Primary producers	
Cyanobacteria	
Diatom films	
Flagellates	*Euglena* spp.
Detritivores (epifauna)	
Fiddler crabs	*Uca* spp.
Shore crabs	*Carcinus* spp.
Blue crab	*Callinectes sapidus*
Mud crabs	*Scylla* spp.
Small mud crabs	*Nassarius* spp.; *Ilyanassa* spp.
Detritivores (infauna)	
Meiofauna	
Copepods	Phylum Crustacea, Class Maxillopoda, Subclass Copepoda
Nematodes	Phylum Nematoda
Flatworms	Phylum Platyhelminthes
Macrofauna	
Bivalves	Phylum Mollusca, Class Bivalva
Crustaceans	Phylum Crustacea
Worms	Several phyla
Burrowing anemones	*Cerianthus* spp.
Burrowing brittlestars	*Amphiura* spp.
Carnivores	
Mullets	*Mugil* spp.
Flounders	*Pleuronectes* spp.
Herons and egrets	Family Ardeidae

Estuaries

Some Characteristic Species of Estuaries Worldwide

Primary producers	
Phytoplankton	
Interstitial bacteria	
Interstitial algae	
Detritivores	
Deposit-feeding polychaetes	Many genera
Suspension-feeding polychaetes	*Nereis* spp.
Snails	
Oysters	*Crassostrea* spp., *Saccostrea* spp., and others
Mussels	*Geukensia demissa* and others
Nematodes	Phylum Nematoda
Ribbon worms	Phylum Nemertinea
Carnivores	
Crabs	Phylum Arthropoda, order Decapoda
Lobsters	Family Nephropidae, Family Palinuridae, and others
Shrimps	
Flatfishes	Order Pleuronectiformes
Dowitchers	*Limnodramus* spp.
Whimbrel	*Numenus phaeopus*
Godwits	*Limosa* spp.
Oystercatchers	*Haematopus* spp.
Plovers	*Charadrius* spp.
Estuarine fishes	
Saltwater spawners	
Mullets	*Mugil* spp.
Atlantic menhaden	*Brevoortia tyrannus*
Estuarine spawner	
Winter flounder	*Pleuronectes americanus*
Anadromous fish	
Salmon	*Salmo* spp.; *Onchorhynctus* spp.
Sturgeon	*Acipenser* spp.
Lampreys	*Petromyzon* spp.; *Lampeta* spp.
Striped bass	*Morone saxatilis*
Alewife	*Alosa pseudoherengus*
Blueback herring	*Alosa aestivalis*

(*Continued*)

Hickory shad	*Alosa medicris*
American shad	*Alosa sapidissima*
Catadromous fish	
American eel	*Anguilla rostrata*
European eel	*Anguilla anguilla*

Salt Marshes

Some Characteristic Species of Salt Marshes

Primary producers	
Cordgrasses	*Spartina* spp.
Sea lavender	*Limonium* spp
Glassworts/Pickleweeds	*Salicornia* spp.
Sea blites	*Suaeda* spp.
Marsh elder	*Iva frutescens*
Rushes	*Juncus* spp.
Herbivores	
Insects	
Canada Goose	*Branta canadensis*
Muskrat	*Ondatra zibethica*
Carnivores	
Killifish	*Fundulus* spp.
Needlefish	*Strongylura marina*
Fiddler crabs	*Uca* spp.
White-clawed mud crab	*Eurytium limosum*
Marsh crab	*Sesmara reticulatum*
Blue Crab	*Callinectes sapidus*
Rails	*Rallus* spp.
Egrets	*Egretta* spp., *Casmerodius* spp.
Herons	*Ardea* spp.
Raccoon	*Procyon lotor*
Detrivores	
Amphipods	Subphyluum Crustacea, Order Amphipoda
Periwinkles	*Littorina* spp.
Ribbed mussels	*Geukensia* spp.
Oysters	*Crassotrea* spp. and others

Atlantic and Gulf Coast Salt Marshes, North America

Primary producers	
Marsh elder	*Iva frutescens*
Blackgrass	*Juncus gerardi*
Salt marsh ox-eye	*Barrichia frutescens*

Salt marsh cordgrass	*Spartina patens*
Smooth cordgrass	*Spartina alterniflora*
Virginia pickleweed	*Salicornia virginica*
Salt grass	*Distichlis spicata*
Black needlerush	*Juncus roemerianus*
Giant cutgrass	*Zizaniopsis miliaceas*
Herbivores	
Coffee bean snail	*Melampus bidentatus*
Marsh periwinkle	*Littoraria irrorata*
Black Duck	*Anas rubripes*
Green-winged Teal	*Anas carolinensis*
Canada Goose	*Branta canadensis*
Snow Geese	*Anser cauerulescens*
Meadow mouse	*Microtus pennsylvanicus*
Meadow jumping mouse	*Zapus hudsonius*
White-footed mouse	*Peromyscus leucopus*
Harvest mouse	*Reithrodontomys raviventus*
Muskrat	*Ondatra zibethica*
Whitetail deer	*Odocoileus virginianus*
Carnivores	
Fiddler crabs	*Uca* spp.
Square-backed marsh crabs	*Sesmara* spp.
Clapper Rail	*Rallus longirostris*
King Rail	*Rallus elegans*
Virginia Rail	*Rallus limicola*
Sora	*Porzana carolina*
Willet	*Catoptrophorus semipalmatus*
Hooded Merganser	*Lophodytes cucullatus*
Great Blue Heron	*Ardea herodias*
Little Blue Heron	*Florida cerulean*
Black-crowned Night Heron	*Nycticorax nycticorax*
Common Egret	*Casmerodius albus*
Snowy Egret	*Egretta thula*
Long-billed Marsh Wren	*Telmatodytes palustris*
Marsh Hawk/Northern Harrier	*Circus cyaneus*
Ring-billed Gull	*Larus delawarensis*
Short-eared Owl	*Asio flammeus*
Mink	*Mustela vison*
Otter	*Lutra canadensis*
Raccoon	*Procyon lotor*
Omnivores	
Song Sparrow	*Melospiza melodia*
Savannah Sparrow	*Passerculus sandwichensis*

(*Continued*)

Seaside Sparrow	*Ammospiza maritima*
Opossum	*Didelphis virginiana*

Pacific Coast Salt Marshes, North America

Primary producers	
Sea lettuce	*Ulva linza*
Green string sea lettuce	*Ulva intestinalis*
Brown alga	*Fucus distichus*
Moss	*Eurohychium stokesii*
Salt marsh grass	*Pucinella phyrgananodes*
California cordgrass	*Spartina foliosa*
Tundra grass	*Dupontia fischeri*
Tufted hair grass	*Deschampia caepitosa*
Wiry saltgrass	*Distichlis spicata*
Shoregrass	*Monanthochloe littoralis*
Sedges	*Carex* spp.
Three-square bulrush	*Scirpus americanus*
Salty Susan	*Jaumea carnosa*
Red chimo daisy	*Chrysanthemum articum*
Virginia glasswort	*Salicornia virginica*
Dwarf glasswort	*Salicornia bigelovii*
Glasswort	*Salicornia subterminalis*
Saltwort	*Batis maritima*
Alkali seaheath	*Frankenia grandifolia*
Palmer's sea heath	*Frankenia palmeri*
Seaside arrowgrass	*Triglochin maritimum*
Saltbush	*Atriplex watsonii*
Saltbush	*Atriplex julacea*
Desert-thorn	*Lycium brevipes*
Goosetongue	*Plantago maritima*
Plant parasite	
Dodder	*Cuscuta salina*
Herbivores	
Savannah Sparrow	*Passerculus sandwichensis*
Song Sparrow	*Melospiza melodia*
California meadow mouse	*Microtus californicus*
Deer mouse	*Peromyscus maniculatus*
Western harvest mouse	*Reithrdodontomys megalotis*
Desert cottontail	*Sylvilagus audubonii*
Brush rabbit	*Sylvilagus bachmani*
Black-tailed jackrabbit	*Lepus californicus*
Mule deer	*Odocoileus hemionus*

Carnivores	
Side-blotched lizard	*Uta stansburiana*
Southern alligator lizard	*Gerrhonotus multicarinatus*
Western fence lizard	*Sceloperus occidentalis*
Ornate shrew	*Sorex ornatus*
Black Rail	*Laterallus jamaicensis*
Clapper Rail	*Rallus longirostris*
Long-tailed weasel	*Mustela frenata*
Striped skunk	*Mephitis mephitis*
Gray fox	*Urocyon cineroargenteus*
Coyote	*Canis latrans*

Plants of European Salt Marshes

Primary producers	
Salt marsh grass	*Pucinella maritima*
Red fescue	*Festuca rubra*
Creeping bentgrass	*Agrostis stolonifera*
Glassworts	*Salicornia* spp.
Mediterranean glassworts	*Arthrocnemum* spp.
Blackgrass rush	*Juncus gerardi*
Spiny rush	*Juncus acutus*
Bulrushes	*Scirpus* spp.
Chaffy sedge	*Carex paleacea*
Sedge	*Desmoschoenus bottnica*
Toad rush	*Juncus bufonis*
Sea pink	*Armeria* spp.
Sea lavender	*Limonium* spp.
Sea plantain	*Plantago maritima*
Sand spurry	*Spergularia* spp.
Arrowgrass	*Triglochin* spp

Plants of Temperate South American Salt Marshes

Primary producers	
Brazilian cordgrass	*Spartina brasiliensis*
Cordgrass	*Spartina montevidensis*
Saltgrass	*Distichlis spicata*
Seashore paspalum	*Paspalum vaginatum*
Sea club-rush	*Scirpus maritima*
California bulrush	*Scirpus californicus*
Three-square bulrush	*Scirpus olneyi*
Totora reed	*Scirpus riparius*
Spikerush	*Elocharis palustris*
Spiny rush	*Juncus acutus*

(*Continued*)

Reed	*Cyperus corymbus*
Glasswort	*Salicornia gaudichaudiana*
Saltbush	*Atriplex hastate*
Sea purslane	*Sesuvium portulacastrum*
Apio Cimarron	*Apium sellowianum*
Mata verde	*Lepidophyllum cupressiforme*
Marsh rosemary	*Statice brasiliensis*
Sea heath	*Frankenia microphylla*
Pickleweeds	*Suaeda* spp.
Patagonian goosefoot	*Halopeplis patagonica*

Plants of Tropical South American Salt Marshes

Primary producers	
Brazilian cordgrass	*Spartina brasiliensis*
Seashore dropseed	*Sporobolus virginicus*
Seashore paspalum	*Paspalum vaginatum*
Alkali bulrush	*Scirpus maritima*
Sea purslane	*Sesuvium portulacastrum*
Saltwort	*Batis maritima*
Beach bloodleaf	*Iresine portulacoides*
Golden leather fern	*Acrostichum aureum*

South African Salt Marshes

Primary producers	
Red algae	*Bostrychia* spp.
Small cordgrass	*Spartina maritima*
Cape eelgrass	*Zostera capensis*
Pickleweed (mid-shore)	*Arthrocnemum perenne*
Pickleweeds (upper shore)	*Arthrocnemum africanum*; *Arthrocnemum pillansii*
Seashore dropseed	*Sporobolus virginicus*
Sea lavender	*Limonium linifolium*
Detritivores	
Mud prawn	*Upogebia africana*
Marsh crab	*Sesmara catenata*
Marsh crab	*Cyclograpsus punctata*
Marsh crab	*Cleistostoma edwardsii*
Barnacles	*Balanus elizabethae*; *Balanus amphititie*
Mangrove snail	*Cerithidea decollate*

Mangroves

Neotropical Mangrove Communities

Common mangroves in the Neotropics	
Primary producers	
Red mangrove	*Rhizophora mangle*
Black mangrove	*Avicennia germinans*
White mangrove	*Laguncularia racemosa*
Buttonwood mangrove	*Concarpus erectus*
Pacific Coast mangrove communities	
Primary producers	
Red mangroves	*Rhizophora harrisonii*; *Rhizophora racemosa*
Black mangroves	*Avicennia bicolor*; *Avicennia tonduzii*
Endemic mangrove	*Pelliciera rhizophorae*
Dragonwood tree	*Pterocarpus afficinalis*
Prickley-pole	*Bactris minor*
Raphia palm	*Raphia taedigera*
Saltwort	*Batis maritima*
Mangrove lily	*Crinum angustifolium*
Mangrove rubber vine	*Rhabdadenia biflora*
Leguminous shrubs	*Machaerium lunatum*; *Dalbergia* spp.
Flute-player's schomburgkia	*Schomburgkia tibicinis*
Herbivores	
Green iguana	*Iguana iguana*
White-tailed deer	*Odocoileus virginianus*
Paca	*Agouti paca*
Carnivores	
American crocodile	*Crocodylus acutus*
Spectacled caiman	*Caiman crocodilus*
Boa constrictor	*Boa constrictor*
Yellow-billed Cotinga	*Carpodacectes antoniae*
Roseate Spoonbill	*Ajaia ajaja*
Mangrove Black Hawk	*Buteogallus subtilis*
Muscovy Duck	*Carina moschata*
Boat-billed Heron	*Cochlearius cochlearius*
Mangrove Cuckoo	*Coccyzus minor*
Mangrove Warbler	*Dendroica petechia*
Rails	*Aramides cajanea*; *Aramides axillares*
White Ibis	*Eudocimus albus*
Black-necked Stilt	*Himantopus mexicanus*
Amazon Kingfisher	*Chloroceryle amazona*
Pygmy anteater	*Cyclopes didactylus*

(*Continued*)

Mexican anteater	*Tamandua mexicana*
Crab-eating raccoon	*Procyon cancrivorus*
Mantled howler monkey	*Allouatta palliata*
White-throated capuchin	*Cebus caucinus*
Central American otter	*Lutra annectus*
Omnivores	
Basilisk lizard	*Basiliscus basiliscus*
Mangrove Hummingbird	*Amazilia boucardi*

Caribbean mangrove communities: Belize Coast

Mangroves	
Red mangrove	*Rhizophora mangle*
Black mangrove	*Avicennia germinans*
White mangrove	*Laguncularia racemosa*
Buttonwood mangrove	*Concarpus erectus*
Animals	
Green sea turtle	*Chelonia mydas*
Hawksbill sea turtle	*Eremochelys imbricate*
Loggerhead sea turtle	*Caretta caretta*
Leatherback sea turtle	*Dermochelys coriacea*
Kemp's ridley sea turtle	*Lepidochelys kempi*
White Egret	*Egretta alba*
Anhinga	*Anhinga anhinga*
Neotropical Cormorant	*Phalacrocorax olivaceaus*
Boat-billed Heron	*Cochlearius cochlearius*
White Ibis	*Eucdocimus albus*
Brown booby	*Sula leucogaster*

Caribbean mangrove communities: Greater Antilles

Mangroves	
Red mangrove	*Rhizophora mangle*
Black mangrove	*Avicennia germinans*
White mangrove	*Laguncularia racemosa*
Buttonwood mangrove	*Concarpus erectus*
Endemic animals	
Cuban crocodile	*Crocodylus rhombifer*
Anole lizards	*Anolis* spp.
Cuban Green Woodpecker	*Xiphidiopicus percusses*
Jamaican Tody	*Todus todus*
Mangrove Warbler	*Dendroica petechia gundlachi*
Clapper Rail	*Rallus longirostris carinaeus*

Caribbean mangrove communities: Lesser Antilles	
Tree	
Dragonwood tree	*Pterocarpus officinalis*
Birds	
Spotted Sandpiper	*Actitis macularia*
Great Blue Heron	*Ardea herodius*
Cattle Egret	*Bubulcus ibis*
Belted Kingfisher	*Megaceryle alcyon*
Lesser Antillean Pewee	*Contopus latirostris*
West Indian Whistling Duck	*Dendrocygna arborea*
Lesser Antillean Bullfinch	*Loxigilla noctis*
Brazilian mangrove communities: Maranhão	
Mangroves	
Red mangrove	*Rhizophora mangle*
Red mangrove	*Rhizophora racemosa*
Red mangrove	*Rhizophora harrisonii*
Black mangrove	*Avicennia germinans*
Black mangrove	*Avicenna schaueriana*
White mangrove	*Laguncularia racemosa*
Buttonwood mangrove	*Conocarpus erectus*
Animals	
Roseate Spoonbill	*Ajaia ajaja*
Scarlet Ibis	*Eudocimis rubra*
Wattled Jacana	*Jacana jacana*
West Indian manatee	*Trichechus manatus*
River dolphin (tucuxi)	*Sotalia fluviatilis*
Brazilian mangrove communities: southern Brazil	
Mangroves	
Red mangrove	*Rhizophora mangle*
Black mangrove	*Avicennia schaueriana*
White mangrove	*Lacungularia racemosa*
Birds	
Semi-palmated Plover	*Charadrius semipalmatus*
White-rumped Sandpiper	*Calictris fuscicollis*
Lesser Yellowlegs	*Tringa flavipes*
Greater Yellowlegs	*Tringa melanoleuca*
Scarlet Ibis	*Eudocimis rubra*
Orange-winged Parrot	*Amazona amazonica*

Indo-Pacific Mangrove Communities

East Africa

Mangroves	
Red mangrove	*Rhizophora mucronata*
Blackwood	*Avicennia marina*
Orange mangrove	*Bruguiera gymnorrhiza*
Mangrove apple	*Sonneratia alba*
Yellow mangrove	*Ceriops tagal*
Endemic mangrove (no common name)	*Xylocarpus benadivensis*
Indian-mangrove	*Lumnitzera racemosa*
Animals	
Green sea turtle	*Chelonia mydas*
Olive ridley sea turtle	*Lepidochelys olivacea*
Nile crocodile	*Crocodylus niloticus*
Hippopotamus	*Hippopotamus amphibious*
Curlew Sandpiper	*Calidris ferruginea*
Roseate Tern	*Sterna dougallii*
Caspian Tern	*Hydroprogne caspia*
Sykes monkey	*Cercopithecus mitis*
Otter	*Lutra maculicollis*
Dugong	*Dugong dugon*

Sundarbans

Mangroves	
Sundri	*Heritiera fomes*
Gewa	*Excoecaria agallaocha*
Cedar mangrove	*Xylocarpus mekongensis*
Cannonball mangrove	*Xylocarpus granatum*
Keora	*Sonneratia apetala*
Orange mangrove	*Bruguiera gymnorrhiza*
Goran	*Ceriops decandra*
Red mangrove (no common name)	*Rhizophora mucronata*
Nipa palm	*Nypa fruticans*
Animals	
Saltwater crocodile	*Crocodylus porosus*
Mugger or Marsh crocodile	*Crocodylus palustris*
Gavial or Gharial	*Gavilis gangeticus*
Water monitor lizard	*Varanus salvator*
Lesser Adjutant	*Leptoptilos javanicus*
Masked Fin-foot	*Heliopais personata*
Bengal tiger	*Panthera tigris*
Chital deer	*Cervus axis*
Barking deer	*Muntiacus muntjak*
Wild pig	*Sus scrofa*

Macaque	*Macaca mullata*
Gangetic freshwater dolphin	*Platanista gangetica*

Myanmar

Mangroves

Red mangroves	*Rhizophora mucronata; Rhizophora conjugate; Rhizophora candelria*
Keora	*Sonneratia apetala*
Cannonball mangrove	*Xylocarpus granatum*
Cedar mangrove	*Xylocarpus moluccensis*
Black mangrove	*Avicennia officinalis*
Smallflower mangrove	*Bruguiera parviflora*
Orange mangroves	*Bruguiera gymnorrhiza; Bruguiera cylindrical*
Sundri	*Heritiera fomes*
Nipa palm	*Nypa fruticans*
Mangrove date palm	*Phoenix paludosa*

Animals

Saltwater crocodile	*Crocodylus porosus*
River terrapin	*Batugar baska*
Oriental Darter	*Anhinga melanogaster*
Little Cormorant	*Phalacrocorax nigers*
Reef Heron	*Egretta sacra*
Ruddy Shelduck	*Todorna ferruginea*
Bronze-winged Jacana	*Metopidius indicus*
Lesser Black-backed Gull	*Larus fuscus*
Edible-nest Swiftlet	*Aerodramus fuciphagus*
Sambar	*Cervus unicolor*
Hog deer	*Cervus porcinus*
Mouse deer	*Tragulus javanicus*
Barking deer	*Muntiacus muntjak*
Tapir	*Tapirus malayanus*
Wild boar	*Sus scrofa*
Asian elephant	*Elephas maximus*

Indochina

Mangroves

Baen	*Avicennia alba*
Tall-stilted mangrove	*Rhizophora apiculata*
Smallflower mangrove	*Brugueira parviflora*
Black mangrove	*Avicennia officinalis*
Mangrove apple	*Sonneratia caseolaris*
Nipa palm	*Nypa fruticans*
Mangrove date palm	*Phoenix paludosa*

(*Continued*)

Animals	
Water monitor lizard	*Varanus salvator*
False gavial	*Tomistoma schlegeli*
Saltwater crocodile	*Crocodylus porosus*
Lesser Adjutant	*Leptoptilos javanicus*
Storm's Stork	*Ciconia stormi*
White-winged Wood Duck	*Cairina scutulata*
Spot-billed Pelican	*Pelicanus philippensis*

Australasian Mangrove Communities

New Guinea	
Mangroves	
Baen	*Avicennia alba*
Blackwood	*Avicennia marina*
Mangrove apples	*Sonneratia* spp.
Red mangrove	*Rhizophora mucronata*
Tall-stilted mangrove	*Rhizophora apiculata*
Smallflower mangrove	*Bruguiera parviflora*
Orange mangrove	*Bruguiera gymnorrhiza*
Sundri	*Heritiera fomes*
Fern	
Golden leather fern	*Acrostichum aureum*
Australia	
Mangroves	
Endemic mangrove	*Avicennia integra*
Grey mangrove	*Avicennia marina*
Red mangrove	*Rhizophora stylosa*
Tall-stilted mangrove	*Rhizophora apiculata*
Large-leaved orange mangrove	*Bruguiera gymnorrhiza*
Mangrove apples	*Sonneratia alba; Sonneratia caseolaris*
Smallflower mangrove	*Brugueira parviflora*
Yellow mangrove	*Ceriops* spp.
Looking-glass mangrove	*Heritiera littoralis*
Cannonball mangrove	*Xylocarpus granatum*
Nipa palm	*Nypa fruticans*

3

Continental Shelf Biome

Continental shelves are the submerged edges of landmasses (see Figure 3.1). They begin at the coast at the extreme low-tide mark and extend seaward to depths of about 600 ft (200 m). Average depth is about 430 ft (132 m). Shelf widths are extremely variable, ranging from no shelf at all along some coasts to shelves nearly 900 mi (1,500 km) wide elsewhere. Plate tectonics has played a major role in determining the width of shelf areas, which today underlie roughly 8 percent of the global sea surface. The broadest shelves, such as those off the east coast of North America, occur on the trailing edges of moving tectonic plates. Narrow shelves mark actively converging plate boundaries such as along the west coast of South America.

As a biome, continental shelves have two main components: the seabed itself with its associated biota; and the neritic zone of the sea, those shallow, sunlit waters above the shelf. Together, the two parts make up some of the most productive and economically important areas of the sea. According to one estimate, 90 percent of the world's catch of shellfish and fish comes from shelf areas. The productivity of aquatic and seabed communities is key to the survival of many seabirds and marine mammals.

The continental shelf biota ultimately depends on nutrients flowing from the land and from the open sea. Stream runoff—its volume and its seasonality—helps determine the size and timing of algal blooms. But the stratification (or lack thereof) of the water column influences whether those nutrients will be available to the phytoplankters at the beginning of food chains. Winds, tides, and fronts are all involved in mixing the layers and returning settled particles to the euphotic zone near the surface where the phytoplankters photosynthesize. At certain west coast locations,

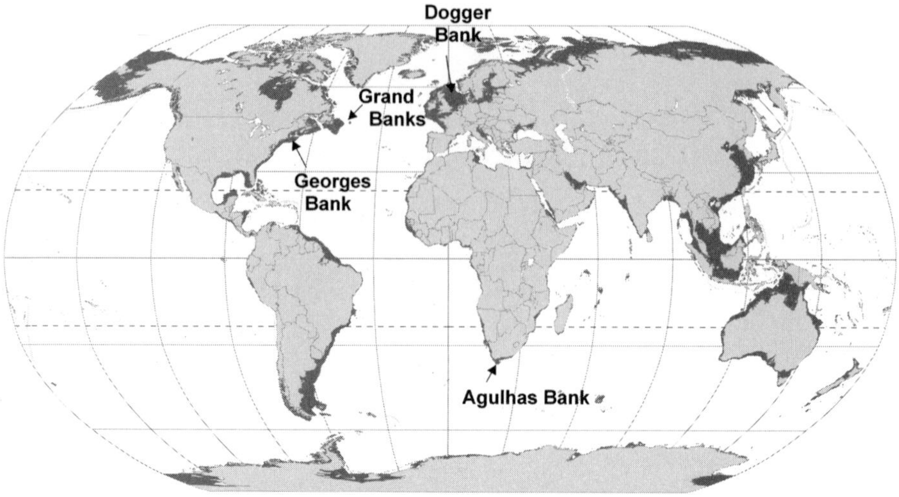

Figure 3.1 Continental shelves vary in width depending upon the geologic history of a landmass. *(Map by Bernd Kuennecke.)*

wind-driven upwelling brings cold waters up from depth and with it needed nutrients. Ocean currents, also wind-driven, deliver materials from the adjacent open sea, materials that may have circulated through the oceans of the world.

Overlaps between continental shelf and coastal biomes occur in the sublittoral or subtidal zone along the shore. It is therefore difficult and somewhat arbitrary to assign some habitat types and the organisms that dwell in them to one or the other. In this book, those that are exclusively or primarily intertidal—mudflat, salt marsh, and mangrove—appear in the chapter on the coastal biome. Estuaries are included in the same chapter, because in geomorphic terms, they are coastal features, and they are the site of many of the coastal communities just mentioned. This chapter focuses on shallow areas permanently inundated by seawater and features seagrass meadows, kelp forests, fishing banks, upwelling ecosystems, and coral reefs.

The Shelf Environment

Geology

Continental shelves are underwater extensions of continents and continental islands. At various times in their geological history—especially during Pleistocene glacial periods, when sea levels dropped—they were dry land well above the high-tide mark and subject to stream and glacial actions. Much of the present surface topography results from erosion and deposition that occurred when the area was above sea level. Valleys were cut, floodplains and river deltas were built, and glacial materials were deposited. Now submerged once again, wave action and tidal currents sort and redistribute the loose materials. Coarser-grained particles—coarse

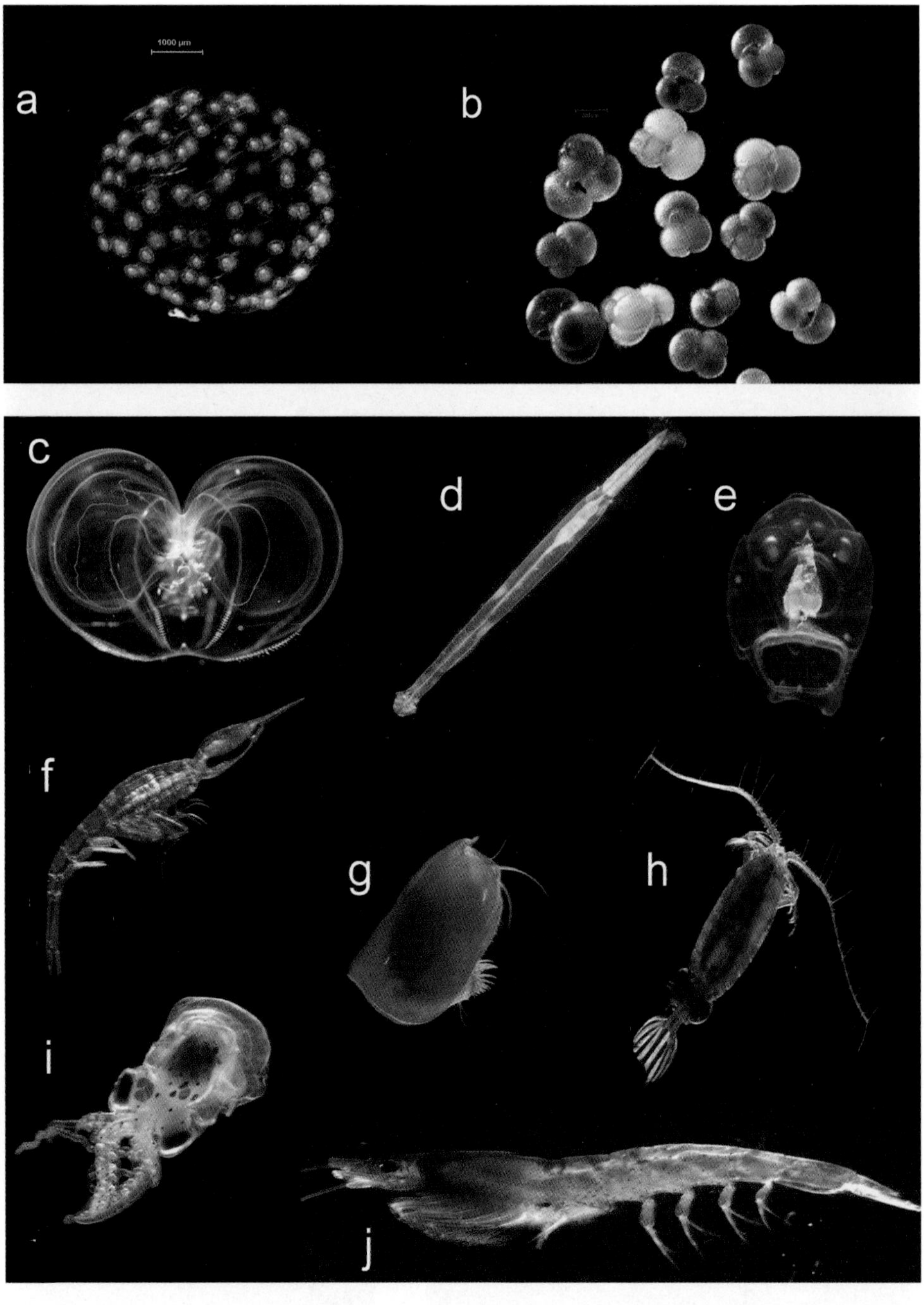

Plate I. A few of the many members of the zooplankton. Microzooplankters include: (a) radiolarians, and (b) foraminiferans. Macrozooplanketers include: (c) ctenophore or comb jelly, (d) chaetognath or "arrow worm," (e) jellyfish larva, (f) marine amphipod, (g) ostracod, (h) copepod, (i) juvenile octopus, and (j) krill. *(Microphotography (a) and (b) by C. de Vargas, Station Biologique de Roscoff and Census of Marine Zooplankton. Microphotography (c) and (d) by Larry Madin, Woods Hole Oceanographic Institute and Census of Marine Zooplankton; Microphotography (e)–(i) by Russ Hopcroft, University of Alaska, Fairbanks, NOAA, and Census of Marine Zooplankton; Microphotography (j) by Nancy Copley, Census of Marine Zooplankton.)*

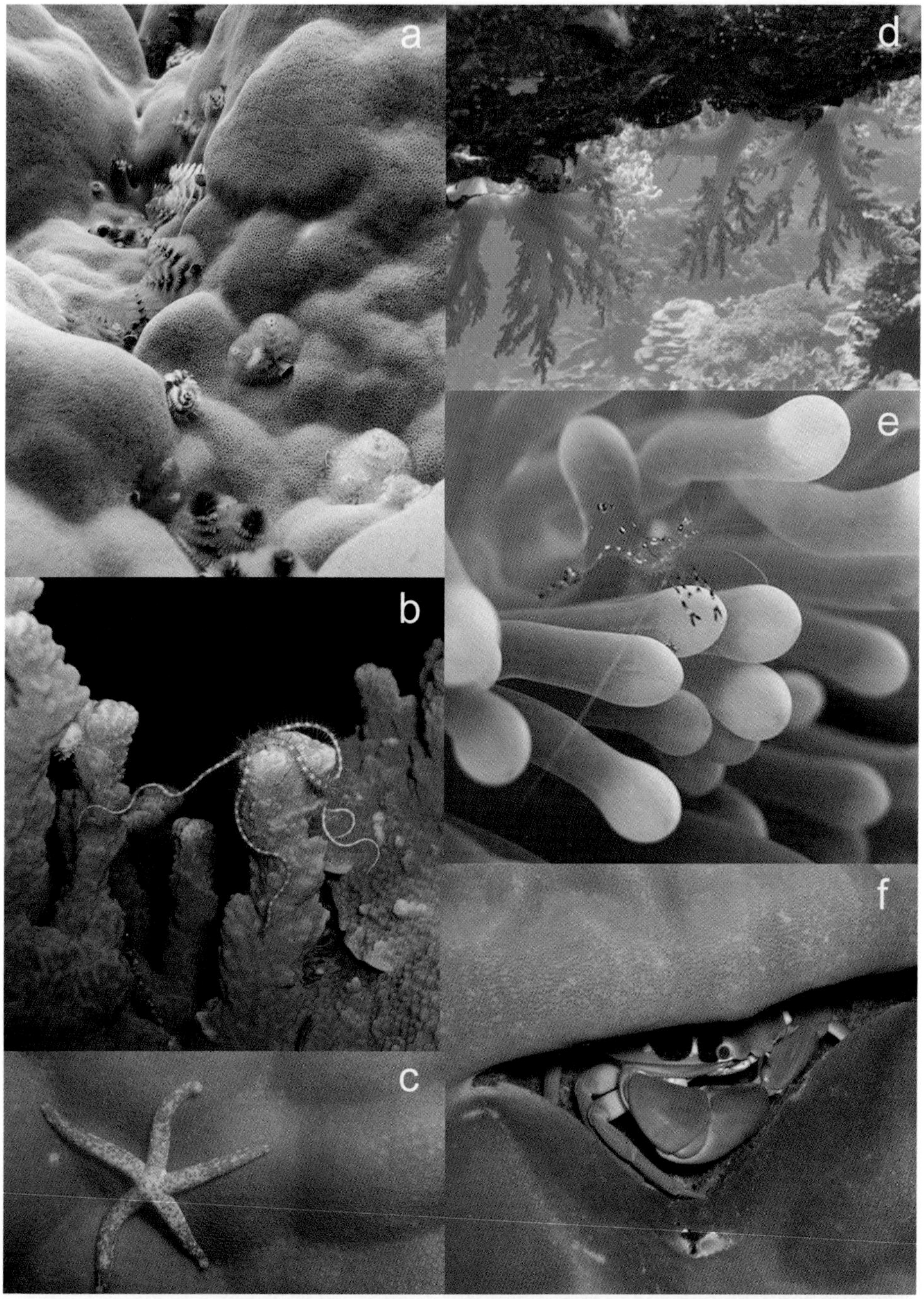

Plate VI. A small sample of tropical reef invertebrates from the Indo–West Pacific region, including: (a) Christmas tree worms (polychaetes), (b) brittlestar, (c) sea star, (d) soft corals, (e) a translucent shrimp on an anemone, and (f) spotted reef crab (*Carpilius maculates*) lodged in Porites coral. *(Photos © Katrina Adams, Kosrae Village, Kosrae, Micronesia, www.kosraevil lage.com. Used with permission.)*

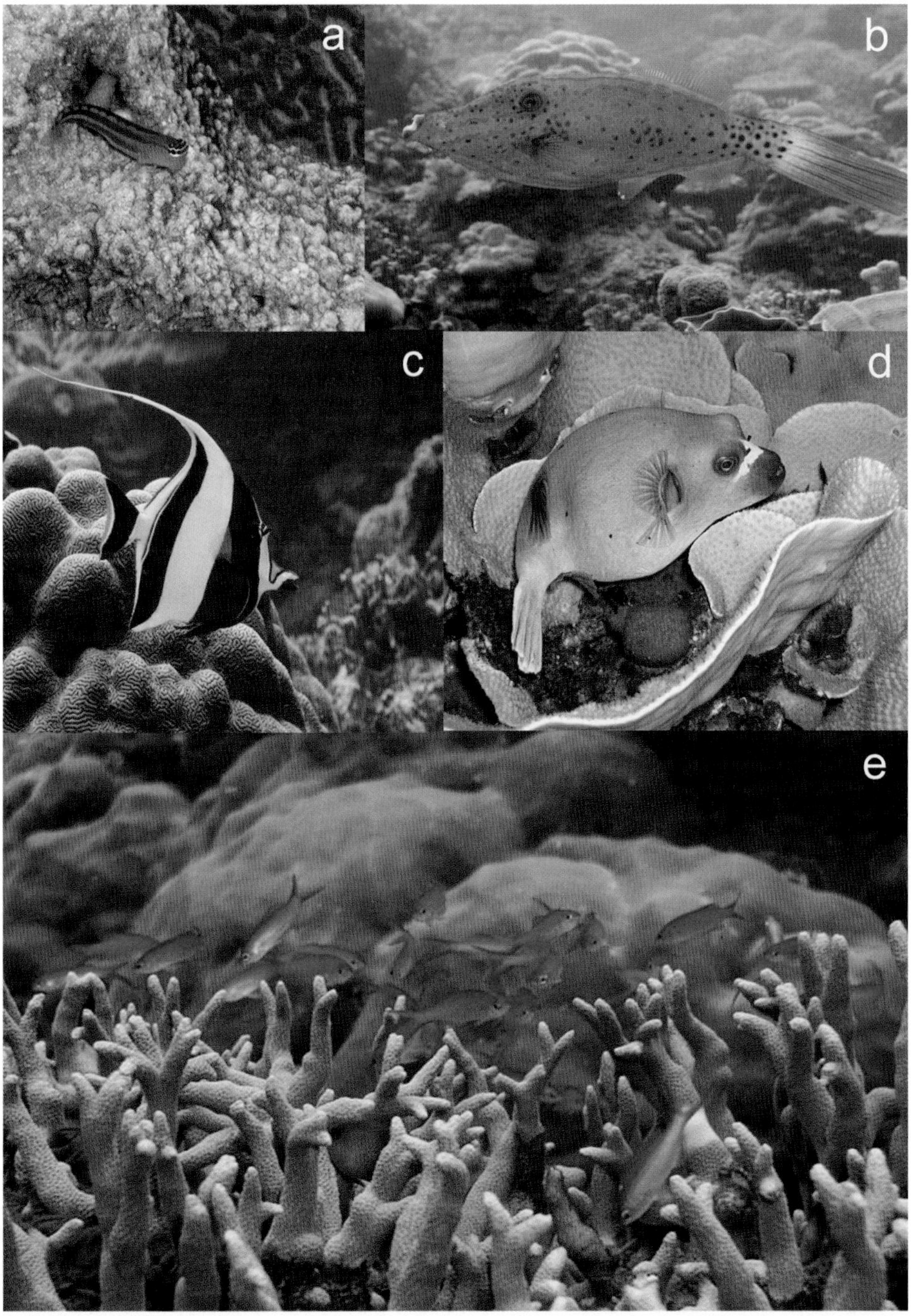

Plate VII. A few of the thousands of fish found on Indo-Pacific coral reefs, including: (a) Blenny, (b) Moorish idol (*Zanchus cornutus*), (c) scribbled filefish *(Aluterus scriptus*), (d) black spotted puffer (*Arothron nigropunctatus*), and (e) school of purple queen anthias (*Pseudoanthias pascalus*). *(Photos © Katrina Adams, Kosrae Village, Kosrae, Micronesia, www.kosraevillage.com. Used with permission.)*

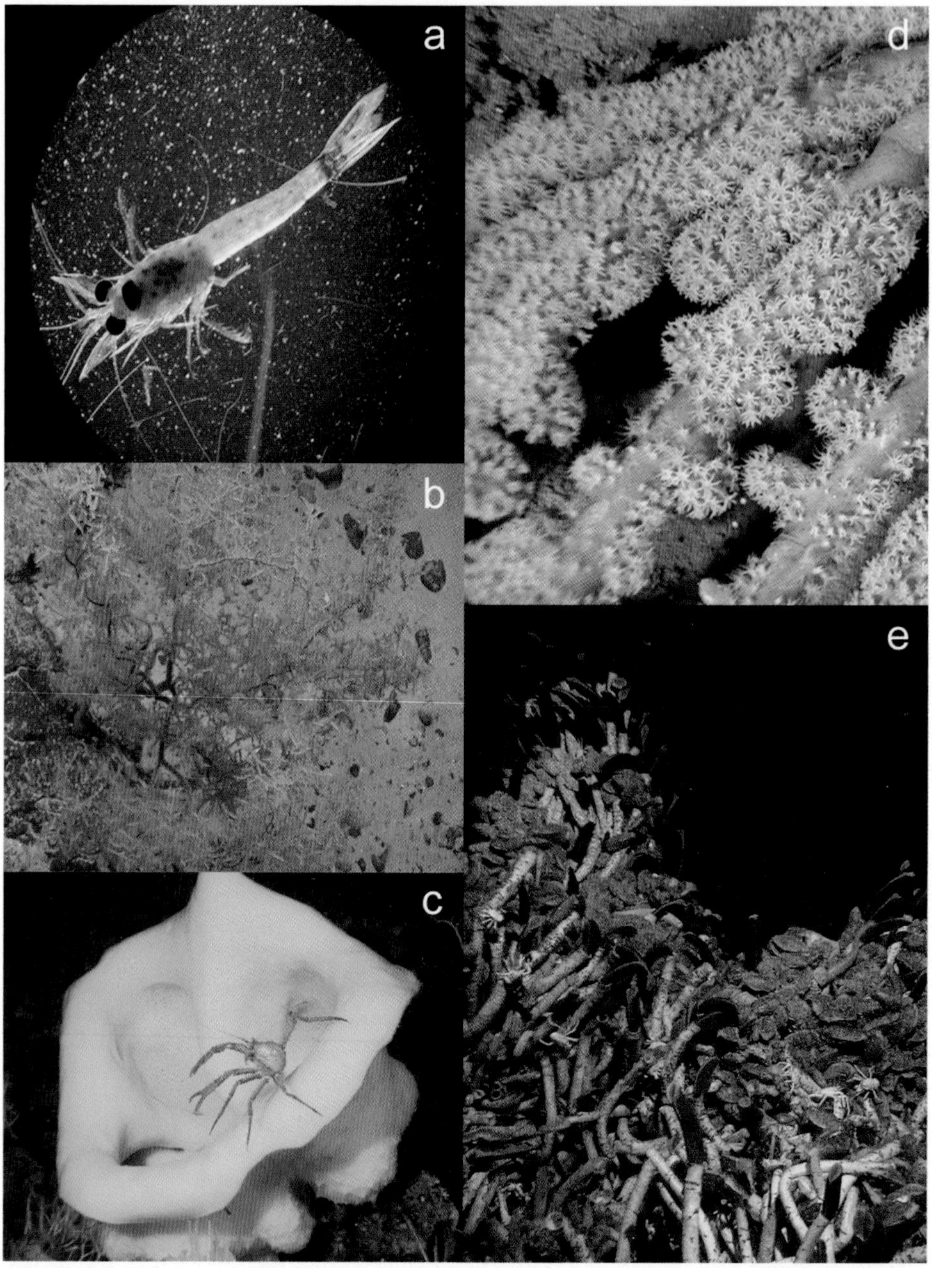

Plate VIII. Life in the deep sea: (a) Mysid shrimp, *Memysis anomala*. *(Microphotography (a) by S. Pothoven, NOAA.)* (b) Black coral at Manning Seamount. *(Mountains of the Sea Research Team, Sea Research Foundation's Institute for Exploration crew, and NOAA.)* (c) Crab on a sponge at Davidson Seamount. *(NOAA and MBARI.)* (d) Extended polyps of gorgonian soft coral. *(NOAA's Olympic Coast Marine Sanctuary.)* (e) *Riftia* vent worms. *(Cindy Van Dover, NOAA OceanExplorer.)*

sands, pebbles, and cobbles—tend to occur in most areas because these larger particles are not apt to be dislodged and swept away by strong waves and currents. Finer particles become suspended and carried out to sea beyond the edge of the shelf. The surface of shelves can be quite irregular and in places there may be plateaus as well as deeper valleys and basins. Some plateaus rise close to the sea's surface, creating shoals known as banks. The Grand Banks of Newfoundland, Georges Bank off New England, and Dogger Bank in the North Sea were until recently the sites of the world's great cod fisheries. Catches of other fish as well as crustaceans were—and, in some cases, still are—of considerable value.

The largest areas of continental shelf occur in the Northern Hemisphere, a by-product of plate tectonics and the current locations of landmasses on the planet. Most were directly affected by the great ice sheets of the late Pleistocene in that they are formed from or at least covered by deep deposits of glacial till, originally in the form of ground, recessional, and terminal moraines as well as other, smaller glacial landforms. Melting ice released huge volumes of sediments as outwash, and this material is also deposited offshore. In these unconsolidated substrates, diverse infaunas and epifaunas may thrive.

Another material that has contributed to the construction of geomorphic features on continental shelves was formed by living organisms. The shells of micro-zooplankton and molluscs and the exoskeletons of hard corals and sponges, all rich in calcium carbonate, have accumulated in thick deposits in certain areas to form reefs and carbonate banks. Living coral reefs, features of clear tropical waters, are one the most species-rich ecosystems on Earth.

On shelves that in the geologic past were covered with shallow seas in warm, dry climate regions, seawater salts precipitated out as the water evaporated. Evaporites accumulated into thick layers. In some locations, as along the Gulf Coast of the United States, the result was salt domes in which petroleum and natural gas are trapped.

Wave-cut platforms and large boulders make for hard, rocky reefs and seabeds in some areas. These provide somewhat rare stable habitats for attached seaweeds and animals. Kelp forests grow on such surfaces and are yet another species-rich ecosystem on the continental shelf.

The shallowness of the water above a continental shelf is significant for the growth of phytoplankters since sunlight is able to penetrate the water column. However, these tiny organisms also require nutrients, and agents that mix the water column are vital in returning sinking particles to the euphotic zone. Mixing occurs in several ways: wave action (often intensified by winds), tidal currents, tidal or shelf-sea fronts, shelf-edge or shelf-break fronts, and upwelling. Some processes are location-specific. Close to the shore, waves and tides are constants. On open Atlantic coasts, storm waves can affect the seabed to depths as great as 260 ft (80 m). Waves and currents result in ever-shifting sands on the seabed, which is challenging for members of the infauna. In addition, they cause physical stress on attached benthic seaweeds and animals through pounding and abrasion. Generally speaking, biomass is greater some distance offshore where these forces are not as strong and where fronts or upwelling carry nutrients to the surface waters. Nonetheless, waves and currents are not entirely negative factors in the environment. They are important in oxygenating the water and sediments, removing wastes, circulating nutrients, moving gametes, and dispersing larvae.

Fronts

A tidal or shelf-sea front is the boundary or contact zone between inshore waters that are tidally mixed and stratified waters beyond the tidal influences. In temperate regions of the world ocean, a stratified water column usually develops in spring and summer as the surface waters warm or precipitation and runoff increase. In the tropics, the water column may be stratified year-round. The warmed surface waters are less dense than deeper, cooler water and float on top, creating the stratification and preventing the mixing of the layers except during major storms. Nutrient particles tend to sink out of reach of phytoplankters drifting near the light-rich surface, so primary production is low on the stratified side of the front. However, the mixed inshore waters are especially nutrient-rich in springtime, when runoff from the land normally increases. Nutrients diffuse across the front along a density gradient from the mixed inshore body water mass into the surface layer of adjacent stratified mass. At depth is a return flow, since the concentration of nutrient particles is greater in the cold water near the base of the stratified water column than in the adjacent mixed waters (see Figure 3.2).

Even though this cycle replenishes nutrients in the inshore waters, the highest concentration of phytoplankters develops near the front on the stratified side. The front thus becomes the place where consumers such as zooplankters, fish, and seabirds are most abundant. The geographic position of this type of front changes with the phases of the moon. It moves a few miles out to sea into deeper water as the time of spring tides approaches and then back toward land near the time of neap tides.

Shelf-break fronts occur at the outer edge of continental shelves where the surface suddenly plunges some 10,000 ft (3000 m) down the continental slope toward the abyssal plain. The mechanics of these fronts are not well understood, but one idea is that they are caused by internal waves generated by the tide. Each time the tide rises, water from the open sea flows onto the continental shelf. Each time the tide falls, water moves off. This back-and-forth motion generates a wave at the boundary between the lighter surface layer and the denser lower layer and creates turbulence in the water column and localized mixing within the water column. Where studied in the Atlantic Ocean at the edge of the continental shelf off the coast of Brittany, France, the amplitude of the internal wave was about 200 ft (60 m), and its effects were noticeable for nearly 20 mi (30 km) landward into the shelf waters and an equal distance out to sea. Because tides are a daily occurrence, mixing occurs and nutrients are bought up to the surface every day of the year along these fronts. The productivity of the phytoplankton is increased throughout

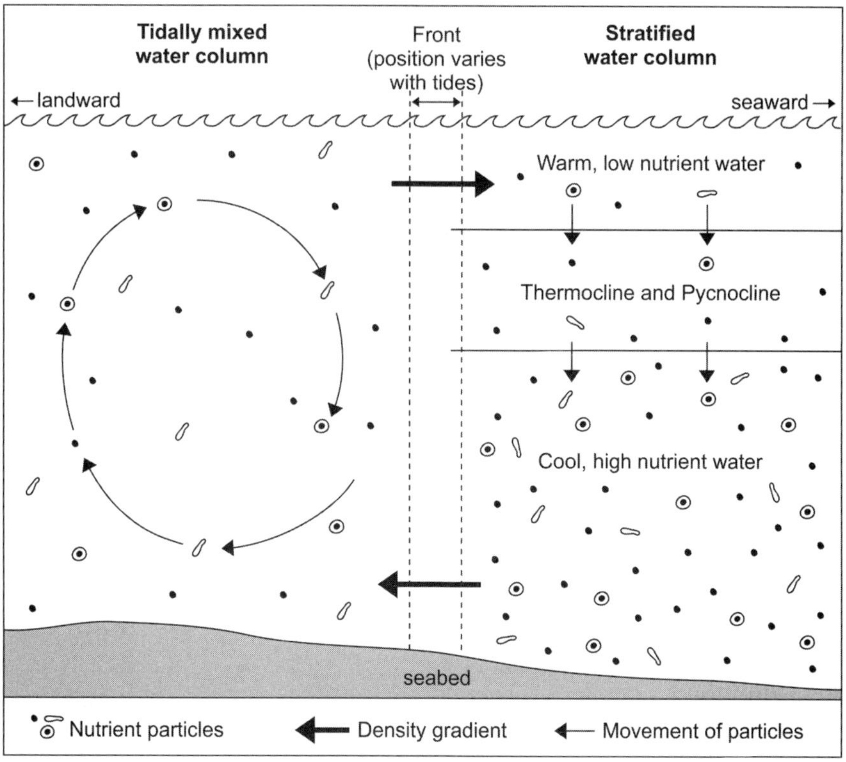

Figure 3.2 An ocean front is the contact zone between a stratified body of water and a well-mixed one. Differences in temperature and the amount of dissolved materials creates pressure gradients which allow the flow of nutrients between the bodies. *(Illustration by Jeff Dixon.)*

the year, and this enhances the production of zooplankters and the whole chain of benthic and pelagic consumers.

Upwelling

Upwelling along coasts is wind-driven. Where steady winds blow parallel to coasts with narrow continental shelves, semipermanent large-scale regions of upwelling develop when the Coriolis Force directs the winds and therefore the warm surface waters offshore. Colder water from depth, rich in nutrients, rises to replace the nutrient-poor waters so removed. Products of global atmospheric circulation patterns, four major upwelling areas exist, each associated with an eastern boundary current—the Humboldt, Benguela, California, and Canary currents, respectively. A fifth major area of upwelling occurs in the Indian Ocean off the coast of Somalia and the Arabian Peninsula. A seasonal phenomenon lasting about four months, the upwelling is controlled by the monsoons. Lesser areas with upwelling of short duration occur sporadically elsewhere in association with strong storms.

Life in the Continental Shelf Biome

Too Much of a Good Thing

Situations of too many nutrients or too much turbulence exist, and these reduce rather than enhance productivity on the shelf. At the mouths of estuaries, for example, plumes of brackish water are heavily laden with sediments. Although nutrients are abundant, turbidity limits the penetration of light and reduces the production of benthic algae. Close to shore, coastal upwelling may cause so much mixing that phytoplankters are carried downward out of the euphotic zone, so the increase of nutrients at the surface does them no good.

As in the Coastal Biome, the distribution of benthic organisms on the continental shelf is largely determined by the nature of the substrate. At the coast, the shelf merges with the sublittoral or subtidal zone of the Coastal Biome, and primary productivity comes from seagrasses, seaweeds (especially kelps), and phytoplankters. These areas provide planktonic food for the larvae of many forms of marine life and shelter for juveniles. Rocky seabeds and reefs have distinct seaweed zones and, below them, animal zones. Sandy seabeds are dominated by animal life, especially tube-dwelling and burrowing invertebrates such as molluscs, sea cucumbers, urchins, and crabs. Flatfish and stingrays may lurk just beneath the surface waiting to ambush prey.

Shifting sands and gravels, continually disturbed by waves, are inhabited by motile animals such as echinoderms and crustaceans. Sand, however, may be held in place by living organisms. Purplish calcareous seaweeds, green seaweeds, and seagrasses all trap and bind fine particles. Stable sands provide habitat for an infauna that would be susceptible to burial or suffocation in areas of shifting sediments and thus host a greater variety of organisms than moving sands. Living organisms become part of the habitat. Seagrasses provide attachment sites for epiphytic algae. Giant kelps create a three-dimensional underwater "forest." Off New Zealand, huge horse mussels use byssal threads to bind sediment grains together, stabilizing the surface and attracting worms and small crustaceans to the mussel bed. The bivalves themselves become habitat for sessile hydroids, soft corals, and other invertebrates adding even greater complexity to the system.

The benthic fauna dominates in areas in which phytoplankton productivity has seasonal pulses, such as at tidal fronts or in temperate waters in general. Mostly particle feeders, the filter-feeders such as oysters, mussels, and clams, strain phytoplankters and particulate organic matter (POM) from the water column. The fecal pellets they expel contribute to the food supply of suspension-feeding clams and deposit-feeders in detritus food chains. Demersal fish are plentiful and characteristic. Most are both predators and scavengers. Other carnivores include nudibranchs (sea slugs) that scrape encrusting invertebrates, such as bryozoa, soft corals, and sponges, off shells and rocks. Pelagic fish such as herring and mackerel are particularly abundant in areas in which high phytoplankton production is a year-round feature—such as at shelf-break fronts or in the five major regions of upwelling. Under these conditions, zooplankton populations have time to grow to sizes able to consume the bulk of phytoplankton production. Large zooplankton populations, mostly copepods, feed krill and small fish, the mainstays of the diets of larger carnivorous fish, penguins and other seabirds, and baleen whales.

Shelf communities vary with latitude and climatic regimes in a pattern resembling Longhurst's marine biome scheme (see Chapter 1). In fact, the same scientist identified seven regional ecosystems appearing on shelves, and each is described as follows.

Regional Ecosystems

Polar, permanently covered by ice. This type of shelf occurs in northern and northeastern Greenland and almost completely surrounds Antarctica. At these extreme latitudes, months without sunlight are followed by months with low-angle solar radiation 24 hours a day. When ice is less than 6 ft (2m) thick, light can penetrate and a dense cover of diatoms may grow on its underside. These algae support polychaetes, copepods, and amphipods. Benthic invertebrates are abundant and diverse. They serve as a rich food supply for squid and large numbers of a few species of fish. Off Antarctica, small euphausids (krill) are the main food for pelagic fish such as the Antarctic silversides (*Pleurogramma antarcticum*) and for crabeater seals (*Lobodon carcinophagus*).

Polar, seasonal ice cover. Seasonal ice cover or broken pack ice is common off Greenland, off North American shores from Newfoundland to the Aleutians, and across Arctic Eurasia from Finland to the Sea of Okhotsk. Off the Antarctic coast, parts of the eastern Ross Sea and a few other points experience similar conditions. In summer, diatoms dominate the phytoplankton, fed upon by large copepods, krill, and salps. Occurring in huge swarms, these invertebrates are consumed by large numbers of baleen whales and seals. Especially in the Northern Hemisphere, production of algae exceeds the ability of the first-level consumers to harvest them, so many die and settle to the bottom, where they support a rich and diverse community of benthic macroinvertebrates. Fish in the Arctic are mainly demersal and include members of the cod and haddock family (Gadidae), rockfish family (Sebastidae), and wolffish (*Anarhichus* spp.). In the Antarctic, small perch-like fish (known as notothenioids) are endemic to the region and are about the only type of fish found. Sea mammals such as gray whale, walrus, and bearded seal feast on benthic invertebrates in the Arctic, but have no counterparts in the Antarctic.

Mid-latitude shelves. These areas have a spring bloom of diatoms followed by an autumn bloom of dinoflagellates. The seasonal pulses in phytoplankton production are reflected in population cycles among a zooplankton composed largely of copepods. Close to shore, small copepods are abundant; farther out, larger species dominate. Peak phytoplankton production overwhelms a slow population growth response by zooplankters so that much goes unconsumed. Detritus food chains therefore dominate. Vast schools of herring-like fish (family Clupeidae) and mackerel and tuna (family Scombridae) may form in the pelagic zone in northern areas. Demersal fish such as cod, haddock, and flounder are also abundant. Overall fish diversity is much greater than in polar regions of continental shelf. Some 200 species in more than 50 families have been recorded.

Topography-forced summer production areas. In widely scattered areas of the mid-latitudes, tidal currents move nutrient-rich bottom waters upward wherever surface features on the shelf obstruct the flow. Such areas occur in southern parts of the North Sea, in the Gulf of Alaska, in the temperate North Pacific, on the Falkland Shelf, and off New Zealand. The phytoplankton bloom occurs in mid-summer, but the animal life of these regions is quite similar to that of the mid-latitude shelves.

Coastal upwelling regions along eastern boundary currents. In many of these regions, the shelves are narrow and no rivers bring in nutrients, yet productivity is high as a result of nutrient-rich cold water brought up from depth. Typically, diversity is low, but each species may occur in huge numbers. The phytoplankters are typically large chain-forming or colonial diatoms. Large copepods (two genera predominate: *Calanus* and *Calanoides*), euphausids, and filter-feeding crabs consume the plankton. The many large cells and abundant fecal material settling to the bottom result in decomposition and can deplete the oxygen at certain depths. Demersal fish may be abundant at the edge of the shelf. Characteristic are various rockfish. Anchovies and anchovetas are pelagic herbivorous fish that, at least historically, occurred in vast numbers everywhere. Pelagic predators in these waters include sardines, hake, guano birds (cormorants, pelicans, and boobies), sea lions, and—in the Southern Hemisphere—penguins.

Trade Wind belt, tropical wet, or tropical wet and dry climate. These areas are typically associated with large rivers that have their peak discharge during the rainy season, rivers such as the Amazon, Niger, Congo, Indus, and Irrawaddy. This ecosystem type occurs off West Africa in the Gulf of Guinea, off the Atlantic coast of South America from the Guianas to northern Brazil, in the eastern Pacific from southern Mexico to Colombia, and in the Indo-Pacific region, from the South China Sea to the southwestern coast of the Indian subcontinent, including Indonesia and northern Australia. Due to intense sunlight year-round, almost the entire neritic zone may lie above the thermocline so that the water column is a single warm, nutrient-poor layer with little chance of mixing except when wave action is extreme during tropical storms. The phytoplankters are typically small cells, dominated by dinoflagellates. Only where stream discharge occurs will there be sufficient nutrients to support seasonal diatom blooms. Small copepods consume the small algal cells, but most diatoms settle to the bottom. The fish fauna can be quite diverse; a large percentage are pelagic.

Trade Wind belt, dry coasts with little stream discharge. Areas with this type of shelf environment are found off islands and archipelagoes in the Caribbean Sea, in parts of the Arabian Sea and the Red Sea, and off the coasts of northeast Australia and northeast Indonesia. The substrate is characterized by coral reefs and unconsolidated carbonate sands. The depth of the water's surface layer changes little during the year and remains warm. With no input of nutrients via streamflow, the water is clear and nutrient-poor. The sparse phytoplankton consists of the tiniest cells (nano- and picoplankton). Protists and small zooplankters consume the phytoplankton. Most primary production occurs in the benthos among macroalgae, encrusting green algae, red algae, cyanobacteria mats, and seagrasses. And symbiotic algae live in coral polyps as well as in other cnidarians, giant clams, large asidians, and encrusting sponges.

The benthic biota is exceptionally diverse at all taxonomic levels, with coral reefs being among the most recognized hotspots of global biodiversity. Sandy areas are dominated by filter-feeding crabs and filter-feeding clams. Fish are diverse in form and function. Parrotfish (Scaridae) are significant as herbivores and focus on corraline and other algal mats. Complex food webs enmesh fish, invertebrates, and a variety of large predators.

Seagrass Meadows

At the head of tidal inlets and estuaries, in lagoons, and on the lee side of barrier islands, underwater meadows of seagrasses occupy fine sediment substrates in the shallow waters of the subtidal zone. Seagrasses are true flowering plants, members of two ancient families (Hydrocharitaceae and Potamogetonaceae) unrelated to the grasses growing on land. They have roots and stems, and almost all have long linear leaves (see Figure 3.3). Their simple flowers open underwater, where pollen is transported among plants by waves and currents. Most seagrasses are dioecious—that is, they have separate male and female plants. Most have rhizomes from which they reproduce vegetatively to form extensive, often single-species subtidal stands. Adaptation to total immersion in seawater includes the absence of stomata on the leaves. No direct exchange of gases with the atmosphere takes place. Rather the plants utilize the carbon dioxide (CO_2) dissolved in the water and the oxygen (O_2) they themselves produce during photosynthesis. Since their roots are in oxygen-depleted, water-logged sediments, gases must pass from the leaves to the roots by means of internal pathways. Physiological adaptations let the roots withstand oxygen-less conditions at night when photosynthesis does not occur.

Only 49 species of seagrass in 12 genera are known worldwide in environments ranging from cool temperate to tropical. Eelgrass (*Zostera*) and wigeongrass

Figure 3.3 Seagrass are true flowering plants—although not true grasses—sometimes also referred to as submerged aquatic vegetation. *(NOAA, OceanExplorer.)*

(*Ruppia*) tend to dominate in temperate latitudes in both the Northern and Southern hemispheres. Turtlegrasses (*Thalassia*) and tapeweeds (*Posidonia*) are common in subtropical and tropical waters. Although geographically widespread and occurring everywhere except in the Antarctic, seagrasses do exhibit ecological preferences and are patchily distributed where conditions are suitable. Salinity is one factor limiting the occurrence of some species. For example, turtlegrasses and tapeweeds prefer salinities greater than 20, whereas eelgrass withstands salinities as low as 10. Light is another limiting factor. The depth to which seagrasses can grow depends largely on the clarity of the water and hence on the availability of sunlight to plants that are rooted in the seabed. They tend to extend into deeper water in nutrient-poor, phytoplankton-poor tropical waters than in typically more turbid temperate waters. Eelgrass may occur no deeper than 3 ft (1 m) in estuaries along the east coast of the United States, but it can be found at depths greater than 100 ft (30 m) in clear waters off California. Seagrasses grow farther out from the shoreline on gently sloping beaches and are restricted to a narrow belt close to shore on more steeply sloping beaches. Seagrasses may extend into the intertidal zone in certain situations, but generally their upper limits are close to the low-tide mark, since they are unable to endure desiccation or damage from ultraviolet radiation, strong wave action, and/or ice scour. Abrasion by sand held in suspension in the water is a significant factor limiting their occurrence in more exposed sites.

Although few animals feed directly on seagrasses, the meadows are highly productive communities. The leaves are attachment sites for a wide array of epiphytic diatoms, small filamentous algae, and other single-celled plants as well as bacteria and small animals. Red, brown, and green macroalgae may also occur if they can attach to shells or rocks buried in the sediments. Their fronds often break off to form drifting mats that have been reported far out to sea. Benthic microalgae live in the sediments, and phytoplankters float among the swaying blades of grass.

It is estimated that less than 10 percent of the primary production of seagrasses is consumed by herbivores, most of which are vertebrates—sea turtles, dabbling ducks and geese, manatees, and dugongs. Sea turtles have bacteria and protozoa that digest the cellulose in much the same manner as happens in the rumen of cattle. Adult green turtles, widespread in the tropics, prefer new shoots free of epiphytes close to the bottom of the seagrass beds. Slow-growing creatures, they may attain weights up to 440 lbs (200 kg). On coasts around the Indian Ocean, the dugong (*Dugong dugon*) depends on seagrass as its primary food source and grows to lengths of 6–10 ft (2–3 m) and to weights near half a ton (420 kg) on a diet of rhizomes, leaves, and stems digested by their gut microflora. Some sea urchins are also important grazers of live seagrasses. They, too, have bacteria in their guts that break down cellulose. Off Jamaica, *Lytechnis variegatus* feeds on turtlegrass. Elsewhere in the Caribbean, the sea urchin *Diadema antillarium* leaves the protection of coral reefs at night and moves out to graze the meadows surrounding patch reefs.

Many more species browse the epiphytic algae and consume the diverse and abundant protozoa, nematodes, hydrozoans, actinians, tube-dwelling polychaetes, and ascidinians growing on the blades of seagrass. Amphipods and isopods concentrate on the algae, but many snails and some fish ingest both the algae and the small animals.

With so little of the primary production consumed as live plant tissue, most seagrass biomass enters detritus food chains as either POM or DOM (dissolved organic matter), and the majority of invertebrates and fish in seagrass meadows are detritivores. The infauna consists largely of deposit-feeding polychaetes. Crabs, shrimps, amphipods, and fish comprise an epifauna also dependent on organic detritus. Much of the dead material consumed by the crustaceans passes through their gut and is eliminated as feces. In the process, however, it is shredded into small particles that will become suspended in the water and serve as food for filter-feeding mussels, clams, and polychaetes. Among fish detritivores, mullets concentrate on dead seagrasses, but most others consume a mixture of detritus and small crustaceans.

Crabs and fish move through the canopy, hunting prey and scavenging, while seahorses wait in ambush among the blades, and stingrays wait buried in the sediments. Detritus-feeding crustaceans are the most important food items of carnivorous fishes. Even more important than fishes in the overall flow of energy through the meadow ecosystem, however, are decapod crustaceans, both juveniles and adults. Shrimps, crabs, and lobsters feed on a zooplankton composed of copepods, decapod larvae, amphipods, and ostracods. The activities of animals variously crop and disturb the meadows to create a mosaic of microhabitats. Sea turtles can overgraze and leave scars or empty patches that invite pioneer seagrass species to

Figure 3.4 Stingrays are bioturbators that churn seabed sands when they burrow into the bottom to hide or spring up to capture prey. *(Photo © Katrina Adams, Kosrae Village, Kosrae, Micronesia, www.kosraevillage.com. Used with permission.)*

invade. Stingrays (see Figure 3.4) mix bottom sediments (bioturbate), resuspending and moving it around, and in the process oxygenating a thin surface layer. Burrowing shrimp produce a bumpy surface of mounds.

The abundance of shellfish and fish attract waterfowl and raptors. Shorebirds and diving ducks are important predators of invertebrates and small fish; fish eagles and osprey take larger fish.

Abundant food combined with the sheltering structure of the vegetation make seagrass meadows vital habitat not only for sea turtles and sea cows, but for many larval, juvenile, and adult shellfish and finfish, including many of commercial value. In much of the world, seagrass beds are threatened by a combination of factors, including overgrazing, nutrient enrichment, and outright destruction from shoreline development. Sea urchins, green turtles, ducks, geese, and dugongs can all deplete seagrass beds when the habitats become fragmented or reduced in size. Nutrient enrichment is more directly a human problem, because it is commonly caused by inflows of sewage or agricultural runoff into shallow inlets. The influx of nitrates and phosphates stimulates a bloom in the phytoplankton, which clouds the water and diminishes the amount of light able to penetrate to the grasses anchored in the seafloor. Too many nutrients also produce rapid growth in epiphytic algae, which then block sunlight from the grasses' leaves. It is the lack of light that kills off the meadow. An overabundance of suspended sediments, often associated with upstream urban development or poor agricultural practices, has the same effect.

Construction of ports, industries, residences, and recreation sites along shallow soft-sediment coasts involves dredging and filling. Seagrasses may be buried outright, or smothered by suspended sediments in the process. Warming sea temperatures seem to lower the resistance of seagrasses to naturally occurring fungi and slime molds. Such temperature stress was noted on both sides of the North Atlantic during a warming period in the early 1930s.

Seagrass meadows are essential nursery habitats for a variety of sea life, as well as critical habitat for endangered sea turtles and dugongs. They are vital wintering grounds for Northern Hemisphere migratory ducks such as American Wigeon and geese such as the Brant, which are among the few birds that graze living seagrasses. Efforts to protect or restore them are under way in many places around the world.

Banks

Plateaus, or banks, rise above the general surface of the continental shelf to create shoals, areas of very shallow water. Obstructing ocean currents, they force localized upwelling and bring nutrient-rich waters to the surface. Tidal fronts or shelf-break fronts as well as the nearby convergence of ocean currents with different physical properties can further augment the supply of nutrients in these sunlit waters and create some of the world's most productive fishing grounds. Four such areas are described below.

Grand Banks, Newfoundland, Canada

Several submarine plateaus on the seaward edge of the Atlantic shelf of North America south and east of Newfoundland and Labrador form the Grand Banks. The banks stretch over a distance for 450 mi (730 km) and cover an area of 108,100 mi^2 (280,000 km^2). The shallow water above them ranges in depth from 120 ft (36 m) to 600 ft (185 m). The cold Labrador Current flows south, hugging the coastline and contacts the northward flowing warm waters of the Gulf Stream off to its east. The mixing currents not only increase the nutrient supply available to phytoplankters, but also generate the dense fogs and strong storms for which the banks are infamous. Additionally, a shelf-edge front contributes a flow of nutrients to the banks.

The Grand Banks provide spawning, nursery, and feeding areas for fish and shellfish. Historically, they were best known for Atlantic cod, which were being harvested by Basque and Portuguese fishermen as early as the 1400s, even before Columbus "discovered" America. (Of course, Native American fishermen were catching fish there long before then!) Other commercially important species taken on the banks were haddock, Atlantic halibut, ocean perch, turbot or Greenland halibut, yellowtail and witch flounders, American plaice, crabs, shrimp, and scallops. Huge populations of cod and Atlantic herring supported nearly 30 species of marine mammals, including beluga whale, northern right whale, fin whale, humpback whale, and grey seal. Except for the Beluga whale, all of these are now endangered.

Georges Bank

East of Cape Cod, Massachusetts, at the southwestern end of the banks that begin off Newfoundland, is Georges Bank. A large, oval underwater plateau, it rises more than 300 ft (100 m) above the seabed of the Gulf of Maine and

End of the Great Cod Fishery

Figure 3.5 Codfish were once plentiful demersal fish on Georges Bank. *(Northeast Fisheries Science Center archives. http://www.nefsc.noaa.gov.)*

Fishing vessels from many European countries, the United States, and Canada fished the Grand Banks, including large factory ships from the former Soviet Union. Serious depletion of cod (see Figure 3.5) and other fish stocks was well recognized by Canadian and New England fishermen by the early 1960s. Overfishing and the destruction of the benthic habitats by trawling gear were major problems. In 1977, Canada declared an Exclusive Economic Zone for 200 nautical miles (226 statute mi or 370 km) off its shores and banned foreign fishing vessels from those waters in an effort to manage the fisheries. The so-called Nose and Tail of the Grand Banks and a smaller bank, Flemish Cap, farther to the east, remained international waters. All cod and flounder fisheries on the Grand Banks were closed by 1995 and the catch of other fish species was strictly regulated. Few signs of recovery of stocks are visible today, with the exception of the yellowtail flounder, populations of which have returned to historic levels. Declines in fish populations were followed by increases in the abundance of shellfish and expansion of shrimp and crab fisheries in Canadian waters. International shrimp fisheries exist on the Nose, and turbot and shrimp fisheries are productive on Flemish Cap. International moratoriums have been imposed on the taking of cod and most other fish; but they may not be effective, because these species can still be legally taken as by-catch.

measures 150 mi (240 km) by 75 mi (120 km). At its shallowest point, it is only 100 ft (30 m) below the surface of the water. Currents, tides, and storm waves reshaped glacial deposits to form the bank itself and create its topography. Areas shallower than 160 ft (50 m) have sandy ridges 30–130 ft (10–40 m) high and 295 ft (90 m) long and trending northwest to southeast. The eastern part of the bank is deeper and smooth. A sharp boundary between the two surfaces occurs at 160 ft (50 m) and coincides with the position of the tidal front that develops in summer. Fifteen deep submarine canyons slice through the southeastern edge of Georges Bank.

Water circulates counterclockwise in the Gulf of Maine but is deflected into a clockwise flow over the bank. The divergent flows keep the two water masses separate and lead to the formation of a tidal front in the summer, when Gulf waters become stratified, but waters over the bank remain well mixed. Tidal currents are responsible for the continued mixing of the bank's water column and for keeping the waters cooler than the surface layer of the Gulf. The tidal front draws up nutrients and deep cold water from the Gulf of Maine, which is fed by the cold Labrador Current. Nutrient enrichment feeds an exceptionally high rate of primary production in the shallow waters above the bank, a spawning, nursery, and feeding ground for cod, haddock, herring, flounder, lobster, scallops, and clams. The larvae of cod, haddock, and yellowtail flounder consume the abundant zooplankters. The tides and circulating currents help keep the larvae, as well as fish eggs, in the rich waters of the bank. The irregular surface of coarse glacial deposits shelters juvenile cod and the invertebrates they eat. Strong currents flowing over gravel at the eastern edge of the bank oxygenate the lower waters and make conditions ideal for spawning herring, which lay their eggs on the bottom. All in all, more than 100 kinds of fish have been reported from Georges Bank, and many species of seabirds and cetaceans—including the endangered northern right whale—come to feed upon them.

Overfishing has led to the commercial extinction of most of the important fish. Halibut had disappeared by 1850, even though fishing then meant small boats and handlines with one or two hooks. Modern steam- and diesel-powered trawlers increased the efficiency of fishing ships in the 1920s, at about the same time that the frozen fish industry got its start in Gloucester, Massachusetts, and made fish fillets and fish sticks available to an ever-growing market (30 years or so later, this included square "fillets" for fast-food restaurants). After World War II, factory ships from the Soviet Union, Japan, and other countries arrived on the banks. Each ship could haul in 100 tons an hour. Sharp declines in groundfish and small pelagic fish such as herring and mackerel were noted by the 1960s. In 1974, factory ships flying foreign flags were banned, but New England fishermen expanded their efforts. Cod, haddock, herring, and sea scallop populations declined precipitously. By the late 1990s, a large portion of the bank was closed to fishing, but cod and other groundfish stocks continued to decline as lobster, dogfish, and skates increased.

Dogger Bank, North Sea

Dogger Bank marks a divide between the central and southern North Sea. The continental shelf here is a sediment-filled depression produced by plate movements. Coarse sediments of glacial origin accumulated in the central part of the sea and determined its present configuration, including the presence of Dogger Bank. The bank is a gravelly moraine some 200 mi (324 km) long and 75 mi (120 km) wide. A veneer of sand tops it, ranging in thickness between 3 and 33 ft (1–10 m). The shallowest part of the bank is in the southwest, where the sea is less than 65 ft (20 m) deep.

Ocean currents in the North Sea are complex. Atlantic water enters from the north and meets waters from the Strait of Dover. Most of the North Sea water column becomes stratified in the summer months, whereas water over the bank stays well mixed. Tidal fronts are therefore established near the edges of the bank, resuspending and redistributing sediments and nutrients. However, winds stir up the water column frequently enough over the shallower parts of the North Sea to keep phytoplankton production high on Dogger Bank throughout the year.

Dominant benthic invertebrates are heart urchin, a bivalve, and large polychaetes such as "sand masons." Other bivalves on the bank include the banded wedge shell and the clam *Nucula tenuis* in shallow areas and *Nucula nitida* and *Thyasira flexuosa* in deeper places. Dogger Bank serves as a spawning ground for mackerel, herring, cod, whiting, plaice, sole, sand eels, and sprat. Seabirds such as Northern Gannets, Northern Fulmars, and Black-legged Kittiwakes come in great numbers to feed on the fish. White-beaked dolphins, white-sided dolphin, and harbor porpoise also congregate on these rich feeding grounds.

The North Sea was one of the world's great fishing grounds in the nineteenth and early twentieth centuries. Cod, haddock, and whiting stock have all declined since the 1980s, and plaice suffered a sharp decline in the 1990s. Overfishing and beam trawlers whose gear damages benthic communities are implicated. Drilling for oil and gas and laying pipelines has also disturbed the seabed. The North Sea is one of the world's busiest shipping lanes and always under threat of oil spills, noise pollution, and the introduction of alien species. The establishment of wind farms is an additional concern, because the huge wind mills must be anchored to the seafloor.

Agulhas Bank, South Africa

South Africa's richest fishery lies immediately off its southern coast on one the few broad continental shelf areas on the African continent. The bank runs from Cape Point in the west to East London in the east. The region in general is the meeting place of the cold Benguela Current and the warm Agulhas Current. Yet marine conditions vary enough across the bank's east-west expanse that distinct environments divide it into western, central, and eastern sectors. Each region has distinct thermocline properties, primary productivity rates, production patterns for zooplankton, and habitat and spawning grounds for commercially important open-water species.

In the Southern Hemisphere summer, the waters over the Agulhas Bank become stratified, largely due to the inflow of warm waters from the Agulhas Current. Easterly winds in summer and autumn drive the current and create intermittent coastal upwelling in the eastern and central regions of the bank. Shelf-edge upwelling also occurs in the east at this time of year. In winter, strong westerly winds blow and mix the water column over much of these two sectors, although shelf-edge upwelling continues and can introduce weak stratification. The western section of the bank, under stronger influence from the Benguela system, experiences nearly continuous upwelling during the summer, especially on the western sides of capes and headlands. Primary productivity is highest in the western sector, particularly in coastal areas dominated by upwelling. Species diversity is highest in the east.

West-coast fisheries are entwined with those of the Benguela upwelling region (see below). Shallow water rock lobsters are one commercial catch that comes from the western bank. Pilchard and Cape anchovy, which were once important west coast fisheries, have shifted to the southern or central region of the Agulhas Bank, where shallow water hake and most of South's Africa's sole are also taken.

Shark Heaven

The Agulhas Bank is home to a marvelous array of sharks of seemingly every size. An estimated 140 species inhabit either the cold waters along the west coast or the more temperate waters to the east or both. The most dreaded and thus the most exciting is the great white. In fact, shark-watching cages are located along South Africa's coast so tourists can gain a safe glimpse of these fearsome animals. But great whites are not the only attraction. Harmless whale sharks—at 40 ft (12 m) the world's largest shark; tiger sharks, and short-fin makos are all there. East of Cape Agulhas, in warm waters, 11 kinds of small catsharks occur. The tiniest, the tiger catshark, is only about 18 inches (45 cm) long. All this high diversity is possible because to the convergence of two ocean currents over the shallow bank. Here, where the Indian Ocean meets the Atlantic Ocean, the cold Benguela Current meets the warm Agulhas current and creatures common to each are brought together.

From June to November a visitor to South Africa's southern coast can watch the migration of southern right whales returning to their breeding and calving grounds from a winter spent feeding in Antarctic waters. Often they come within a few yards of the shore. Bryde's whale is common in autumn and early winter off the southeast coast; and humpbacks pass in migration twice a year (June–July and September–November) as they move between feeding grounds in the Southern Ocean and wintering grounds in the Indian Ocean off Mozambique.

Upwelling Ecosystems

Four of the world's five major upwelling areas occur with eastern boundary currents in the Atlantic and Pacific oceans (see Figure 3.6). The fifth, found in the northwestern Indian Ocean, is the product of the Asian monsoon. The cold waters brought up from depth increase aridity on the adjacent landmasses, so that each upwelling region lies just offshore from an extreme desert environment. Nutrients brought up from depth support rich pelagic fisheries, especially of anchovies, which in turn support large breeding populations of seabirds, particularly the

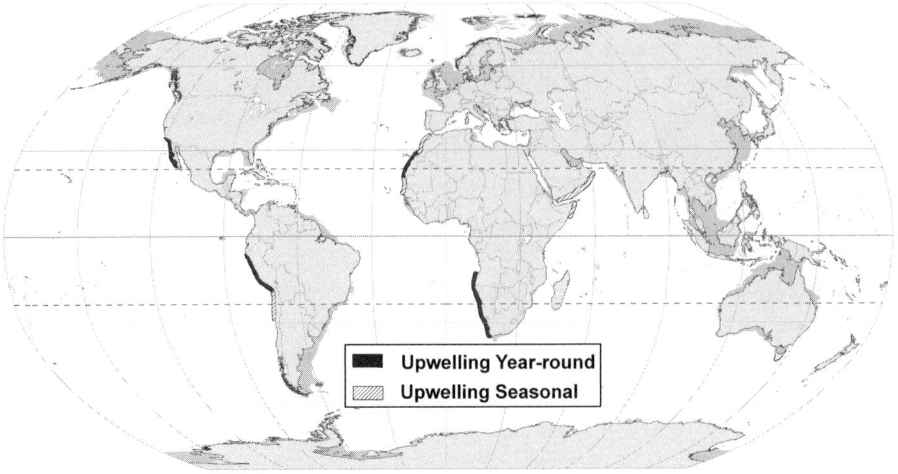

Figure 3.6 World's major upwelling areas. *(Map by Bernd Kuennecke.)*

so-called guano birds such as boobies, cormorants, and pelicans (see Figure 3.7). Upwelling is accentuated on headlands and islands, so these are preferred nesting and roosting sites for tens of millions of birds. In the Southern Hemisphere, penguin colonies also occur on these coasts and offshore islands.

Peru's coastal waters, associated with the Humboldt Current, have the highest rates of primary productivity of the five major upwelling regions. Northwest Africa, near Cap Blanc (white from guano), and the Benguela Current region in southwestern Africa have somewhat lower rates, whereas productivity in the California Current upwelling region is considerably lower than the other three. The Somalian upwelling area has high production, but unlike the others, which are essentially permanent phenomena, it is limited to only four months out of the year.

Upwelling regions account for at least 40 percent of the world's fisheries catches. In all areas, pelagic clupeids—anchovies, anchovetas, and sardines—dominate the fish biomass. Flatfish are important demersal species near shore. Hake and, in the Atlantic, rosefish can be found farther offshore. Horse mackerel and chub mackerel mass in the lower parts of the thermocline. In addition to the large colonies of seabirds mentioned above, these fish-rich waters also typically support colonies of fur seals and sea lions.

The Humboldt Current System

The cold Humboldt Current is associated with permanent cells of upwelling off the coast of Peru and seasonal upwelling off Chile. As already stated, it has the highest primary productivity of all five regions. Not surprisingly, then, it also has the most productive fisheries. Until the 1970s, Peru led the world in tons of fish caught each year, almost of all it anchovies and sardines. Peru and Chile together still account for 15–20 percent of the world's marine catch even though the upwelling area is less than 1 percent

Guano: The High Stakes in Bird Droppings

Figure 3.7 Guano birds: pelicans are seen on rocks to right; cormorants on distant rocks on the left. *(Photo © Elisa Locci/Shutterstock.)*

In the dry climate regions formed in association with cold eastern boundary currents, the "poo" or guano of boobies, cormorants, pelicans, and—off Namibia—penguins once accumulated into deposits as much as 25 ft (8 m) thick on rocky headlands and offshore islands. Even prehistoric peoples recognized the value of these bird droppings and used them as fertilizer on their fields. In Peru, the Inca protected the birds and determined when and by whom the guano could be harvested. In the nineteenth century, guano mining boomed as a major industry to supply European and American demands for fertilizer. Between 1875 and 1900, Peru exported some 20 million tons worth 2 billion dollars. Wars were fought to control guano-rich areas. In 1879, Bolivia lost its coastal lands to Peru, a change in the world map still contested by Bolivians. The United States passed a law in 1856 allowing its citizens to claim any uninhabited guano island as American territory.

The guano boom was over when deposits around the world were stripped and when modern agriculture began to use synthetic nitrate and phosphate fertilizers. In Peru, the fish that fed the guano birds—anchovies—became the focus of the economy. They were processed into fish meal for export as animal feed. A couple of severe El Niños and overfishing depleted the fishery, leading to a serious decline in seabird populations. Today, some guano is still collected. It is primarily sold to organic farmers.

Anchovies Versus Sardines

Anchovies and sardines are major fisheries on a global scale, yet both of these small fishes undergo dramatic basin-wide population peaks and crashes. When anchovies boom, sardine populations crash and vice versa. Declines have sometimes been blamed solely on overfishing, but recent research by Japanese biologists suggests that 50-year cycles are related to ocean temperature changes. Optimal temperature for the survival of anchovy larvae is 72° F (22.2° C), whereas that for sardine larvae is 61° F (16.2° C).

of the ocean's surface area. Most of this catch was rendered into fish meal for poultry and livestock feed. Overfishing and a devastating El Niño in 1972–73 ended Peru's dominance of world fish production, and soybeans came to replace fishmeal as the main source of animal feed in Europe and the Americas (and now, everywhere).

The drastic decline of fish, especially anchovies, in the early 1970s led to high mortality in the guano bird populations, once estimated to number 35–45 million. They have yet to recover. The Guanay Cormormant may have a population of about 4 million birds, the Peruvian Booby, about 3 million, and the Peruvian Pelican only about 400,000. Today, 23 islands (including the Ballestas Islands) and 10 headlands in Peru are managed by a state-owned company to conserve the bird populations. Even though it is no longer profitable, the company still mines guano. If bird populations and guano accumulation are sufficient, a given deposit will be harvested every five to seven years. The guano bird reserves also protect dwindling populations of Humboldt Penguin and the endemic and highly endangered Peruvian Diving Petrel and serve as breeding grounds for Southern sea lions and the South American fur seal.

The Benguela Current System

The Benguela Current is unique among the upwelling areas in that warm currents affect both its northern and southern boundaries. It is composed of two subsystems, the Northern Benguela off the coast of southern Angola and northern Namibia and the Southern Benguela off southern Namibia and South Africa. They are separated by the strongest upwelling cell in the world near Lüderitz, Namibia. Sardines and anchovies were the most important fish species, but stocks began to collapse in the south in the 1960s and in the north in the late 1970s. Southern stocks recovered slowly. Adult anchovies and sardines migrate to the warm, stratified waters of Agulhas Bank to spawn. A coastal current then carries eggs and larvae northward into the southern Benguela system. The Northern Benguela ecosystem seems to have changed entirely after the disappearance of anchovies and sardines. Jellyfish and detritus-feeding gobies now dominate. All pelagic fish occur in low numbers, threatening hake and horse mackerel fisheries with commercial extinction.

The Canary Current System

Different seasonal patterns in upwelling differentiate the Canary Current system into three regions. The northern Moroccan coast experiences summer upwelling. In the central region of south Morocco and northern Mauritania, upwelling occurs all year. In the south, off southern Mauritania and Senegal, upwelling is a winter occurrence. The south has tropical conditions in the summer, and the alternating water temperatures are related to seasonal changes in the fish fauna. In the summer, tropical species such as tunas migrate as far as 20° N; whereas temperate sardines or pilchards extend their ranges southward into the region in winter. West African fisheries in the Canary Current were once dominated by large demersal fish, but they were overexploited and seem to have been replaced with octopuses, shrimps, and pelagic fish. Octopuses are now an important commercial West African fishery.

Somali–Arabian Sea Upwelling System

In the northwestern Indian Ocean, two coastal upwelling systems are regulated by the southwest monsoon. The continental shelf along the shores of East Africa and southern Arabia in the western Arabian Sea is on average only 5.5–20 mi (9–35 km) wide. Coast-parallel southwesterly winds begin in April or May, driving an equatorial ocean current in the Southern Hemisphere toward the Somali Coast. Along the coast, these waters become a northward-flowing Somali Current. A cold wedge of water appears around 5° N and weak upwelling begins along the northern branch as a result of the winds. As the monsoon strengthens, a clockwise gyre known as the Great Whirl develops in the northwestern Indian Ocean and moves more water offshore, generating a strong cold water upwelling along the northern Somali coast.

A second area of upwelling occurs off southern Arabia along the entire coast of Yemen and Oman during the summer monsoon. Offshore flows carry thin streams of cool surface waters far into the Arabian Sea. These wisps of cool water may last in the warm waters of the Arabian Sea for a few weeks. Since the coastal currents are moving eastward, upwelled water is also carried into the warm waters of the northeast Arabian Sea.

Weak coastal upwelling can occur along the northwest coast of India during the winter or northeast monsoon. Water temperatures may be only about 3.6° F (2° C) cooler than normal, 79° F (26° C).

The highly productive areas along Somali's east coast support commercially important small pelagic fish such as the oil sardine, mackerel, scads, jacks, and anchovies. Other fish include porcupine fish, splitfins, and driftfish. Indian oil sardine is the most important catch.

The Yemen-Oman upwelling region fish fauna is also predominantly small pelagic fish. Many of the same species occur there as along the Somalian coast. The oil sardine is the main fish off Yemen; the horse mackerel is the major catch, by weight, off Oman.

Kelp Beds and Forests

Off sheltered to moderately exposed rocky coasts in cool temperate regions of the ocean, kelps grow in profusion and serve as the base of species-rich animal communities.

Kelps

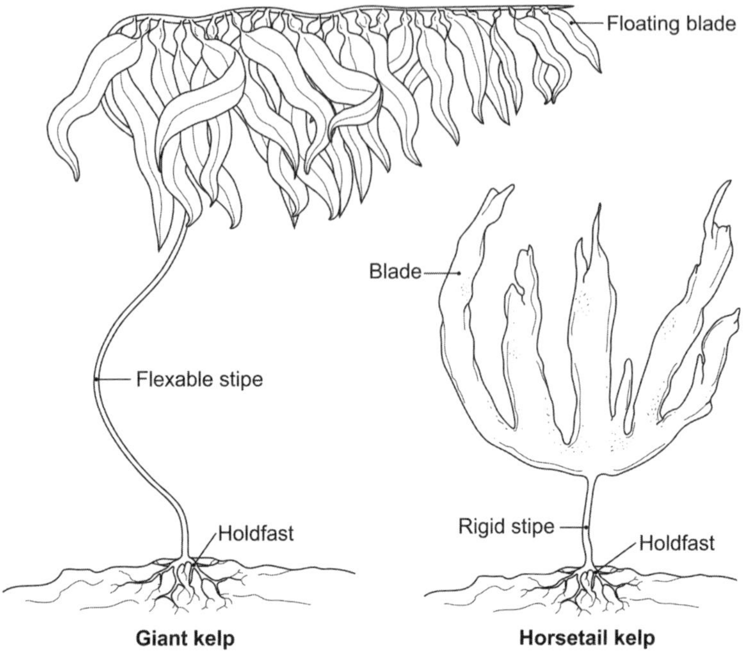

Figure 3.8 Typical perennial kelps. *(Illustration by Jeff Dixon.)*

Kelps are large, rubbery brown algae in the orders Fucales and Laminariales. The basic growth form has three parts: a root-like holdfast, a stipe, and flat blades or fronds (see Figure 3.8). Branched or unbranched, flexible or rigid, stipes may bear single or multiple blades. Some kelps are equipped with flotation devices—air-filled bladders—to hold the blades in sunlit waters at or near the sea surface. Others rely on stiff stipes to keep the blades high in the water column. Kelps may be annuals, or they may possess perennial holdfasts and shed blades and stipes for part of the year. Each growthform is adapted to different conditions of water depth, wave action, and disturbance. Kelp forests contain macroalgae standing at least 15 ft (5 m) off the seabed, whereas kelp beds have plants less than 3 ft (1 m) high.

While typically associated with cool waters in the temperate zone, kelp forests have recently been discovered near the Equator in cold water at depths of 40–200 feet (12–60 m) off the Galápagos Islands. A mathematical model based on data from satellites and oceanographic instruments had predicted the occurrence of kelps (*Eisenia galapagensis*) at this location.

Kelps are almost exclusively subtidal in occurrence. If the water is clear, the slope of the continental shelf gentle, and a hard substrate present, they can grow in water 65–130 ft (20–40 m) deep and as far as 6 mi (10 km) offshore. The many long plants reaching from the seafloor toward the sea surface give the impression of a forest complete with an understory of smaller kelps and red algae. As in a true forest, a three-dimensional habitat forms that allows a variety of animals to live at and utilize different levels as well as different resources (see Figure 3.9).

Kelp forests grow in both hemispheres from subpolar latitudes equatorward until summer water temperatures exceed 68° F (20° C). (In warmer areas, coral reefs occupy rocky reefs offshore.) Cold ocean currents and areas of cold water upwelling let kelp forests flourish off some subtropical coasts (see Figure 3.10).

Wave action keeps kelp blades in constant motion, which maximizes their exposure to sunlight and aids in the absorption of nutrients. Upwelling and wind-driven mixing of the water-column ensure an abundant and continually renewed supply of nutrients.

Kelp forests and beds are highly productive and retain most nutrients in the system by quickly recycling them. Waves erode the ends of blades and uproot kelps, disturbances that release DOM and POM that enter the microbial loop via bacteria (see Chapter 1). The bacteria may be consumed directly by zooplankters or larger filter-feeders or they may ride the "snow" to the seafloor, where they will be consumed along with the snow by sessile filter-feeding benthic organisms such as

Figure 3.9 The kelp forest creates a three-dimensional habitat. *(Photo © Paul Whitted/ Shutterstock.)*

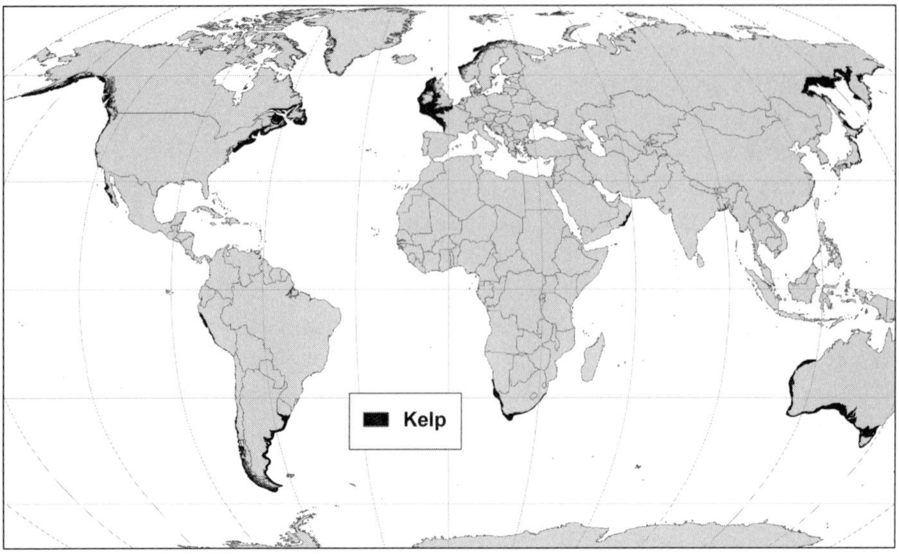

Figure 3.10 Distribution of kelp beds and forests. *(Map by Bernd Kuennecke.)*

mussels, barnacles, sponges, and tunicates. Uprooted kelp may sink to the bottom or may float as drift algae—alive and still photosynthesizing—out to sea or onto the beach, becoming wrack. In shallow water, drift algae is eaten by sea urchins. On the beach, dead kelp is fed upon by terrestrial amphipods and isopods and becomes the source of energy for detritus food chains, wastes from which wash back to the sea.

Sea urchins are important members of kelp communities. Their grazing may determine the landward boundary of kelp beds, but normally they have little impact on kelps growing in deeper waters offshore. However, for reasons not yet well understood, sea urchin populations occasionally grow to tremendous sizes and devastate kelp beds. All fleshy algae can be eliminated during such outbreaks, leaving only a low cover of diatoms, encrusting red coralline algae, and closely cropped filamentous green algae. Once they have laid bare a patch of the forest, the urchins advance in fronts across adjacent areas, clearing them, too. Recovery of a stand of kelp may take four to six years.

Regional Expressions

Although different species and genera dominate the kelp flora and fauna, basic patterns in zonation, food chains, and sea urchin-kelp relationships are repeated in each oceanic region. *Laminaria* species are dominant kelps in the North Atlantic and in the northwest Pacific. Their blades are held in the water column by strong stipes and are so completely submerged at high tide that kelp beds are invisible from shore. The giant kelp that dominates the eastern Pacific along the coasts of both North and South America, as well as off New Zealand, is buoyed by gas-filled bladders and floats conspicuously on the sea surface regardless of water level. So, too, are the large *Eklonia* kelps that form the canopy of kelp forests off the west coast of southern Africa, the east coast of southern Japan, and southeast coasts of Australia.

Sea Urchin-Kelp Relations

Sea urchin irruptions may be part of natural population and ecological cycles in which a given area of rock reef alternates between kelp bed and sea urchin barren. Or they may be related to releases from heavy predation, such as occurred off the west coast of North America. Overhunting of sea otters led to their near extinction and coincided with large increases in urchin numbers. Sea otters eat sea urchins and molluscs such as abalone that also graze kelps. When, with international protection, sea otter populations rebounded, a dense kelp forest returned to favorable habitats along the coast. Off Nova Scotia, sea urchin population peaks coincided with the demise of the cod, an urchin predator, from overfishing; but a cycle of population growth followed by population crashes brought about by disease seems also to occur.

Northwest Atlantic kelp beds. Dominant kelps in the Gulf of Maine and off Nova Scotia include horsetail kelp, sugar kelp, and sea colander. Irish moss (a red alga) dominates the understory, but red fern—a filamentous red alga—is also prevalent and may form its own belt at the bottom of the zone. Crustose coralline algae of several genera cover the seabed. Grazers on kelp include limpets, periwinkles, and sea urchins. Snails graze on sea colander, filamentous red algae, and diatom films, while isopods concentrate on the coralline ground layer. Green sea urchins can be dominant elements. When sea urchins are rare, the kelps and other macroalgae are abundant; when urchin numbers are high, the kelps are overgrazed and coralline algae dominate.

The red algae understory is habitat for motile invertebrates such as shrimps, amphipods, isopods, and juvenile crabs. Sessile invertebrates attach to the fronds of algae. Kelps may host colonies of hydroids, and red algae can have a coating of hydroids, tunicates, and the spat of mussels.

Predators include lobsters, the Jonah crab, green crabs, sea stars, and fishes such as winter flounder, haddock, eelpout, and wrasse. Sea ducks such as Red-breasted Mergansers, Common Goldeneye, and Old Squaw consume both invertebrates and small fish.

Northeast Atlantic. Kelp beds on the continental shelves of Atlantic Scandinavia and the British Isles are quite similar to those on the opposite side of the Atlantic. They show clear zonation. Horsetail kelp grows in the shallower waters of the sublittoral fringe. Beyond, in somewhat deeper water, is a belt of sugar kelp. Both have short, flexible stipes and simple strap-like blades kept in sunlit water by both gas-filled bladders and wave-generated turbulence. Deeper still is a zone of *Laminaria hyberborea*, which has stiff stipes and grows up to 7 ft (2 m) long. Grazing by the edible sea urchin apparently sets is lower limit.

Northeast Pacific. Perennial giant bladder kelps that may grow 200 ft (60 m) long form the dense upper canopy of the nearshore kelp forest. Strong holdfasts attach them to rocky reefs 15–60 ft (5–20 m) below the sea surface. Other brown algae that may form canopies are elkhorn kelp and the annual bull kelp, feather boa kelp, and a sargassum. Laminarians, whose flexible stalks or stipes hold their fronds more than 6 ft (2 m) off the seabed, occur as an understory, below which grow foliose red and brown algae and articulated corallines. The rocky reef itself is covered with filamentous and encrusting algae species.

The holdfast of a giant kelp may live 4–10 years with individual fronds being replaced every 6–12 months. The giant kelp is highly productive and supports a community of detritivores, herbivores, and carnivores that may number 1,000 or more species. More than 100 species are reported to live amid the holdfasts. Invertebrates associated with California kelp beds include purple and red sea urchins, abalone, Kellet's whelk, Knobby sea star, and spiny lobster, as well as sea cucumbers and octopuses. Together with the surfgrasses of the lower eulittoral zone, kelp forests offer shelter and nursery habitat for many open-ocean species. Location and environmental conditions permit a mixing of northern and southern species off the coast of California. The result is a high diversity of fishes, some of which—such as chubs, grunts, damselfishes, wrasses, gobies, and croakers are representatives of families more closely associated with the tropics. Others such as surfperches, rockfishes, and greenlings have affinities with northern cold-temperate species.

North Pacific kelp forests were once browsed by the now extinct Stellar's sea cow. The keystone role of sea otters in regulating sea urchin populations, and thus helping to maintain kelp forests, is described in the sidebar on p. 147.

Southern Hemisphere

Southeast Atlantic. The west coast of southern Africa, from the Cape of Good Hope north into Namibia, is bathed by the cold Benguela Current and is home to one of the world's great kelp forests. A dense canopy of the giant bamboo kelp, which may grow 45 ft (15 m) long, is visible from shore. Split-fan kelp forms a subcanopy 3–8 ft (1–2.5 m) high. Like the giant kelp off the coast of California, bamboo kelp has a long flexible stipe and gas-filled bladders on the tips of fronds that keep it floating on the surface. When the tips of fronds are broken, POM and DOM are released into the water and consumed by bacteria as part of the microbial loop. Detritus from the bacteria is consumed by filter-feeding and deposit-feeding animals such as ribbed mussel, sponges, tunicates, sea cucumbers, and barnacles. Waves prevent grazers such as sea urchins and snails from climbing up the stipes and feeding on the canopy; but at times, the kelp is bent down to the seafloor, where it is trapped beneath and consumed by abalones. Sea urchins feed on microalgae and drift algae, and snails feed on the understory kelps. Other herbivores in the kelp forests include limpets and fish such as the hottentot and strepie. The main carnivore is the rock lobster, which primarily consumes ribbed mussels. It in turn is consumed by dogfish sharks, Cape fur seals, and seabirds such as Bank Cormorants.

Southeast Pacific. Between 18° and 42° S latitude along the west coast of South America, the cold eastern boundary current of the South Pacific—the Humboldt Current—as well as upwelling bring cold-temperate conditions to the tropics. The narrow continental shelf off Chile has a band of kelp and kelp-like brown algae in the shallowest waters of the subtidal zone. In deeper water, the brown algae are joined by a red alga, and grazers include the black sea urchin, a large chiton, and the black snail. Marine otters are among the predators feeding on crustaceans, molluscs, and fishes. The Humboldt Penguin breeds on offshore islands, as do Southern sea lions; both hunt fish in the kelp forest.

Along the coasts of southern Chile (42°–55° S), cold waters from the Southern Ocean circulate. Strong prevailing westerly winds mix the water column, making the illuminated surface waters nutrient-rich. Just offshore is a conspicuous belt of kelp forest 150–325 ft (50–100 m) wide with a floating canopy of giant kelp, the same species found off California. A smaller kelp, *Lessonia flavicans*, forms an understory with its 5–10 ft (2–3 m) long fronds; and fleshy and foliose red algae form a shorter substory. The seafloor beneath is covered with crustose red algae. Marine otters and Southern sea lions feed in these southern waters. Magellanic Penguins are the counterparts of the Humboldts found closer to the Equator. The same community of kelps and large marine animals is found on the southern most Atlantic coast of Argentina and, except for the marine otter, off the Falkland Islands.

Coral Reefs

Coral reefs are great limestone structures built up over millennia by living organisms that secrete calcium carbonate skeletons. They are features of continental shelves where the water is warm and clear, typically shallow seas in the tropics. The most familiar reef-builders are the stony corals, but red and green coralline algae are often more important. Marine scientists say that tropical reef, biogenic reef, or algal reef are more appropriate names, but the term coral reef endures in common and scientific usage.

Coral reefs are famous for their enormously high biodiversity and are frequently compared to tropical rainforest in this regard (see Figure 3.11). More than 100,000 marine animal species from just about every known phylum are reef-dwellers, and perhaps a million more are still to be discovered. Among them are almost 1,500 kinds of reef-building coral. In addition, all algal divisions are represented in the flora. Some species are obligate reef inhabitants; some are more general in their ecological preferences. Broad distributional patterns emerge within this extraordinary variety of life. Almost 92 percent of the world's reefs occur in the Indo-West Pacific, a biogeographic region with its own distinctive assemblage of reef corals, fishes, and other organisms. Three other reef biogeographic regions exist: the East Pacific, West Atlantic, and East Atlantic (see Figure 3.12).

Reef fauna had lived in warm shallow seas for 100 million years in what was once a single world ocean. In the late Cenozoic, plate tectonics tore Pangea apart and the ocean was divided into separate basins. The widening of the Atlantic Ocean separated reef-building corals on either side of the Atlantic. Completion of the Panamanian isthmus isolated the western Atlantic from the eastern Pacific. Mass extinctions accompanied consequent changes in ocean circulation patterns and temperature and were followed by local speciation. As a result, most corals and most reef species in other taxa are endemic to the biogeographic region in which they are found. By far the greatest number of species today are in the Indo-West Pacific. The West Atlantic, with only a small fraction of the species-richness of the Indo-West Pacific, is next in diversity, followed by the East Pacific and East Atlantic, respectively. Although coral reefs have existed for millions of years, most modern living reefs are no more than 10,000 years old, having either come into being or experienced renewed growth as the sea level rose at the end of the last glacial period.

Each living reef represents a massive accumulation of dead skeletons with only a thin coating of living tissue. Reef structures in the Indo-West Pacific commonly

Figure 3.11 Coral reefs are famous for the great diversity of animals living in, on, and near them. *(Photo © James R. Woodward. Used with permission.)*

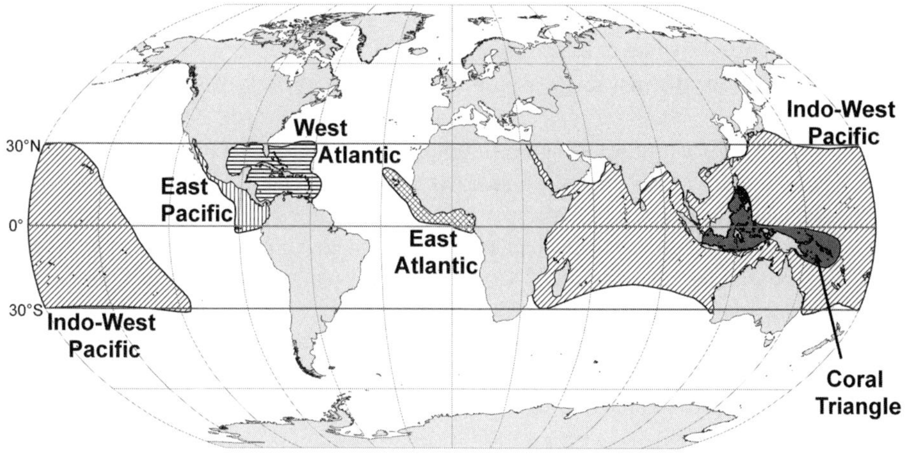

Figure 3.12 Major coral reef regions of the world. *(Map by Bernd Kuennecke.)*

are 0.75 mi (1 km) or more thick; Enewetak Atoll, probably more than 50 million years old, is more than 4,265 ft (1,300 m) thick. Those in the East Pacific are seldom more than 3 ft (1 m) thick.

Coral reefs are more or less confined to tropical seas where water temperatures do not drop below 68° F (18° C) or rise much above 97° F (36° C). Warm western boundary currents can extend the distribution of living reefs poleward into the subtropics. Fairly diverse communities of reef-building corals exist at 28°–35° latitude in the North and South Pacific, the North Atlantic, and the North and South Indian oceans. The extreme latitudinal limits for reef-building corals are 38° N in the Azores and 38° S in Victoria, Australia. The exact limiting factors are yet to be discovered. Temperature and the growth of macroalgae (in more nutrient-rich waters) are implicated. Areas of upwelling of cold water and areas of high sediment load—such as at the mouths of large tropical rivers—lack coral reefs. It may be that environmental conditions outside the tropics interfere with the secretion of calcareous skeletons and make it impossible for stony corals to exist.

Reefs are complex constructions of living corals and algae. They are continually being broken

The Coral Triangle

The global center of marine biodiversity lies among the islands of Southeast Asia in area that has been designated the Coral Triangle (see Figure 3.12). An area about half as big as the United States is home to about 75 percent of all known reef-building corals, some 500 species. Although the Triangle's boundaries were drawn to delineate areas of high coral diversity, the area also contains the world's highest diversity of coral reef fishes, some 3,000 species. Biodiversity, furthermore, is extremely high in terms of formaniferans; the solitary, mobile, non-reef-forming fungiid corals; and habitat diversity. With slight adjustment, the boundaries of the Coral Triangle would also enclose the world's greatest diversity of mangrove.

As a center of tropical marine biodiversity, the Coral Triangle is a top priority for conservation efforts aimed at maintaining global biodiversity. Also at stake is the livelihood of the 2.5 million people who live in the region and depend on the reefs for their subsistence or commercial fisheries.

into loose rubble by both physical and biological processes. Debris is moved around and sorted by waves and tidal currents. Some is deposited on the reef; some is washed away by storms. Reefs assume one of three basic forms (see Figure 3.13):

- **Fringing reefs** appear to be an extension of rocky coast shorelines in the tropics (see Plate V). Coral larvae (planulae) settle out and grow in well-lit shallow waters above a hard substrate to which they can attach. Successive generations grow on top of the lifeless skeletons of the preceding one and create a shallow limestone platform in the subtidal zone. After a few thousand years, the living coral will extend above the extreme low-tide mark. Upward growth of the reef halts, since corals can tolerate neither drying out from being exposed to the atmosphere nor the pounding of waves. The reef at this stage builds horizontally, growing outward from its seaward edge.
- **Barrier reefs** are separated from land by shallow lagoons 0.5–6 mi (1–10 km) wide. The bulk of the reef is a wave-cut platform on an extinct reef that may be 100,000 years or more old. New reef growth on the seaward edge of the platform for the last 10,000 years constructs an offshore ridge that rises close to the sea surface. The young reef's outer margin is marked by a line of breakers. The Great Barrier Reef off eastern Australia is the world's largest. Actually a chain of smaller reefs, it stretches 1,430 mi (2,300 km) from north to south and covers an area of 18,500 mi^2 (48,000 km^2). It dwarfs the second-longest reef, the Belize Barrier Reef in the Caribbean, a mere 135 mi (220 km) in length.
- **Atolls** are reefs that encircle a lagoon more than 6 mi (10 km) across and have no land at the center. The reef may trap enough coral debris to form a necklace of low islands. Charles Darwin hypothesized in 1842 that atolls began as reefs fringing volcanic islands. With time, as it became extinct, the volcano subsided and left behind a ring of coral close to the sea surface. Aldabra Atoll, some 200 mi (320 km) north of Madagascar in the Indian Ocean, is one of the world's largest atolls. It measures 21 mi (34 km) by 9 mi (14 km).

Coral reefs cover 3 percent of the area of tropical continental shelves. This amounts to less than 0.2 percent of the total ocean surface area. Yet these living structures are extremely important economically as well as ecologically. An estimated 25 percent of the fish catch of developing countries comes from tropical reefs. As major tourist attractions, reefs generate revenue for individuals, corporations, and nations. In addition, fringing and barrier reefs determine the physical structure of

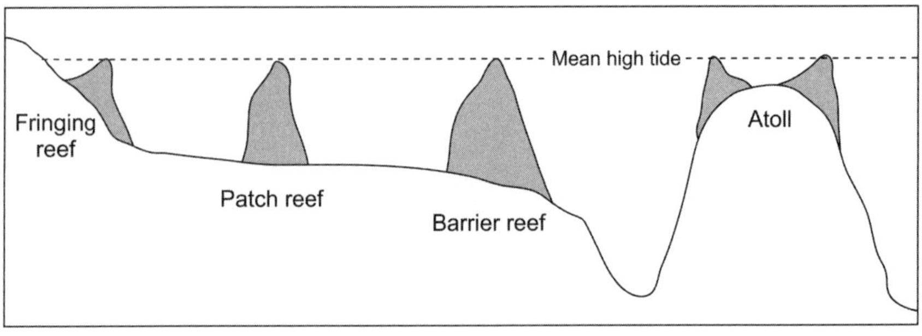

Figure 3.13 Types of coral reef. *(Illustration by Jeff Dixon. Adapted from Kaiser et al. 2005.)*

coastline and how accessible the land is to ocean-going vessels. They provide valuable ecosystem services by protecting the coast from erosion by wave action and by sheltering seafood-rich seagrass and mangrove communities. In turn, seagrass meadows and mangrove prevent siltation, which would smother reef organisms, and provide an abundant supply of food to the reef's herbivores and carnivores alike.

Structure of a Reef

Seven distinct zones relate to the shape and functioning of a reef (see Figure 3.14). The reef front descends steeply to depths of 15–50 ft (5–15 m). Exposed to wave action, it receives a constant supply of nutrients and plankton, including invertebrate and fish larvae, and is the area where most of the active growth of coral polyps and coralline algae occurs. On windward reef fronts, a self-perpetuating system of deep grooves or channels alternating with spurs or buttresses of dead coral develops. The buttresses project seaward and serve to dissipate the energy of incoming waves. As water rushes up the channels, it picks up coarse coral sands that had been lying on the channel bed. The suspended sediments abrade the reef front, deepening and widening the grooves so that the spurs may come to project seaward nearly 1,000 ft (300 m). The reef front flattens below its precipitous escarpment and at depths of about 60 ft (18 m) becomes a narrow shelf. This shelf is likely the remnant of a wave-cut limestone platform dating back to the lower sea levels of the Pleistocene. Below this flat area, the reef slope descends to the seabed of the continental shelf, covered by broken corals and other debris from the reef above.

In the Indo-Pacific region, on the windward reef front, a reef crest commonly forms on top that may poke above the low-spring-tide level. Since corals do not thrive in exposed situations, the crest becomes an algal ridge encrusted with coralline algae. Storm waves crashing over the ridge concentrate boulders and other rubble behind it, shaping the debris into tongues of gravel that stretch onto the reef flat. Everyday wave action removes sand and finer particles from the boulder zone and deposits them in the lagoon. The power of the breakers keeps debris from accumulating immediately behind the algal ridge, so a shallow moat may separate the boulder zone from the algal ridge. The reef flat is a ridge or plateau of broken coral skeletons and other intermediate-size rubble. It may be exposed at low tide, but on windward reefs, it is kept moist by sea spray.

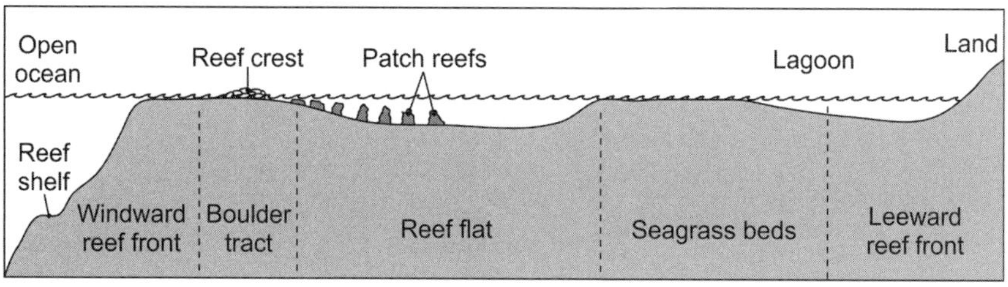

Figure 3.14 Generalized structure of a reef. *(Illustration by Jeff Dixon.)*

Lagoons have soft-sediment floors built of the finer debris from the reef and often host seagrass meadows and a wide range of invertebrates. In the Caribbean, lagoons are typically 15–50 ft (5–15 m) deep, but Indo-Pacific atolls may be more than 200 ft (70 m) deep. Projecting up from the lagoon floor, are small, island-like patch reefs ringed by white coral sand. The sand is kept clear of vegetation by foraging fish that use the patch reef as shelter. Patch reefs may grow to heights that bring them close to the low tide mark, but usually they are much deeper and expand horizontally instead of vertically. Surrounded by the abundant food supplies of the lagoon, they can be the most diverse part of the reef system.

Leeward reef fronts are sheltered from strong wave action, receive fewer nutrients and plankters, and grow more slowly than the more exposed windward reefs. They lack spurs and grooves and algal ridges, boulder zones, moats, and gravel tongues.

Reef-building or stony corals. Corals are colonial cnidarians. The mature animal is a polyp that closely resembles a tiny sea anemone (see Figure 3.15). The body, 0.04–0.1 in (1–3 mm) in diameter, is essentially a tubular sac, a stomach, with a single opening surrounded by numerous tentacles. Reef-building corals (order Scleratinia) secrete calcium carbonate from the base of the polyp to form a hard cup-like calyx in which the polyp sits. When disturbed or otherwise threatened, the polyp withdraws its tentacles and flattens itself against the walls of the cup. Periodically, it lifts up off the bottom of the calyx and secretes a new basal plate on which to rest and the limestone skeleton grows upward. On average, reefs grow about 10 ft (3 m) higher every 1,000 years, fast enough for them—so far—to keep pace with postglacial sea-level rise.

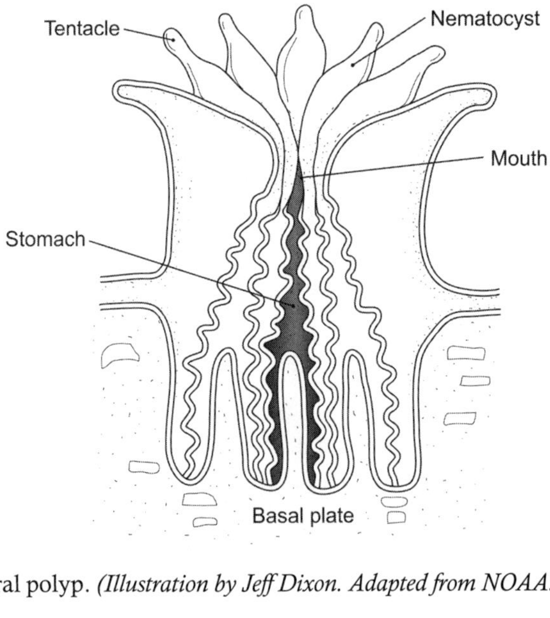

Figure 3.15 Coral polyp. *(Illustration by Jeff Dixon. Adapted from NOAA.)*

The whole colony grows in size and numbers of individuals through asexual reproduction—budding. A mature polyp divides to produce two genetically identical individuals—that is, it makes clones of itself. Polyps formed by budding remain attached to each other by a thin layer of tissue over the top of the limestone wall separating them. In time, all neighboring polyps are interconnected. Colonies may come to contain thousands, even hundreds of thousands, of tiny individuals.

Colonies assume a variety of physical forms (see Figure 3.16) depending on the species of coral or, in some cases, where on the reef they live. Branching corals exhibit obvious "branches" coming off "stems." They tend to be fragile and easily damaged by storm waves. Elkhorn corals, a variation on the branching form, have arms flattened like moose antlers. Digitate corals, considered by some to be a type of branching coral, form clusters of upright columns somewhat resembling the knees of bald cypress. Table corals have their branches fused into fans held up above and parallel to the surface of the reef, while foliose corals produce broad plates arranged in flower-like whorls. Encrusting corals spread over the reef as a thin layer in close contact with the surface. In contrast, massive corals grow into large mounds or balls reminiscent of a brain or a barrel cactus. Finally, in the Indo-Pacific are mushroom corals, large caps perched on stalks. Zonation of growthforms is evident across gradients of wave action and current strength as well as light intensity, which varies with depth and water clarity. On the windward reef crest, encrusting corals and streamlined branching and massive forms occupy the surf zone. Thick branches oriented so that onrushing water will flow along the branch rather than smash into it at a right angle make branching forms surf-resistant. Similarly, ridges on massive forms will run parallel to the flow of water. On less-exposed reef fronts, branching forms dominate at depths affected by wave action and become increasingly flattened as depth increases. The more sheltered the area the greater the variety of growthforms. Below the base of the waves, however, in the subreef zone, massive forms dominate and soft corals become more abundant. Up on the reef flat, in relatively still water, only or two stony coral species grow, often in separate bands. Branching forms cluster near the windward side and massive forms toward the leeward. If exposed to air at extreme low tides, the tops of these coral colonies can die back, leaving only an outer ring of living polyps as a mini-atoll.

The establishment of new coral reefs is possible because corals also undergo sexual reproduction. Many species are hermaphroditic and produce both eggs and sperm, while others have separate male and female polyps. For most (85 percent) fertilization occurs after gametes are released into the water. To maximize the probability that eggs and sperm from sessile animals will meet, mass spawnings in which all polyps release their gametes at the same time are characteristic—and spectacular. The synchronization is not simply among polyps of the same species, but among all coral species on a reef. Billions of gametes stream into the water. On Australia's Great Barrier Reef, almost all corals spawn one or two days after the November full moon. Elsewhere the dates vary, and whether moonlight or the warmest water of the year is the primary stimulus is still not known. It is likely that once spawning

(a)

(b)

(c)

Figure 3.16 Coral colonies assume a variety of forms: (a) A massive brain coral appears in the foreground. *(Photo © James R. Woodward. Used with permission.)* (b) A pillar coral represents the digitate form. *(Photo by Commander William Harrigan, NOAA Corps. Florida Keys National Marine Sanctuary.)* (c) Elkhorn coral is an example of the branching form. *(NASA.)*

begins, chemical cues are involved and one colony's reproductive orgy signals those downstream to release gametes. In the Gulf of Mexico and Caribbean Sea, mass spawning occurs in August. In the West Pacific, mass spawning occurs in Okinawa (26° 30′ N) near the full moons of May and June; in Guam (14° N) a week to 10 days after July's full moon; and in Palau (7° 15′ N) in March, April, and May.

Not all corals are spawners. About 15 percent are brooders, and after the internal fertilization of eggs, embryos develop in the mother polyp, which then releases fully formed larvae called planulae. Brooders, too, follow the lunar cycle.

Whether developed internally or externally, coral larvae swim toward the light and join the plankton in the surface waters. They can settle in one to three days, but may float for as long as a month. Currents can carry them many hundreds of miles away from their home reef. If and when they arrive at suitable hard substrates, they settle and undergo a metamorphosis that turns them into polyps. The presence of coralline algae seems to be a necessary condition for settling. Such long-distance dispersal of larvae is essential in recruiting new individuals to degraded reefs or in establishing entirely new populations.

Coral polyps acquire food in a number of ways. As cnidarians, they possess stinging cells (nematocysts) on their tentacles, which they use to catch large zooplankters. They also filter organic detritus out of the water. Corals produce large volumes of sticky mucus, strands of which drape across the colonies and trap viruses, bacteria, and other plankton as well as particles. Hairs (cilia) on the tentacles move captured material either directly to the mouth or to the tips of the tentacles where it is evaluated. If deemed edible, the tentacle delivers the particle to the mouth; if not, it is cast into the water. Other benefits to the coral may accrue from the mucus. It provides a waterproof coating to prevent desiccation should the polyp be exposed to dry air during low tide. The mucus regularly dries up and is shed, letting corals cleanse themselves of wastes and other debris. It also serves as a nursery for brooders' newly released planulae. Recent studies suggest that some of the bacteria attracted to the nutrient-rich slime may produce antibiotics that defend against disease-causing bacteria and fungi.

Beyond these somewhat standard means of feeding, corals also have internal food factories, the zooxanthellae, symbiotic algae that dwell in their gut. Dinoflagellates, mostly of the genus *Symbiodinium*, these algae photosynthesize by using CO_2 and nutrients from both the wastes of the polyp and direct uptake from seawater. The coral polyp receives any sugars and other organic compounds that are produced and that the algae do not need themselves for survival and growth. These algae give corals their color and are also the reason corals need to grow in shallow well-lit water. When severely stressed, corals eject the zooxanthellae and the reef

Coral Fights

Coral colonies compete with each other for space on the reef. Branching forms tend to grow faster than others and will overtop them. This reduces the light available to the underlying corals and slows their growth to such a degree that they die out. Other corals more aggressively attack neighboring colonies of other species. Some extend thread-like parts of their gut out of their mouths and other pores and into the enemy polyps, whereupon they proceed to digest them. An apparent hierarchy exists determining which species eat which others. Yet another form of coral warfare involves those species that can transform some of their tentacles into long "sweepers" that brush over the enemy polyps and kill them. The dead coral skeletons left behind by either attack method become a temporary demilitarized zone colonized by coralline algae.

becomes white, a phenomenon known as coral bleaching. Studies show that polyps do not necessarily depend on the algae for food, but that photosynthesis is critical to the deposition of the coral's carbonate skeleton. The zooxanthellae, in turn, can live outside the polyp as free-living members of the phytoplankton. Indeed, planulae derived from external fertilization acquire their zooxanthellae from the sea after they settle. Larvae produced by brooders receive the algae directly from the parent polyp.

The Reef Community

A paradox arises. Highly productive, species-rich coral reefs occur amid low-nutrient tropical waters sometimes described as the deserts of the sea. Tight nutrient cycling, a nearly closed ecosystem in which what is produced on the reef stays on the reef, is part of the answer to the riddle. Complex food webs use and reuse matter in a web of species interactions beginning with the producers, algae.

Algae. Macroalgae have key roles in a reef community. Red and green coralline algae are important reef-builders as well as primary producers on the reef. They concentrate calcium carbonate and magnesium carbonate to form internal supporting structures coated with a thin layer of plant tissue. Red corallines include encrusting forms that impart a pinkish or purplish hue to the reef. More upright, knobby forms are also common. The green corallines are mostly members of the genus *Halimeda* and have hard jointed plates segmented like the pads of a prickly pear cactus. Since some species have holdfasts that attach to sandy substrates and others to rocky substrates, the genus is widespread. *Halimeda* skeletal remains are a major source of calcareous sediments in the reef habitat, rivaling or surpassing that derived from corals.

Noncoralline algae form turfs. Filamentous forms grow everywhere and are grazed by invertebrates and fish. They may be the most important primary producers in food chains that lead to human consumers. Large seaweeds such as *Sargassum*, a brown kelp-like alga, are indicators of degraded reefs. They invade when reefs have been physically destroyed or polluted with too many nutrients.

The phytoplankton appears to contribute little to the overall primary production of a reef. The smallest types—picoplankters and nanoplankters—are dominant. Larger cells such as diatoms are generally in low numbers in all tropical waters. The zooxanthellae living in coral polyps and some other invertebrates are the most important dinoflagellates in the system.

Phytoplankters fuel detritus food chains. They leak DOM and produce the POM that is consumed by filter-feeding and suspension-feeding animals, including some corals. Direct consumption of living cells by the zooplankton as well as benthic invertebrates does occur, however. One way or another, most of the products of photosynthesis stay in the reef ecosystem.

Animals. Fishes are the most important consumers on a reef and have major influences on the structure of the reef ecosystem. However, a nearly unimaginable number of other animals also live there. Many are unique to a particular reef system or biogeographic region. No attempt is made here to describe any single fauna in detail. Instead a general picture must suffice to hint at the overwhelming complexity of animal communities and relationships found on coral reefs around the world.

The zooplankton consists largely of crustaceans such as cumaceans, mysids, ostracods, shrimps, isopods, amphipods, and copepods. Polychaetes and formaniferans are also plentiful. While some feed on living algal cells, most are primarily detritivores. They hide by day in nooks and crannies in the reefs and emerge at night to feed.

The benthos teems with larger invertebrates. In addition to stony corals are a number of other sessile cnidarians, including horny corals (order Gorgonacea), soft corals (order Alcyonacea), zoanthids (order Zoanthidea), thorny or black corals (order Antipatharia), sea anemones (order Actinaria), and carallimorphs (order Callimorpharia). Sponges, bryozoans, and ascidians are still other attached reef animals. Hard corals tend to dominate the upper parts of the reef front. A transition zone of hard and soft corals then occurs and sponges, sea whips, and gorgonians finally replace stony corals at depths of 100–230 ft (30–70 m), depending on water clarity and how far the sun's rays penetrate. Sessile invertebrates may be detritus-feeders, suspension-feeders, or carnivores. An equally diverse list of motile invertebrates forage on the coral surface, including polychaetes, gastropods (for example, cowries and limpets), crustaceans (amphipods, isopods, tanarids, and majid crabs), and echinoderms (sea urchins, sea stars, brittlestars, crinoids, and holothurians) (see Plate VI). Limpets (*Acmaea* and *Fissurela*) graze on algae and are usually the most common molluscs on reefs.

Two echinoids—in the Atlantic, the long-spined sea urchin, and in the Indo-Pacific, the crown-of-thorns starfish—have major but contrasting impacts on coral reefs. The sea urchins are grazers that emerge from crevices in the reef at night to forage on algal turfs. Constant cropping of the turf creates an open, low vegetation dominated by filamentous algae with space for coral planulae to settle. The result is a healthy and diverse coral and algae community that supports innumerable invertebrates and fishes. In 1983, disease spread throughout the Caribbean and killed the urchins. The die-off revealed their importance on the reef when algal biomass dramatically increased and coral reefs became algal reefs dominated by thick turfs and leathery, brown algae. Net primary productivity declined as did the survival of coral recruits. Resident coral colonies became overgrown with algae and died as macroalgae took over. Almost no recovery of coral or sea urchin populations has occurred since.

In the Indo-Pacific too many rather than too few echinoids is the problem. The crown-of-thorns feeds on corals, especially branching species. It everts its stomach, secretes digestive enzymes into the polyp, and within four to six hours absorbs the organic material so produced. Since at least the mid-1950s, there have been a series of irruptions in which population explosions of crown-of-thorn spread across the Indo-Pacific from the Ryukyu Islands through the South Pacific to Panama and parts of the Great Barrier Reef. Anywhere from 50 to 100 percent of corals died as reefs were consumed at a rate of 2.3 mi^2 (6 km^2) a year. Some massive corals (*Porites* spp.) survived. Again community change followed as crustose and filamentous algae came to dominance. Herbivorous fishes increased abundance, and sometimes soft corals and sponges replaced reef-building corals.

Recovery occurs in stages as dispersing planulae arrive and find suitable areas for settlement on encrusting coralline algae. It takes 10–15 years for coral to regain its pre-irruption cover on a reef, but much longer for the original diversity to build back. For a long time, affected reefs have communities dominated by massive corals and a patchwork of recovery stages.

Schools of brightly colored, strongly patterned fish swim about coral reefs in a dizzying display of biodiversity (see Plate VII). At least 4,000 species from 100 families are known. A thousand or more different kinds may occur on a single reef. The hordes make species and gender recognition a challenge, and distinctive colors and patterns help out. Unlike the corals with their high degree of endemism, all families, most genera, and many fish species are widespread, found in all tropical regions. A large proportion are strictly reef-dwellers, including damselfishes, parrotfishes, wrasses, surgeonfishes (or tang), rabbitfishes, Moorish idols, butterflyfishes, and angelfishes. Less confined to the reef habitat but nonetheless abundant are blennies, gobies, grunts, and cardinalfishes. Strange-looking puffers, boxfishes, and triggerfishes are less numerous but highly visible components of the community. Among larger predatory fishes that hunt fishes smaller than themselves as well as invertebrates are squirrelfish, groupers, snappers, and emperors.

With so many kinds of fish in the reef community, only a generalized description of some of the more important types can be presented here. Reef fish organize into feeding guilds, and convergent evolution among unrelated species results in fishes that utilize the same food resources having similar morphological and behavioral adaptations. When larvae or juveniles, most fishes feed on the plankton, and as adults, a large part of the fish community still concentrates on zooplankters as their main food source. Most feed during daylight hours. Small plankton-eating fish hunt by sight and capture the small (less than 0.12 in or 3 mm), usually transparent, copepods that are high in the water column during the day. The mouth of small planktivores such as damselfishes and butterflyfishes is typically upturned and the usually toothless jaws protrude, giving the head a shape that lets the eyes focus forward. A fish slowly sneaks up on its wary prey, hovers nearby, and suddenly extends its mouth to snatch the morsel. The fish themselves are vulnerable to large sight-hunting predators, so must be alert and able to escape quickly into the safety of the coral substrate. They have streamlined bodies and forked caudal fins (tails) for fast swimming and move in schools that quickly implode and flash away into the reef at any sign of danger.

Diurnal plankton-feeders are most numerous along the reef front and in strong currents where zooplankton is brought in from the sea and hence is most plentiful. Some are full-time residents of the reef front; others take shelter in other parts of the reef at night. Regardless, half an hour before sunset, the daytime planktivores leave the water column and retreat into solitary shelters in the reef, the smallest being the first to disappear. For 15–20 minutes a "quiet period" pervades the reef, and few fish are seen. Then about 30 minutes after sunset, the nighttime plankton-feeders ascend from their hiding places, again the smallest coming out first.

Nocturnal feeders such as squirrelfishes—with the disturbing habit of swimming upside down—mouth-brooding cardinalfishes, and bigeyes find greater numbers of zooplankters in the water above the reef and larger ones than the diurnal fish had available to them. In addition, so-called semipelagics, small benthic organisms that rise into the water column at night, abound. Polychaetes, ostracods, copepods, mysids, isopods, amphipods, and the larvae of crustaceans become a rich food source all over the reef. Nocturnal planktivores hunt by sight and have large eyes, as well as the large, sharply upturned mouths of diurnal planktivores, but with small teeth. Many are red, a color that appears black in dark waters, rendering them nearly invisible, at least on moonless nights. They are not as vulnerable to predators as their daytime counterparts and tend not to be as streamlined in body form as diurnally active fish, nor have as deeply forked caudal fins. They also tend not to school, but feed all over the reef in a more dispersed fashion. During the day, however, when they rest close to the reef among large corals or in crevices and caves, they are gregarious.

Clownfishes and Anemones

An unusual alliance has developed among certain damselfishes—the clownfishes or anemonefishes of *Finding Nemo* fame—and sea anemones. The small, brightly colored fishes dart among the nematocyst-armed tentacles of the anemone for protection from predators. The fish is covered with mucus containing a chemical that stops the anemone from firing its stinging cells when contact is made with the fish. Whether the fish obtains the chemical from the anemone or is stimulated to produce it itself by close contact with its host is unknown. The relationship benefits the anemone because the bold little fish aggressively chases off butterflyfishes and any others that might nip off an anemone tentacle. The fish also clears away debris and possibly parasites. Twenty-eight species of clownfish and 10 species of anemones in the Indo-Pacific have evolved such a mutualistic relationship.

Herbivorous fish that consume the algal turf, such as surgeonfishes and rabbitfishes, can play keystone roles on coral reefs, making space for coral colonies to grow and planulae to settle. Those that scrape coralline algae from the reef, such as the parrotfishes, may be more damaging and create a lot of the coral sand found on reefs. Herbivores typically have laterally compressed bodies with a small-gaped mouth at the end of a distinct snout. The pectoral fins are strong as they are needed to maintain the fish's position and precise orientation while it feeds. Their teeth are fused or closely spaced, and they eat by rapidly and continuously nibbling as they slowly swim along the reef. They are nonselective feeders and consume invertebrates and detritus along with algal material. The teeth are used for acquiring food, not for chewing or crunching it. Plates in the pharynx grind ingested shelled invertebrates or coralline algae. Among the detritus is the nitrogen-rich fecal matter from planktivores. Feces may be an important source of nitrogen for herbivores in this rather nutrient-poor water, and their consumption of it concentrates nitrogen in the reef ecosystem. All grazers are diurnal and fend off predators with weaponry. Rabbitfishes have venomous fin spines; surgeonfishes have blade-like plates at the base of their tails, from which they derive their name. Another part-time grazer of algae and seaagrasses, the puffers, when faced with predators, quickly blow themselves up like balloons by swallowing seawater. They also produce lethal toxins that become concentrated in their livers.

The relation between grazing fish and algae is evident in the distribution of both on the reef. Fish are few in areas where wave action is strong, so algal biomass is greatest in the shallow surf zone. At depths of 6–35 ft (2–10 m), the crevices and holes in the coral provide shelter, so fish numbers are high and algal biomass low. Below 35 ft (10 m), the structure of the reef offers fewer places of refuge for fish, so their numbers once again decline. Algae are not entirely defenseless against the grazing. Many produce toxic or merely unpalatable compounds to ward off predators.

Among the resident carnivores on the reef, relatively few fish feed on live coral polyps. The main predators come from three families—butterflyfish, triggerfishes, and puffers, but some filefish are also coral specialists. The main carnivore guilds are small-mouthed diurnal fish such as the thick-lipped wrasses and demersal gobies that pick out small sessile invertebrates, and medium-size nocturnal or crepuscular hunters that ambush larger and more mobile prey. Some of the latter hide in the coral rubble and sands of the reef bed and ambush invertebrates and small fishes passing above them. Well-camouflaged scorpionfishes, flatheads or crocodile fish, and various flatfishes hunt in this manner.

The abundance of small and medium-size resident fish supports larger piscivorous fish such as groupers. These are heavy-bodied fishes with large mouths and jutting lower jaws with small teeth that ambush their prey. They tend to hide in dark recesses in the reef, camouflaged by dark mottled or blotchy coloration patterns, though some are rather stunning: the coral grouper, for example, is crimson with neon blue dots. Snappers are common predators on some reefs. They have sharp, conical, somewhat recurved teeth with which to hang on to the crustaceans and small fish they catch.

The rich food supply concentrated on reefs in a somewhat sterile ocean attracts jacks, barracudas, and cartilaginous fish such as sharks and rays from the open sea. These predators prowl the outer reef not only to find prey but also to take advantage of the rather strange symbiotic relationship some larger marine animals have with cleaner fishes. The latter are usually small wrasses (especially *Labroides* spp.) less than 4 in (10 cm) long, gobies, or butterflyfishes. They set up territories or cleaning stations to which large fish come each day by the thousands. The cleaners advertise they are open for business and not to be eaten with bright stripes and jerky "dancing." They remove parasites from the scales, gills, and mouths of their clients and in turn are assured of a constant food supply. The bright red-and-white banded coral shrimp provides similar services.

Extremely important to reef dynamics is a group of organisms known as bioeroders. These animals either weaken the reef superstructure by boring into it or gnaw away at the corals and coralline algae at the surface, reducing the skeletons to small particles. Internal bioeroders include microborers such as bacteria, algae, and fungi, as well as macroinvertebrates such as boring sponges, polychaetes, peanut worms, barnacles (*Lithotyria*), and bivalves. Boring sponges can be responsible for 30–40 percent of the fine sediments on a reef. They have special cells that secrete enzymes to break down coral into loose chips. Bivalves such as *Lithophaga* spp. burrow about 2.5 in (10 cm) into the limestone reef by secreting an acid and using their shells to scrape off softened rock. There may be as many as 10,000 molluscs with burrows per square meter. External bioeroders include chitons, urchins, limpets, hermit crabs, pufferfish, and parrotfish. The weakened reef becomes vulnerable to erosion by wave action and collapse. All coral reefs undergo constant change and renewal as old parts break off and living parts enlarge. In a healthy reef, growth stays ahead of erosion. Storms and other disasters, however, may tip the balance in favor of erosion and destroy a reef. In these cases, recruitment of larvae from afar is necessary if the reef is to recover.

Coral reefs are delicate ecosystems vulnerable to a multitude of threats. Ongoing global climate changes are paramount. Corals are sensitive to changes in temperature, light, and water quality. A small rise in temperature during El Niño events can cause coral bleaching, especially among branching forms growing in shallow areas. Warming temperatures also may cause sea levels to rise too rapidly for reef accretion to keep pace. Increased rainfall in the tropics, predicted to accompany rising temperatures, means increased runoff and more sediments and nutrients washing onto fringing and barrier reefs. Increased nutrients stimulate the production of phytoplankters, which, when they bloom, block sunlight from attached algae and zooxanthellae and, when they die and decay, reduce the amount of dissolved oxygen in the water.

More immediate threats come from human abuses. Many fishermen use destructive practices to harvest seafood from the reef, including dynamiting and poisoning and dragging heavy trawls over the reef bed. The growing tourism industry, especially if unregulated or poorly managed, means more people, more boats, more pollution, and more physical damage. The growing popularity of saltwater aquariums among hobbyists poses the real threat of overcollection of the smaller, spectacularly colored reef fishes so valuable in the aquarium trade. At the same time, the jewelry industry is depleting corals to meet a growing demand for necklaces and earrings made of the stony red material.

Further Readings

Books

Lippson, Alice Jane, and Robert L. Lippson. 1984. *Life in Chesapeake Bay*. Baltimore: The Johns Hopkins University Press. Excellent drawings and discussion of life in the seagrass meadows and shallow waters of Atlantic embayments from North Carolina north to Canada.

Pitkin, Linda. 2001. *Coral Fish*. Washington, DC: Smithsonian Institution Press. Pictures and descriptions of major types of fishes represented on coral reefs.

Videos

BBC. 2002. "Coral Seas." Programme 6, *Blue Planet, Seas of Life*. Available on DVD.

Thirteen/Online. 2007. "Sharkland." Thirteen/WNET New York and Educational Broadcasting Corporation. http://www.pbs.org/wnet/nature/sharkland/index.html.

Appendix

Biota of the Continental Shelf

Seagrass Meadows

Primary producers	
Eelgrasses	*Zostera* spp.
Wigeongrasses	*Ruppia* spp.
Turtlegrasses	*Thalassia* spp.
Tapeweeds	*Posidonia* spp.
Herbivores	
Green sea urchin	*Lytechnis variegatus*
Green sea turtle	*Chelonia mydas*
American Wigeon	*Anas americanus*
Brant	*Branta bernicla*
Dugong	*Dugong dugon*
Detritivores	
Mullets	*Mugil* spp.

Banks

Grand Banks

Fish	
Atlantic herring	*Clupea harengus*
Atlantic cod	*Gadus morhua*
Haddock	*Melanogrammus aeglefinus*
Atlantic halibut	*Hippoglossus hippoglossus*
American plaice	*Hippoglossoides platessoides*
Ocean perch	*Sebastes marinus*
Turbot	*Scophthalmus maximus*
Greenland halibut	*Reinhardtius hippoglossoides*

(*Continued*)

Yellowtail flounder	*Limanda ferruginea*
Witch flounder (grey sole)	*Glyptocephalus cyno*
Whales	
Beluga whale	*Delphinapterus leucas*
Northern right whale	*Eublaena glacialis*
Fin whale	*Balaenoptera physalis*
Humpback whale	*Megaptera novaengliae*
Seal	
Grey seal	*Halichoerus grypus*

Dogger Bank

Benthic detritivores	
Heart urchin	*Echinocardium cordatum*
Bivalve	*Fabulina fibula*
Sand masons	*Lanice conchilega* and *Owenia fusiformis*
Banded wedge shell	*Donax vittatus*
Clams	*Nucula tenuis, Nucula nitida,* and *Thyasira flexuosa*
Fishes	
Atlantic mackerel	*Scomber scombrus*
Herring	*Clupea spp.*
Atlantic cod	*Gadus morhua*
Whiting	*Merlangius merlangus*
Plaice	*Pleuronectes platessa*
Sole	*Solea solea*
Sand eel	*Ammodytes marinus*
Sprat	*Sprattus sprattus*
Fish-eaters	
Northern Gannets	*Morus bassanus*
Northern Fulmars	*Flumarus glacialis*
Black-legged Kittiwake	*Risa tridactyla*
White-beaked dolphin	*Lagenorhynchus albirostris*
White-sided dolphin	*Lagenorhynchus acutus*
Harbor porpoise	*Phocoena phocoena*

Agulhas Bank

Commercially important species	
Rock lobster	*Jasus lalandi*
Pilchard	*Sardinops sagax*
Cape anchovy	*Engraulis capensis*
Hake	*Merluccinus capensis*
Sole	*Austroglossus pectoralis*

Sharks	
Great white shark	*Carcharadon carcharias*
Whale shark	*Rhincodon typus*
Tiger shark	*Galeocerdo cuvieri*
Short fin makos	*Isurus oxyrinchus*
Whales	
Southern right whale	*Balaenoptera australis*
Bryde's whale	*Baleonoptera edeni*
Humpback	*Megaptera novaeangliae*

Upwelling Ecosystems

Humboldt Current System

Main fish	
Anchovy	*Engraulis ringens*
Fish-eaters	
Guanay Cormorant	*Phalacrocorax bouganvillii*
Peruvian Booby	*Sula variegata*
Peruvian Pelican	*Pelecanus thagus*
Humboldt Penguin	*Spheniscus humboldti*
Peruvian Diving Petrel	*Pelecanoides garnotti*
Southern sea lion	*Otaria byroni*
South American fur seal	*Arctocephalus australis*

Benguela Current System

Main fishes	
Sardines	*Sardinops sagax*
Anchovy	*Engraulis enrasiclus*

Somali-Arabian Sea System

Main fishes	
Oil sardine	*Sardinella longiceps*
Mackerel	*Scomber japonica*
Horse mackerel	*Trachurus indicus*
Scads	*Decapterus* spp.
Jacks	*Caranax* spp.
Anchovies	*Stolephorus* spp.
Porcupine fish	*Diodon* spp.
Splitfins	*Synagrops* spp.
Driftfish	*Cubiceps* spp.

Kelp Forests: Northern Hemisphere

Northwest Atlantic

Primary producers	
Horsetail kelp	*Laminaria digitata*
Sugar kelp	*Laminaria saccharina*
Sea colander	*Agarum cribosum*
Irish moss	*Chondrus crispa*
Red fern	*Ptilota serrata*
Crustose red algae	*Lithothamnion* spp., *Clathromorphum* spp., and *Phymotolithon* spp.
Herbivores	
Limpets	*Tectura* spp
Periwinkles	*Littorina* spp.
Snail	*Lacuna vincta*
Sea urchin	*Stongylocentrus droebachiensis*
Isopods	*Idotea* spp.
Carnivores	
Jonah crab	*Cancer borealis*
Sea stars	*Asteria* spp.
Winter flounder	*Pseudopleuronectes americanus*
Haddock	*Melanogrammus aeglefinus*
Eelpout	*Macrozoarcus americanus*
Wrasse	*Tautogolabrus adsperus*
Red-breasted Merganser	*Mergus serrator*
Common Goldeneye	*Bucephala clangula*
Old Squaw	*Clangula hyemalis*

Northeast Atlantic

Primary producers	
Horsetail kelp	*Laminaria digitata*
Sugar kelp	*Laminaria saccharum*
Cuvie or Tangle	*Laminaria hyperborea*
Herbivores	
Edible sea urchin	*Echinus esculentus*

Northeast Pacific

Primary producers	
Giant kelp	*Macrocystis pyrifera*
Kelps	*Pterogophora californica*, *Laminaria* spp.
Herbivores	
Purple sea urchin	*Strongylocentrus purpuratus*
Red sea urchin	*Strongylocentrus franciscanus*
Abalones	*Haliotus* spp.

Carnivores	
Kellet's whelk	*Kelletia kelletii*
Knobby sea star	*Pisaster giganteus*
Spiny lobster	*Panulirus interruptus*
Sea cucumber	*Parastichopus* spp.
Octopuses	*Octopus* spp.
Sea otter	*Enhydra lutris*
Stellar's sea cow[a]	*Hydrodamalis gigas*

Note: [a]Extinct.

Kelp Forests: Southern Hemisphere

Southeast Atlantic

Primary producers	
Bamboo kelp	*Ecklonia maxima*
Split-fan kelp	*Laminaria pallida*
Herbivores	
Abalone	*Haliota midea*
Sea urchin	*Parechinus angulosus*
Snails	*Turbo* spp.
Hottentot	*Pachymetopon blochii*
Strepie	*Sarpa salpa*
Carnivores	
Rock lobster	*Jasus lalandii*
Dogfish sharks	Family Squalidae
Cape fur seal	*Arctocephalus pusillus*
Bank Cormorant	*Phalacrocorax capensis*
Cape Gannet	*Morus capensis*
African Penguin	*Spheniscus demersus*
Detritivores	
Isopod	*Ligia dilatata*
Sponge	*Polymastia mamillaris*
Sponge	*Tethya* spp.
Tunicate	*Pyura stonolifera*
Sea cucumber	*Pentacta doliolum*
Sea cucumber	*Thyone aurea*
Barnacle	*Notomegabalanus algicola*

Southeast Pacific: Northern and Central Coasts of Chile

Primary producers	
Kelp	*Durvillaea antarctica*
Kelp-like brown alga	*Lessonia nigrescens*
Red alga	*Mesophyllum* spp.

(*Continued*)

Herbivores	
Black sea urchin	*Tetrapygus niger*
Chiton	*Acanthopleura echinata*
Black snail	*Tegula atra*
Carnivores	
Cormorants	*Phalacrocorax gaimardi* and *Phalacrocorax bouganvillii*
Pelicans	*Pelecanus occidentalis* and *Pelecanus thagus*
Humboldt Penguin	*Spheniscus humboldti*
Marine otter	*Lontra feline*
Southern sea lion	*Otaria byroni*

Southeast Pacific: Southern Coast of Chile

Primary producers	
Giant kelp	*Macrocystis pyrifera*
Kelp-like brown alga	*Lessonia flavicans*
Fleshy red alga	*Epymenia falklandica*
Foliose red alga	*Gigartina skottsbergii*
Carnivores	
Magellanic Penguin	*Spheniscus magellanicus*
Marine otter	*Lontra feline*
Southern sea lion	*Otaria byroni*

Coral Reefs

(See the appendix to Chapter 4 for an outline of coral taxonomy.)

Some major teleost (bony) fish families associated with coral reefs

Damselfishes	Pomacentridae
Parrotfishes	Scaridae
Surgeonfishes	Acanthuridae
Rabbitfish	Siganidae
Moorish idols	Zanclidae
Wrasses	Labridae
Butterflyfishes	Chaetidontidae
Angelfishes	Pomacanthidae
Grunts	Haemulideae
Cardinalfishes	Apogonidae
Blennies	Blennidae
Gobies	Gobidae
Boxfish	Ostraciidae
Puffers	Tetraodontidae
Triggerfish	Balistidae
Filefish	Monacanthidae

Squirrelfish	Holocentridae
Rock cods and groupers	Serranidae
Snappers	Lutjanidae
Emperors	Lethrinidae
Bigeyes	Priacanthidae
Jacks	Carangidae

4

Deep Sea Biome

Deep sea refers to those regions of the ocean and seafloor beyond the edge of the continental slope (see Figure 4.1). This vast area covers 65 percent of Earth's surface. Water depth ranges from −650 ft (−200 m) to the extreme of −36,198 ft (−11,033 m) at the bottom of the Mariana Trench. Average depth is −12,470 ft (−11,033 m); however, 60 percent of the ocean is deeper than this. Much of the sea bottom consists of a flat abyssal plain approximately 3.5 mi (6 km) below sea level and generally covered by muds and oozes. The monotony of the plain is interrupted by mid-oceanic ridges and seamounts, both of which offer hard surfaces for sessile invertebrates, and oceanic trenches—all three features of tectonic origin. The abyssal plain gives way near landmasses to the continental rise, lifting up to about 1.25 miles (2 km) and then the steeply inclined continental slope, which extends to the edge of the continental shelf.

The deep sea is the least-known part of our planet. Only in recent decades, with technologically advanced means of sampling the conditions and life at great depths, has mere exploration been replaced by scientific study. Since the 1950s, ideas about life in the deep sea have turned previous beliefs upside down. Use of submersibles and ROVs (remote-operated vehicles) has revealed, among other things, a surprisingly high diversity of species, seasonal pulses of food inputs from the euphotic zone, primary production via chemosynthesis at hydrothermal vents and cold seeps, and periodic disturbances in what had been thought to be an unchanging habitat. What follows is a general overview of what has been learned to date. Some estimates say that less than 0.1 percent of the biome has been

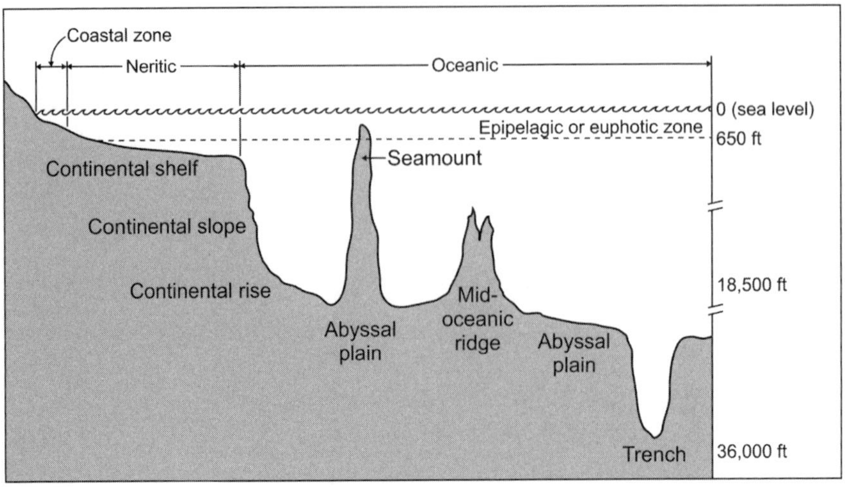

Figure 4.1 Regions of the ocean floor. *(Illustration by Jeff Dixon.)*

Exploration of the Deep: HOVs, ROVs, and AUVs

Exploration of the deep sea awaited technological advances that allowed descent to depths far greater than the 60 feet (18 m) possible in helmeted diving suits. Otis Barton's 1930s bathysphere, a hollow steel ball with windows that was attached to a ship by cable, was a major breakthrough. In it, he and William Beebe reached a depth of −3,000 ft (−914 m). Auguste Piccard reworked the design and developed a self-propelled bathyscape suspended beneath a float. In December 1960, his son Jacques Piccard and U.S. Navy Lt. Donald Walsh descended in a later model, the *Trieste*, to −35,810 ft (−10,916.5 m) and rested on the bottom of Challenger Deep in the Mariana Trench. To this day, they are the only people to have visited the deepest part of the ocean.

After World War II, the U.S. Navy became interested in mapping the seafloor and in 1964 contracted for the first submersible—essentially a three-person mini-submarine—the *Alvin* to be operated by the Woods Hole Oceanographic Institution. Ever since, the *Alvin* has played a key role in deep sea research. In 1977, John Corliss and Robert Ballard were aboard the *Alvin* over the Galapagos Rift where they discovered "black smokers" and giant tubeworms. Perhaps more famously, the *Alvin* carried Ballard to view the *RMS Titanic* at the bottom of the Atlantic Ocean in 1986. The aging *Alvin* will soon be replaced by a new human-operated vessel (HOV) able to reach depths of −21,000 ft (−6,500 m) compared with *Alvin*'s −14,700 ft (−4,500 m).

A number of other deep sea vehicles aid modern exploration of the seas. Among them are unmanned undersea robots, ROVs (remotely operated vehicles) tethered to and powered by a research vessel, and AUVs (autonomous underwater vehicles), small untethered vehicles. Japan's ROV, the *Kaiko*, has reached the floor of the Mariana Trench. The Monterey Bay Aquarium Research Institute's Dorado class AUVs can descend to −19,000 ft (−6,000 m).

sampled, so knowledge is always improving as scientists continue to peer into this vast frontier, the largest biome on Earth.

Physical Environment

In many ways, the physical conditions of the deep sea are more stable and uniform than those of other marine biomes. Nonetheless, this is an extreme environment and life has adapted in sometimes bizarre ways. Salinity is 35 with only a few exceptions, such as in the Mediterranean and Red Seas where it reaches 39, and in the hypersaline basins in the Gulf of Mexico where it is about 300. Pressure increases 1 atmosphere for every increase in water depth of 35 ft (10 m). Biochemical processes run at slower rates under high pressure, necessitating the molecular evolution of pressure-insensitive enzymes among dwellers of the deep. Temperatures remain at about 28° F (−2° C) on the abyssal plain and hardly vary at all below −2,500 ft (−800 m). Cold, too, slows chemical reactions and also requires molecular changes in enzymes. Pressure and temperature impacts are probably major factors limiting the colonization of the deep sea by shallow-water species.

Oxygen dissolved in water has two sources: direct exchange with the atmosphere and as a product of photosynthesis by phytoplankters occurring in the surface layer of the sea. Most water in the euphotic zone high above the deep seafloor is fully saturated. This water descends to the seafloor in the great global conveyer belt of vertical oceanic circulation (see Chapter 1, Figure 1.12). A mid-water layer of low oxygen content occurs at 1,000–3,500 ft (300–1,000 m) as a result of biological processes. Oxygen is consumed by zooplankters feeding on sinking algal cells and by bacterial decay of dead plankton. Low oxygen areas also occur in basins cut off by topographic barriers from bottom circulation and in oceanic trenches that lie near land and its abundant sources of organic detritus.

Near the bottom ocean, currents usually flow too slowly to erode sediments or dislodge benthic organisms. Tidal forces still exist at these depths, however, and are sufficient to bring in food and take out wastes. Several times a year, the bottom may be disturbed by benthic storms, strong currents that can pile sediments into drifts and smother animals.

Sediments that blanket the deep seafloor come from both land and sea. Rivers and wind carry weathered rock material to the sea. Most material is deposited close to the continent; only the finest muds settle out onto the abyssal plain. Plankters produce many microscopic particles that sink to the seafloor; of particular significance are the shells of plankton. Diatoms, radiolarians, and silicoflagellates contribute a rain of silica shells; foraminiferans, coccolithophores, and pteropods have shells of calcium carbonate that sink to the bottom. When more than 30 percent (by volume) of the sediment is composed of these products of living organisms, it is called a biological ooze. Both silica and calcium carbonate dissolve in seawater as they descend; but below a certain depth, the carbonate dissolves more rapidly.

Thus, the composition of the ooze varies with depth. In shallow water, such as on the Atlantic Mid-oceanic Ridge, a calcareous ooze forms; while in deeper water a silaceous ooze is characteristic. Near land, the biological component of sediments never reaches as high as 30 percent so oozes do not exist there.

Hard substrates are scarce but can be found on exposed basalts at tectonically active sites, namely mid-oceanic ridges. The steep slopes of seamounts can prevent accumulation of fine sediments, so attachment sites for sessile organisms can also be found there. Pebble- to cobble-size manganese nodules (concretions of iron and manganese) lie on the seafloor, especially beneath the central gyres of the Pacific Ocean, and offer hard-substrate habitats for some organisms. Solid surfaces of biological origin, such as the tubes, tests, and shells of invertebrates and the skeletons of whales and large fish, also occur.

Seamounts

Seamounts are steep underwater mountains, by definition rising at least 3,500 ft (1,000 m) above the seafloor, but not reaching sea level (in which case, they would be islands). Since most begin as volcanoes at hot spots or along the converging boundaries of two oceanic plates, most occur in long chains. Some once stood above sea level as volcanic islands, but erosion and the sinking that followed their extinction have lowered them. Seamounts that extend from the northwestern end of the Hawaiian Islands are really the oldest parts of the island chain.

Other volcanoes never got large enough to break through the sea and into the air. Average in height for a seamount, Fieberling Guyot stands 2.5 mi (4 km) above the seafloor and is comparable in size to Mount Rainier.

Seamounts interfere with ocean currents and force an upwelling of cold deep water around their sides. The phenomenon is called a Taylor Column because of its tower-like shape. Taylor Columns are ecologically significant because cold, upwelled water is rich in nutrients and will support abundant sea life in an otherwise sparsely populated region of the ocean. Horizontal currents deflected by the seamount create turbulence that both mixes the upper layers of water and creates a current that rotates above the feature. The circling current may help keep nutrients and larvae in place above the seamount.

An estimated 50,000 seamounts occur in the Pacific Ocean. About 100,000 may occur in all the oceans combined.

Hydrothermal Vents

Heat from Earth's interior is released at tectonically active sites such as divergent plate boundaries or along back-arc spreading ridges at convergent oceanic plate boundaries (see Figure 4.2).

In both instances, rising magma fractures overlying sediments or oceanic crust and seawater works its way down the faults toward the hot, molten material, where it becomes superheated. Minerals dissolve and become concentrated in the water, which if it finds a closed conduit, will become a fast jet of rising water reaching

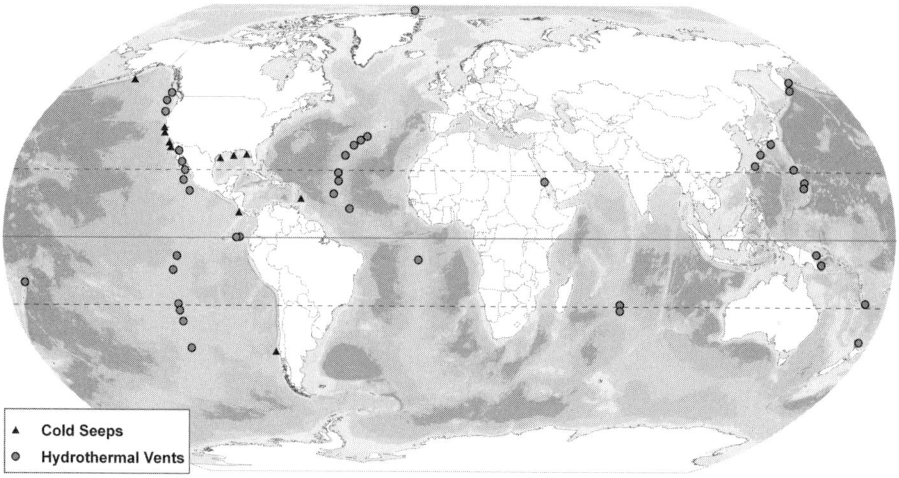

Figure 4.2 Location of known hydrothermal vents and cold seeps. *(Map by Bernd Kuennecke.)*

temperatures near 750° F (400° C). When the superheated water contacts the cold bottom waters of the sea, the dissolved load—mostly sulfur compounds—precipitates out and builds tall towers or chimneys (see Figure 4.3). A "black smoker" forms when a plume of water containing dissolved hydrogen sulfide and other

Figure 4.3 White smokers at Champagne Vent, in the Marianas Arc. *(NOAA/OceanExplorer.)*

dissolved sulfur minerals is released through a chimney or vent formed of precipitates. Often, these plumes rise more than 1,000 ft (300 m) into the water above. Water also seeps through chimney walls and cools enough—to within a range of 35°–210° F (2°–100° C)—for specialized animals to occupy the vent. The hydrogen sulfide yields its energy to chemosynthetic microbes that are the beginning of vent food chains.

Hydrothermal vents may occur in clusters 30–350 ft (10–100 m) across or in large fields over the same body of hot magma. The many vents on the East Pacific Rise are closely spaced with distances between clusters measured in tens of yards or at most a few miles. On the less active Atlantic Mid-oceanic Ridge, vents are much less numerous and more widely separated, often 100 miles or more apart. They are temporary features on the seafloor. Individual conduits become clogged and closed or the whole system moves away from the heat source as the seafloor spreads or a nearby volcanic eruption covers them with lava. Although some fields may remain active for 10,000 years, individual vents probably have much shorter life spans.

Cold Seeps

Methane and/or hydrogen sulfide is slowly emitted through sediments in certain locations along continental margins, on both active and passive plate boundaries. Different sets of conditions set the stage for the development of these cold seeps, slow outflows of oxygen-depleted fluid at temperatures hardly different from those of the surrounding bottom waters. Only 24 have been discovered so far and only half of these have been closely examined. Water penetrates faults formed in compacting sediments overlying subduction zones (on active margins) or salt domes (on passive margins). Any organic carbon that is in the water is oxidized by either biological or geochemical processes to become methane (CH_4). The methane then reacts with sulfates in the seawater to form sulfides. Together, dissolved methane and hydrogen sulfide rise back to the seafloor, where they provide energy for chemosynthetic bacteria. As at hydrothermal vents, bacteria form symbiotic relationships with certain invertebrates and make possible a living community in the total darkness of the deep sea. Cold seep communities have been discovered at depths ranging from nearly −1,000 to almost −20,000 ft (−300 to −6,000 m).

Life of the Deep Sea

Except at hydrothermal vents and cold seeps where microorganisms fixing chemical energy from sulfides and methane are primary producers, the life of the deep sea is animal life (see Plate VIII) ultimately depending on organic detritus sinking from the upper parts of the water column. Benthic communities have high species diversity and vary according to the nature of the substrate and water depth. Pelagic communities appear to be less diverse.

Soft-Sediment Communities

Most phyla, classes, and orders found in shallow water soft-sediment communities are represented in the deep sea, too; but lower taxonomic levels—species, genera, and families—are usually different in the two habitats. Unique inhabitants of the abyssal plain, oceanic trenches, and other soft bottoms deeper than −1,500 ft (−500 m) are xenophyophores, huge single-celled animals related to foraminiferans. The largest known of these benthic deposit-feeders is *Syringammina fragillissima*, which has a diameter of about 8 in (20 cm). Looking something like a bunch of loose lettuce, it is covered in a slime that traps silt, fecal matter, and the shells of dead microorganisms to create a hard, protective test and may be important in benthic community as a bioturbator, resuspending food particles. More "ordinary" members of the community are foraminiferans, nematodes, and certain types of copepods less than 100–500 μm in size and larger polychaetes, bivalves, isopods, amphipods, and tanaid crustaceans. The largest animals include sea anemones, brittlestars, sea stars, sea cucumbers (holothurians), and demersal fishes.

Most animals of the deep benthos are deposit-feeders. On the seafloor, sessile forms and slow, infrequent movers extend some type of structure—for example, a proboscis or palp or tentacle—to collect material. The slow-moving ones must stop to feed. Motile sea cucumbers ingest sediments as they crawl across the surface. Subsurface deposit-feeders eat as they burrow into the sediments. The proportion of sessile forms decreases as depth increases and, at least among polychaetes, so does body size.

Suspension-feeders such as sea anemones, glass sponges, horny corals, sea pens, and stalked barnacles use a variety of methods to gather resuspended or downward drifting particles. Some barnacles and amphipods wave a bristled limb through the water. Brachiopods, tunicates, bryozoans, and some bivalves secrete mucus to trap floating particles and use cilia to transfer them to their mouths. Some formaniferans extend a sticky pseudopod into the water.

Little is known of the predators of the deep, since it has been difficult to observe them or obtain specimens. Some organisms are omnivores, consuming sediments, live prey, and dead organic material. Marine biologists call this feeding guild "croppers." Among them are sea stars, octopuses, and some polychaetes, decapods, and fishes.

Some zonation is apparent in the bathyl zone, where species have narrow depth ranges related to changes in the type of sediment, physiological limitations of the animal, food availability, and probably competition from other species. Less of a pattern exists in the abyssal zone.

Hard-Bottom Communities

Hard substrates are rare in the deep sea. New oceanic crust on mid-oceanic ridges and at hot spots, eroded slopes, manganese nodules, and the skeletons of living and dead animals provide a solid two-dimensional habitat that can host an epifauna. Dominants on these surfaces are relatively large attached or sedentary suspension-feeders such as sponges and corals. They depend on near-bottom currents to bring in food and transport their larvae to fresh sites. Most of the motile inhabitants, such as crustaceans, cephalopods, and fishes, move slowly, but they are capable of bursts of speed when faced with danger or pursuing of prey.

Deep Sea Coral Communities

Only about 10 years ago did the existence of deep sea or cold-water corals become known, and new discoveries are made and new understandings reached every day. Studies using deep sea submersibles and ROVs reveal an abundance of species in all the world's oceans; indeed more kinds of corals live at depths greater than −600 ft (−200 m) than in warm tropical coral reefs. (See the appendix for an outline of coral types.) Deep water corals live on exposed, hard substrates below the euphotic zone. They can be found on the edge of the continental slope, atop salt domes (off Louisiana), in submarine canyons, and on seamounts (see below). Since they live beyond the reach of sunlight, deep sea corals do not have symbiotic zooxanthellae, but instead they depend on food they can filter from the water. Most are non-reef-builders but do build other structures such as mounds, "forests," and "gardens." Only the true or stony corals build reefs; the tuft coral and ivory tree coral are two of the few that do so in the deep sea. Deep water reefs or banks occur from depths of −200 ft (−70 m) to more than −3,500 ft (−1,000 m), where there are strong currents or upwelling. Over centuries the coral structures have trapped sediments and broken pieces of coral to form mounds as much as 150 ft (50 m) high. If these piles of debris remain unconsolidated they are called bioherms; if they become consolidated, they are known as lithoherms.

Tuft coral is a dominant builder and member of deep reefs in the western Atlantic from Nova Scotia to Brazil and into the Gulf of Mexico. It also occurs in the eastern Atlantic and eastern Pacific. From North Carolina to southern Florida, both bioherms and lithoherms develop at depths of 1,200 to −3,000 ft (−370 to −900 m). On their reefs, the fauna consists mainly of sponges (70 known species) and cnidarians (58 kinds of corals and anemones). At least 67 fish inhabitants have been identified, some widespread, others more restricted in distribution. Among those common to all reefs in the region are blackbelly rose fish, morid cod, red bream, roughy, conger eel, and wreckfish. Top carnivores include groupers, snappers, and sharks.

More common than stony corals in the deep sea are hydrocorals (for example, lace corals and fire corals) and ocotocorals (gorgonians, sea fans, soft corals, and stoloniferans), colonies of which may form "forests" or "gardens." Lace coral colonies may be erect or encrusting. The erect *Stylaster cancellatus* can grow 3 ft (1 m) high. Close relatives (congeners) are the main builders of three-dimensional gardens found near the Aleutian Islands, in the California bight, and off both the Atlantic and Gulf coasts of Florida. Black corals, such as the Christmas tree coral, grow to heights of 10 ft (3 m) in deep water on the Pacific and Atlantic continental slopes of North America. Some of the globally occurring gorgonians are also massive. In Alaskan waters, the gorgonian *Primnoa pacificum* may stand more than 20 ft (7 m) tall, and it is not uncommon for primnoids in other parts of the world to attain similar heights. All of these large colonial structures provide attachment sites and shelter for a variety of other animals.

Deep sea corals grow and reproduce very slowly, and colonies may live for centuries. Red-tree coral colonies off Alaska are more than 100 years old. Along the edge of the continental shelf of the southeastern United States, colonies of the white, tree-like tuft coral, the most common cold-water coral, are 700 years old. And gold corals off Florida have been aged at 1,800 years. Slow-growing, slow-reproducing species are also slow to recover from disturbance. Today, bottom-trawlers that drag heavy, weighted nets across the seabed are the greatest threat to deep sea coral communities. The demand of the jewelry industry for the hard precious corals—black corals, red or pink corals, gold corals, and bamboo corals—also depletes coral colonies and destroys the habitat of the animals that live with them.

Seamount Communities

In the nutrient-poor waters of the open sea, seamounts and the cool water above them are highly productive areas that promote the development of distinct communities. The shallowest ones have kelps and encrusting coralline algae growing on hard substrates and phytoplankters in the water. Vertically migrating zooplankters may get trapped in the eddy of the Taylor Column and sometimes attract dense shoals of mysid shrimps, squid, and lantern fish. Orange roughy congregate at seamounts and consume zooplankters, shrimps, and squids. Pelagic predators such as sharks, rays, tuna, and swordfish come in from the open sea to feed on the smaller carnivores. The Japanese eel spawns over seamounts.

Suspension-feeding stony corals, horny corals, black corals, sea anemones, sea pens, hydroids, sponges, tunicates, and crinoids dominate on deeper seamounts. Attached or sedentary, they depend on a strong flow of water to carry particles to them, remove their wastes, and disperse their eggs and larvae. Motile organisms are also part of the epifauna. Among them are polychaete worms, sea stars, sea urchins, sea cucumbers, molluscs, crabs, and lobsters.

Perhaps the most fascinating habitats on seamounts are deep sea coral forests and gardens constructed by cold-water corals (see above). Colonies develop on rocky outcrops where swift currents remove sediments and bring in food particles. On steep, pointed seamounts, the most suitable areas are on the summit; on guyots (flat-topped seamounts), corals grow at the edge of the flat top, where currents are strongest. Corals provide places where other suspension feeders can climb above the seafloor into the water flow and where small crustaceans can hide from predators. Thus a rich community of invertebrates and predatory vertebrates develops.

On the New England Seamount Chain that extends into the western Atlantic off Cape Cod, Massachusetts, seamount summits are about 5,000 ft (1,500 m) below the sea's surface. Marine biologists using the submersible *Alvin* have identified 24 coral species living between the depths of −7,000 ft (−2,200 m) and −3,600 ft (−1,110 m). Among them are the widely occurring bubblegum corals, 7 ft (2 m) tall whip corals, and bioluminescent bamboo corals that give off blue-green light when disturbed.

About 75 mi (120 km) southwest of Monterey, California, the Davidson Seamount rises from its base near −12,000 ft (−3,650 m) below sea level to within 4,000 ft (1,250 m) of the sea surface. The seamount is deeply ridged and coral forests cover the ridges. Mounds of bubblegum coral 7 ft (2 m) high and 7 ft (2m) wide grow with soft mushroom corals, black corals, and pink corals. Living amid these corals are small blue polycheates, basket stars, octopuses, and fishes.

Seamounts in the Gulf of Alaska support red-tree corals, bubblegum corals, bamboo corals, and black corals. Certain galatheid crabs and brittlestars are only known from these seamounts, but more widespread brittlestars and shrimps also inhabit the coral forests.

Seamounts in the great chain that extends across the Pacific from the Emperor Seamounts at the western end of Aleutian Trench along the Hawaiian Ridge to a point southwest of the big island of Hawaii are known for their precious corals. The existence of coral forests was discovered by chance when biologists tracked the endangered Hawaiian monk seal, the last surviving species in a primitive group of pinnipeds, to its deep water feeding grounds. Apparently, the seals are attracted to the abundance of fish resident on the coral beds.

The fauna of seamounts is distinct from the animal life of the surrounding deep sea. More strictly seamount species live near the summit than at the base, where animals more typical of the deep seabed become dominant. Many seamount species have limited geographic distribution and may be confined to a single chain or even individual peak. The distance between seamounts and the retention of larvae above them by the Taylor Column may prevent dispersal and promote local speciation.

Bottom-trawling for lobsters and fish has had disastrous impacts on seamounts, negatively affecting the populations of the target catch as well as of by-catch corals, crustaceans, sharks, and other fishes. Deep sea fish grow slowly and are long-lived. An orange roughy, for example, might live 100 years. Such animals reproduce slowly and cannot withstand heavy fishing pressure, as witnessed by the rapid decline of orange roughy fisheries soon after the fish gained acceptance on the dinner tables of Europe and North America in the early 1980s, when nearshore stocks of popular food fishes had become seriously depleted. Unlike other deep sea fish, which have gelatinous bodies, the orange roughy is a heavy-bodied fish with firm and flavorful flesh. Habitat for corals and associated animals is destroyed by deep sea trawls. The consequences to the ecosystem of the removal of top carnivores remain unknown.

Hydrothermal Vent and Cold Seep Communities

Both deep sea environments formed by the release of hydrogen sulfide and/or methane are known for the remarkable symbiotic relationships that have arisen between some bacteria and their invertebrate hosts. The bacteria are chemosynthesizers that use chemical energy to produce organic carbon compounds. The main hosts for bacteria utilizing H_2S come from three groups of animals: vestimentiferan tubeworms, vesicomyd clams, and bathymodiolid mussels. Tubeworms are totally dependent on the primary producers for food and have no gut of their own, but special tissue that houses the bacteria. They are found at hydrothermal vents and range in size from a fraction of an inch (a few millimeters) to about 3 ft (1 m) long. The largest known, *Riftia pachyptila*, occurs on the East Pacific Rise.

Bivalves make up most of the biomass at cold seeps, and they also occur at hydrothermal vents. Clams such as *Escarpia* are filter-feeders; however, they have greatly reduced digestive systems and must have their chemosynthetic partners to survive. They have large, modified gills to accommodate the bacteria, but they take up the H_2S required by their gill residents through the foot. Clams' gills capture the dissolved carbon dioxide and oxygen that the bacteria need. The giant vent clam, *Calyptogena magnifica*, can attain a length of nearly 8 in (20 cm).

Mussels (see Figure 4.4) also host bacteria in gill tissues, but unlike the clams, they have fully functional digestive systems. Particulate organic matter (POM) filtered out of the water seems to be only a dietary supplement, however. Some 17 species of mussels are known from vents and seeps; most are in the newly described subfamily Bathymodiolinae. The largest, *Bathymodiolus thermophilus*, can

Figure 4.4 Vent mussels. Galatheid crabs and shrimp graze bacteria on the mussel shells. *(NOAA/OceanExplorer.)*

be as large as the giant vent clam. Methane-based symbiotic relationships at cold seeps associated with salt domes off Louisiana and mud volcanoes near Barbados involve mussels and three other bivalve families.

Some shrimps (family Bresilidae), too, have symbiotic relationships with sulfur-dependent bacteria and swarm around vents and seeps. Those known from hydrothermal vents include *Rimicaris exoculata* and *Chorocaris chacei*, both of which crop filamentous sulfur bacteria that they "farm" on specialized mouthparts.

Some free-living bacteria also are chemosynthetic. Those that dwell in the 300–1,500 ft (100–500 m) plume emerging from vents aggregate in clumps resembling marine snow and are a food source for the zooplankton. If the vent is in shallow water (<650 ft or 200 m), zooplankters from upper layers of the water column will migrate down during the daylight hours and become food for vent animals. Elsewhere on rock and animal surfaces, biofilms and filamentous mats form and are food for grazers and deposit-feeding animals living at great depths. On mid-oceanic ridges shrimps are the dominant grazers.

While all the lifeforms mentioned, including the bacteria, depend on sulfur (or in some instances, methane) as their energy source in their dark habitat, they are not totally independent of the photosynthesis occurring near the ocean surface. All require oxygen to release the energy fixed in organic compounds and much of that comes from the tiny phytoplankters by way of deep sea currents.

Top predators at vents and seeps—including the eel-like vent zoarchid fish, which seems to prefer vent snails, limpets, and amphipods—are restricted to these habitats. Vent crabs and squat lobsters target deep sea mussels and tubeworms, while octopuses come in from the surrounding sea to feed on clams, mussels, and crabs.

Most hydrothermal vents are short-lived phenomena, since they are at active plate boundaries. The conduits through which superheated water rises eventually move away from the magma chamber below, or long before that may become clogged with mineral deposits. A dying community draws in scavenging gastropods, decapods, and copepods.

Life on Whale Skeletons and Other Carcasses on the Sea Bottom

Vertebrate bones are rich in lipids, and as they decay in anaerobic conditions, they slowly release sulfides that can be used by chemosynthetic bacteria related to those found at vents and seeps. Dead whales are particularly significant "nutrient-islands" on the deep seafloor. Scavengers of large carcasses are called "parcel attenders." Some arrive almost as soon as the remains land on the seafloor. Some demersal fish and amphipods, decapod shrimps, gastropods, and brittlestars move in for a high-quality feast. Like vultures at a kill in the savanna, they gorge themselves and then hang around, sometimes for weeks, only gradually abandoning the site as the flesh disappears. The energy and nutrients they obtain are transferred to the rest of the community through their wastes and through predation, for carnivores are also attracted to the site.

A study of a baleen whale skeleton in the Santa Catalina basin off California revealed a distinct community of attached vesicomyd clams and mussels (*Idasola washingtonia*) with symbiotic sulfur-dependent algae. Others among the more than 40 members of the macrofauna were many species of polychaetes, some amphipods, and isopods. The most abundant animals were mussels, four limpets, and a crab. White and yellow filamentous bacterial mats (*Beggiatoa* spp.) grew on the bones and were likely the main food supply for grazing limpets.

Almost none of the animals at the carcass were found in surrounding waters nor at cold seeps on the California slope. However, many did also occur at hydrothermal vents at the Juan de Fuca Ridge 1,000 miles to the north and in the Guaymas basin 1,000 miles to the south. Scientists suggest that whale bones on the seafloor around the world may serve as stepping stones for the dispersal of vent animals to newly active sites and wonder whether the giant marine reptiles of the Jurassic once played a similar role after death.

Pelagic Communities

The water habitat of the deep ocean separates into several zones (see Chapter 1, Figure 1.1), each with its own constraints as well as opportunities for life. Particularly below −3,500 ft (−1,000 m) the habitat is relatively uniform. It is totally dark. Depth-related changes in pressure and temperature impose physiological challenges, but the biggest obstacle to species survival may be limited resources. Biodiversity is relatively low in this realm.

Epipelagic zone—sea level to −650 to −852 ft (−200 to −250 m). This depth corresponds with both the euphotic zone and, in temperate regions, the seasonal thermocline. The phytoplankters living here are the primary producers not just for this zone, but for all pelagic and benthic habitats in the deep sea, except those where chemosynthetic organisms occur. Very small zooplankters can capture single algal cells, but most larger ones need bigger packages and rely on globs of "marine snow." The snow sinks to the seafloor and is a vital source of POM for both pelagic organisms that snare it in mid-water and for deep sea benthic organisms confined to the ocean bed. Suspension-feeders, such as krill, also depend on sinking POM.

Most invertebrates living in the epipelagic zone rise toward the surface at night to feed. Since most predators, even the abundant copepods, hunt by sight, natural selection has favored "invisible" zooplankters. All of the dominant forms—salps, siphonophores, medusae, foraminiferans, and chaetognaths—are tiny, transparent gelatinous creatures. Most fish, too, are nocturnal feeders. At day, even with countershading and disruptive patterns on their flanks, they are visible from below in Snell's window.

Mesopelagic zone—at −820 to −3,200 ft (−250 to −1,000 m). No photosynthetically active, living phytoplankters are in this zone or in any of the deeper ones.

Animals must be either detritivores or carnivores to survive. Many of the same groups that dominate the epipelagic waters occur, but they are represented by different species. Copepods and especially the gelatinous siphonophores are abundant. In the upper part of the zone, shrimps are typically transparent with red or orange stripes. The pigment comes from their diet and makes them invisible, since red and orange absorb blue-green light, the only wavelengths penetrating to this depth.

Fishes in the upper part of the zone, such as lanternfishes and hatchetfishes, characteristically have well-developed eyes and musculature, well-calcified skeletons, and gas-filled swim bladders with which to regulate their buoyancy. Their backs are black, flanks are highly reflective, and light-producing organs called photophores line their bellies. Mirror-like platelets regularly spaced along their flanks reflect light at the same intensity as the background, so the fish are invisible when approached from the side. From below, however, they may still be seen against the light in Snell's circle. Light from the photophores may disrupt their silhouette. The many predatory fishes usually have upward-facing eyes set in tubes and upward-tilting mouths.

In the lower part of the zone, fish are dark top and bottom and lack reflective plates on their flanks. At dusk, many migrate into the euphotic zone or the base of the thermocline to feed. Decapod crustaceans are completely red.

Bathypelagic zone—at −3,000 ft to −8,000 ft (−1,000 m to −2,500 m). The highest diversity of pelagic species occurs in this zone, but total biomass is low. Fish typically are black all over. They have small primitive eyes or are blind but have large mouths, especially in comparison with relatives in the mesopelagic zone. Their skeletons are only weakly calcified and they lack swim bladders or possess fat-filled ones. Hearts and kidneys are small, and brains simplified. Bioluminescence is used in a variety of ways at this depth (see Figure 4.5). Species and gender recognition may be accomplished by flashing lights. Some fish have photophores in specialized structures that serve as lures. Others use light to create decoy targets for predators or to set up a "smoke screen." "Headlights" may help others locate their own prey. Vertical migrations to the lighted surface waters no longer take place in this zone.

Fish at this depth must conserve energy since food is limited. They tend to ambush prey rather than swim in pursuit of it. Muscles, which are energy-demanding to maintain, are greatly reduced; and bodies often have the consistency of gelatin. Only strong jaw muscles are kept, so many fishes appear to be large mouths with some fins attached. Long feather-like bristles and antennae may help keep them afloat.

Bizarre life histories have evolved in this zone among the fishes that are usually slow-growing and long-lived. One of the strangest may be that of anglerfishes (see Figure 4.6), which takes gender differences to the extreme. The females fit the stereotype of bathypelagic fish: large, sluggish, tiny eyes, a mouth with a huge gape, and a large stalked lure outfitted with luminescent bacteria. The males—small, fast,

Figure 4.5 Bioluminescence in jellyfish. *(Photo © krishnacreations/Shutterstock.)*

Lighting Up under Water

On land, bioluminescence—light produced by living organisms—is rare and more or less limited to fireflies, glowworms (the larvae and larva-like females of certain beetles), and foxfire (light produced by some wood-decaying fungi). In the ocean, it is common and occurs in taxa ranging from bacteria to fishes. People most often see it when dinoflagellates flash blue-green in the surf or in the wake of a ship, light often mistakenly called phosphorescence.

In the deep sea, lights ripple through comb jellies and jellyfish. A squid squirts a "smoke screen" of light and disappears. An estimated 75 percent of deep sea fishes, especially those living at depths of 1,000–8,000 ft (300–2,400 m), use bursts of light—sometimes to become invisible to those swimming beneath them and other times to signal their presence to potential mates, or to lure prey, or to trick and confuse would-be predators.

Bioluminescence is a chemical process involving two compounds: (1) a "luciferin" that actually produces the light and (2) an enzyme, a "luciferase," that acts as the necessary catalyst. Sometimes the two are bound into a single photoprotein molecule. Whenever light is emitted, the luciferin must be regenerated, a process that requires energy in the form of ATP. That different compounds and different mechanisms exist in different taxa is evidence that bioluminescence has evolved many times as a successful adaptation to life in the dark depths of the sea.

Some organisms manufacture their own light-producing chemicals. Some use those made by others, either by acquiring them in their food or by harboring symbiotic colonies of luminescent bacteria. Squid and fish have special organs called photophores that allow them to regulate light emission. Simple lids of tissue work well for some species. Others have evolved complex systems of reflectors, lenses, and filters.

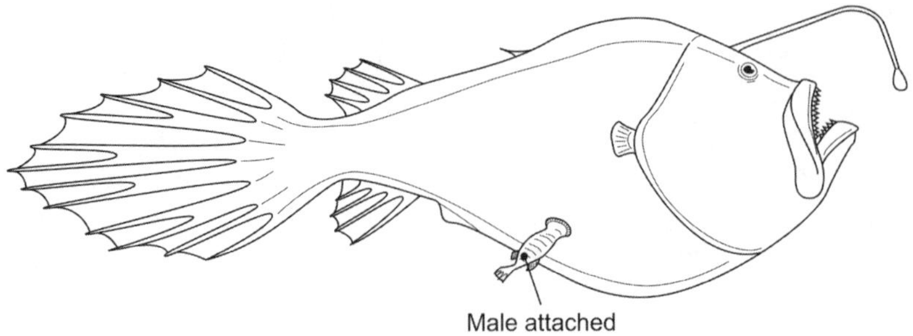

Figure 4.6 A female anglerfish with tiny male attached. *(Illustration by Jeff Dixon.)*

and large-eyed—contrast in just about every way. So that a female does not confuse it with food, the male attaches himself to her and spends most of his life as a parasite but is still able to fertilize her eggs whenever she releases them.

Abyssopelagic zone—at −8,000 ft (−2,500 m) to the benthopelagic zone. This zone may extend into hadal depths greater than −20,000 ft (−6,000 m) in oceanic trenches. Its base is defined by the depth of the seafloor and hence the benthopelagic zone. Food is limited. Few fish occupy this zone, which is inhabited mainly by decapods or, in the deepest parts, mysid shrimps.

Benthopelagic zone—within 300 ft (100 m) of the seabed. Food is more abundant in this zone, and the biomass of the nekton is greater than in the abyssopelagic zone. Benthic organisms float up into this zone, so that the larvae of both pelagic and benthic animals, gastropods, amphipods, and sea cucumbers are available for consumption by pelagic species.

Further Readings

Internet sites

Asare, Amma. n.d. "Bioluminescence." http://www.milton.edu/academics/pages/marinebio/biolum.html.

Haddock, S. H. D., C. M. McDougall, and J. F. Case. 1997. "The Bioluminescence Web Page." http://lifesci.ucsb.edu/~biolum.

Monterey Bay Aquarium Research Institute (MBARI). 2008. "Deep Sea Benthic Fauna Guide." http://www.mbari.org/benthic/fauna.html.

Monterey Bay Aquarium Research Institute (MBARI). 2008. "Mission to the Deep." http://www.mbayaq.org/efc/efc_mbari/mbari_home.asp.

Other online exhibits of the Monterey Bay Aquarium and associated research institute should also be explored.

Video

BBC. 2002. "The Deep." Programme 2 in *Blue Planet, Seas of Life.* Available on DVD.

Appendix

Biota of the Deep Sea Biome

Types of Coral

Lots of things are called corals. The scientific classification of these animals is confusing, and it is continually being revised. This brief outline places groups mentioned in the text.

Phylum: Cnidaria
Only two classes, the Anthozoa and Hydrozoa, have corals. Two other classes contain box jellies and true jellyfish.

Class Anthozoa
Soft corals, sea anemomes, and true or stony corals. Adults polyps have sac-like bodies partitioned radially into separate chambers. Septa or mesenteries form walls between the chambers. Nematocysts in the epidermis and sometimes the lining of the digestive tract are characteristic.

Subclass Zooantharia
Stony corals and sea anemones. Radial symmetry in multiples of six.

Order Scleractinia
Stony corals with cups of calcium carbonate at the base of the polyp

Order Antipatharia
Black corals. Black skeletons usually obscured when alive. One of the precious corals

Order Zoanthidae
Gold corals. One of the precious corals

Subclass Octocorallia

Radial symmetry in multiples of eight. Each polyp has eight feather-like tentacles.

Secrete a tough, elastic matrix into which the polyp can retract. Most have spicules of calcium carbonate with their tissue. Some have calcified holdfasts and internal rods for support. Live on reefs but contribute little to their construction. Colonies bushy, whip-like, or fan-shaped.

Order Alcyonacea

Soft corals. Encrusting or erect colonies, mostly fleshy and flexible with internal spicules giving shape and support. Mushroom or other lobate growth forms.

Suborder Calcaxonia

Family Primnoidae (the red-tree corals)

Family Isididae

Order Gorgonacea

Sea fans, bamboo corals, and tree corals. Also pink and red precious corals. Hardened core covered by a tough outer rind of living tissue.

Order Stolonifera

Organ-pipe coral. Polyps rise from a creeping mat (stolon). Tubular calcareous skeletons.

Class Hydrozoa

Includes the hydrocorals, hydras, and hydroids.

Order Stylasterina

Hydrocorals. Tiny polyps barely visible to the naked eye. Skeletons are fragile and shatter like glass when bumped into.

Scientific Names of Species Mentioned in Chapter 4

Deep Sea Corals

Tuft coral	*Lophelia pertusa*
Ivory tree coral	*Oculina varicosa*
Chrismas tree coral	*Antipathes dendrochristos*
Red-tree coral	*Primnoa resedaeformis*
Gold corals	*Gerardia* spp.
Black corals	*Antipathes* spp.
Red or pink corals	*Corallium* spp.
Bamboo corals	*Lepidisis* spp. *Keratoisis* spp., *Isidella* spp., and *Acanella* spp.

Deep Sea Coral Reef Fishes

Blackbelly rose fish	*Heliocolenus dactylopterus*
Morid cod	*Laemonema melanurum*
Red bream	*Beryx decadactylus*
Roughy	*Hoplostethus occidentalis*
Conger eel	*Conger oceanicus*
Wreckfish	*Polyprion americanus*

Seamount Animals

Deep sea corals	
Bubblegum corals	*Paragorgia* spp.
Whip corals	*Lepidisis* spp.
Bamboo coral	*Keratoisis* spp.
Mushroom corals	*Anthomastus* spp.
Red-tree corals	*Primnus* spp.
Echinoderms	
Basket star	*Gorgonocephalus eucnemis*
Brittlestar	*Asternonyx* spp.
Crustacean	
Galatheid crab	*Gastroptychus iaspus*
Fishes	
Japanese eel	*Anguilla japonica*
Orange roughy	*Hoplostethus atlanticus*
Mammal	
Hawaiian monk seal	*Monachus schaunislandii*

(*Continued*)

Hydrothermal Vents

Giant tubeworm	*Riftia pachyptila*
Vestimentiferan tubeworms	*Escarpia* spp.
Giant vent clam	*Calyptogena magnifica*
Limpet	*Lepetodrilus elevatus*
Vent snail	*Cyathermia naticoides*
Deep sea mussels	*Bathymodiolus* spp.
Amphipods	*Halice hesmonectes*
Shrimps	*Rimicaris exoculata, Chorocaris chacei, Alvinocaris lusca*
Hydrothermal vent crab	*Bythograea thermydron*
Squat lobster	*Munidopsis subsquamosa*
Vent zoarcid fish	*Thermarces cerberus*

Whale Carcasses

Bacterial mats	*Beggiatoa* spp.
Mussel	*Idasola washingtonia*

Deep Sea Animals

Decapod crustaceans	
Shrimps	*Sergia* spp., *Acanthephyra* spp.
Fishes	
Lanternfishes	Family Myctophidae
Marine hatchetfishes	Family Sternoptychidae
Anglerfishes	*Cryptopsaras couesi, Melanocetus johnsoni, Caulophryne* spp., and others

Glossary

Abyssal. Pertaining to zones of great depth in the ocean, generally between 13,000 and 20,000 ft (4,000–6,000 m) below sea level.

Abyssal Plain. The flat ocean floor at depths greater than 13,000 ft (4,000 m), excluding oceanic trenches.

Amphipod. A small crustacean with a body compressed laterally.

Amplitude (of wave). The vertical distance between the crest of one wave and the trough of the next wave.

Annual. Pertaining to an organism that lives for one year or less.

Bank. An underwater plateau on the continental shelf that rises into the euphotic zone.

Benthic zone. The seabed.

Benthos. Collectively, the organisms that live on or in the seabed.

Biogeography. The distribution patterns of living organisms, past and present, and the processes involved in determining those patterns. Also, the science that studies these patterns and processes.

Biogeographic Region. Part of the Earth's surface recognized by having a set of characteristic plant and animal taxa, with some restricted to that area and others shared with other such regions. A division of the Earth determined by taxonomic relationships, not by growthforms as biomes are.

Biome. On land, a geographic region characterized by the dominance of a particular type of vegetation and its associated animals and soils. The lifeforms in the biome are adapted to the climate of the region or some other dominant element of the physical environment, such as edaphic conditions or periodic disturbance. Different taxa may occur in different parts of the same biome. In the oceans, biomes have been delineated according to latitudinal zones and water temperature, or by physical conditions that elicit responses in the phytoplankton.

Biota. All the living organisms of a particular area.

Bioturbator. An organism that mixes the sediments of the sea bed by its activities, such as burrowing, deposit-feeding, and so forth.

Bivalve. A mollusc of the class Bivalvia. Their bodies are encased in two rigid shells joined together by a hinge. Clams, cockles, and mussels are examples.

Bloom (algal). A period of rapid cell division among algae. A population explosion among these single-celled plants.

Byssal Threads. Strong filaments by which some molluscs attach themselves to hard surfaces.

Carnivore. A flesh-eating animal.

Climate. The general weather patterns expected in an average year. The main factors are temperature and precipitation.

Commercial Extinction. The depletion of a fishery to the point at which it is no longer economical to harvest fish or shellfish.

Community. All the species living in a particular area, or a subset of a species, such as all the fishes, all the invertebrates, or all the animals living in the benthic zone. Some sort of interrelationship among the members of a community is often assumed.

Compensation Level. The depth in the sea at which primary production equals respiration and no excess energy is available for growth and reproduction.

Consumer. An organism that derives its energy by eating other organisms (dead or alive) rather than by directly fixing light or chemical energy itself.

Continental Shelf. That part of the continental margin submerged in shallow water less than 600 ft (200 m) deep.

Continental Slope. The steeply plunging edge of a continent that begins at the outer edge of the continental shelf and extends down to the continental rise.

Convergent Evolution. The development of similar morphological or other characteristics in unrelated taxa under similar environmental conditions in separate parts of a biome.

Copepod. A tiny aquatic crustacean with a body that tapers toward the tail and that has long antennae.

Crustose (algae). A thin scaly growthform displayed by some red or coralline algae, as well as certain lichens.

Cyanobacteria. Singe-celled organisms occurring in water (and soil) that are able to fix nitrogen and photosythesize. Once classified as blue-green algae.

Decapod. A member of the class Crustacea that has 10 legs. Crabs, true shrimps, and lobsters are examples.

Decomposer. An organism that breaks down dead organic material into simpler molecules or its inorganic components.

Demersal. Pertaining to free-swimming organisms that live near or at the bottom of the sea.

Detritivore. A consumer that feeds on fragments of dead organic material or particulate organic matter.

DOM. Dissolved organic matter.

Echinoid. A member the class Echinoidea, such as sea stars, sea urchins, and sand dollars.

Ecology. The interrelationships among organisms and the living and nonliving aspects of their environment. Also, the science that studies these interrelationships.

Ecosystem. All the living and nonliving parts of a given area that work together as a single unit to maintain a flow of energy and cycling of nutrients.

El Niño. A seasonal weather phenomenon that affects the equatorial Pacific, especially off the west coast of South America. During these events of December, normal high pressure systems and cold ocean currents that make the coast exceptionally dry are replaced by low pressure, warm ocean waters, high humidity, and even rain. Severe, prolonged El Niños can affect weather patterns around the world.

Endemic. Native to and restricted to a particular geographic area.

Epibiota. All the organisms—plant, animal, microorganism—that live on the surface of the substrate.

Epifauna. All the animals that live on the surface of some substrate.

Epipelon. The water-sediment interface, or the contact zone between the surface of the sediment (substrate) and water.

Eulittoral or Intertidal Zone. That part of the coast that lies between the highest high-tide mark and the lowest low-tide mark.

Fauna. A collective term for all the animal species found in a given area.

Fishery. An area of the sea defined by the type of fish or shellfish caught there, or the marine populations harvested in a particular area.

Flagella. A whip-like appendage on certain phyto- and zooplankters that is used to propel them through the water.

Flagellates. One-celled organisms with flagella. Among them are some green algae and some zooplankters.

Foliose (algae). Leaf-like in appearance.

Front. The contact zone between two masses of water with different physical characteristics.

Gastropod. Molluscs of the class Gastropoda. They have coiling or spiraling shells, an elongated foot, and retractable tentacles. Snails, periwinkles, and limpets are examples.

Grazer. An animal that consumes algae.

Guano. Seabird droppings that often accumulate in thick deposits and are rich in phosphates and nitrates. Before the advent of synthetic fertilizers, guano was mined and sold for agricultural use.

Guild. A group of ecologically similar species that share food resources and have the same general foraging habits.

Guyot. A flat-topped seamount. Named after geographer/geologist Arnold Guyot.

Gyre. The generally circular movement of ocean currents around an ocean basin driven by the atmospheric circulation pattern.

Habitat. The space in which a species lives and the environmental conditions of that place.

Halocline. The depth at which the salinity profile changes rather abruptly.

Herbivore. An animal that consumes plant matter.

Infauna. A collective term for all the animals that live buried in bottom sediments.

Iceberg. Large floating irregularly shaped block of ice that has broken off (calved from) a glacier.

Ice Cap. Domed body of permanent ice and snow that covers a large land area, such as the Greenland ice cap.

Ice Floe. A flat expanse of floating ice.

Ice Pack or Pack Ice. Large floating mass made up of many pieces of ice, such as found in the Arctic and Southern oceans.

Ice Sheet. A vast cover of ice on land that reaches thicknesses of hundreds or thousands of feet and entirely obliterates signs of the underlying terrain, such as the Antarctic ice sheet or the ice that blanketed northern North America and northwest Europe several times during the Pleistocene Epoch.

Ice Shelf. The edge of an ice sheet that protrudes from the continent and floats on the sea. The landward part remains attached to the landmass and is called fast ice.

Ion. A particle bearing a negative or positive charge.

Isopod. A small crustacean with a body that is flattened dorsally or ventrally.

Irruption. A rapid growth in population that occurs irregularly.

ITCZ (Intertropical Convergence Zone). The contact zone between the Trade Winds of the Northern and Southern Hemispheres. Shifts its position north and south of the Equator with the seasons and, when overhead, usually brings rain.

Kelp. A large brown alga or seaweed from either order Laminariales or order Fucales.

Latitude. The distance of a point north or south of the Equator (0° latitude), measured in degrees.

Lichen. A lifeform that consists of a fungus and an alga locked in a symbiotic relationship and classified as a single organism.

Marine Snow. Globs of particulate organic matter that precipitate down from the euphotic zone to the sea bed.

Microbial Loop. The food chain in which dissolved organic matter is leaked from algal and zooplankter cells and consumed by marine bacteria, which then are eaten by zooplankters.

Microhabitat. A small or limited space within a habitat that possesses unique environmental conditions.

Mid-oceanic Ridge. An undersea mountain range formed at the edges of diverging tectonic plates.

Mixing Zone. That upper part of the water column where water is roiled by wind energy so that waters of varying temperature and/or nutrient content are mixed.

Monsoon. A wind that reverses its direction seasonally. An onshore flow typifies the warm season and an offshore flow occurs during the cold season. The Asian Monsoon is most powerful and dominates the climate of the vast Indian Ocean region.

Morphology. The form (shape and size) and structure of an organism.

Motile. Able to move under its own power.

Mysid Shrimp. Also known as opossum shrimp. Small crustaceans only distantly related to true shrimps, which are classified in a different order.

Nautical Mile. At sea distance is measured as a subdivision of the great circle circumference of Earth. The nautical mile, an international and U.S. unit of length, is the length of one minute (1/60 of a degree) of arc of a great circle and is equal to about 6,076 feet (1,852 m). On land, the statute mile is used as the unit of length in the English measurement system. It is equivalent to 5,280 ft (1,609 m).

Nekton. A collective term for the actively swimming animals in the open ocean.

Neritic. Pertaining to the shallow water above continental shelves.

Neuston. A collective term for those animals that hang on water's surface film.

Oceanic (zone). The open sea beyond the continental shelf.

Organic. Pertaining to complex compounds of carbon produced by living organisms.

Pectoral Fins. The fins on the sides of fish behind the gills. They take the place of the forelimbs in terrestrial vertebrates.

Pelagic. Pertaining to the open waters of the sea.

Perennial. Pertaining to plants that live more than two years.

pH. A measure of acidity (0–7) or alkalinity (7–14). The negative logarithm of the concentration of hydrogen ions in solution.

Physiology. The metabolic or life functions and processes of organisms.

Phytoplankton. A collective term for all plants that float in the water unable to move against tides and currents. Many, however, can propel themselves up and down the water column.

Plankter. An individual cell or small organism that floats in the currents or tides unable to change location by itself, except up or down ion the water column.

Plankton. A collective term for all organisms that float in the water unable to move against tides and currents.

Plate Tectonics. The movement of pieces of the Earth's crust (plates) and the rearrangements and deformation of the surface that result.

Pleustron. A collective term for buoyant animals that remain at the sea's surface, half in and half out of the water.

POM. Particulate organic matter.

Primary Producer. An autotrophic organism that can fix energy into the bonds of organic compounds. Most primary producers utilize sunlight and photosynthesize, but in the deep sea (at vents and seeps) the primary producers are chemosynthetic.

Pycnocline. The depth at which a marked change in water density occurs.

Raptorial. Adapted for grasping prey.

Rift. A break in the Earth's crust where adjacent plates are pulling away from each other.

Scavenger. An animal that feeds on carrion (dead animals).

Seagrass. A true flowering plant that lives submerged beneath saltwater. Also known as submerged aquatic vegetation (SAV); turtlegrass and eelgrass are examples.

Seaweed. A marine macroalga, such as Irish moss, sea lettuce, or the kelps.

Sessile. Attached to the substrate; nonmotile.

Settling (by barnacles and other sessile invertebrates). Becoming permanently attached to the substrate.

Shoal. A large school of fish.

Species. A group of individual organisms that can interbreed and produce viable offspring.

Subducting. The movement of one tectonic plate down and under an adjacent plate.

Sublittoral or Subtidal. That zone of the coast below normal low tide and extending seaward to a depth at which wave action no longer disturbs the sea bed.

Substrate. The bottom materials or other underlying layers.

Succulent. A plant that has specialized tissues for storing water.

Supralittoral. The coastal zone above normal high-tide level but affected by sea spray.

Suspension-feeder. Any organism that obtains its food by filtering particulate organic matter out of the water.

Taxon (plural = taxa). Any group at any level in the taxonomic hierarchy.

Taxonomy. The way scientists have classified a group of similar, related organisms into species, genera, families, and higher units. Also, the science that classifies, describes, and names organisms.

Temperate. Mild or moderate temperature conditions.

Thermocline. That depth at which a rapid change in water temperature occurs.

Trade Winds. The strong, constant easterly winds of tropical latitudes.

Trench (ocean). Deep linear landform feature created by the subduction of a tectonic plate bearing oceanic crust. Trenches are the deepest parts of the ocean floor.

Tropics. The latitudinal zone on Earth that lies between 23° 30′ N and 23° 30′ S (that is, between the Tropic of Cancer and the Tropic of Capricorn).

Turbidity. The measure of the amount of sediment or particulate matter suspended in water.

Upwelling. The upward movement of cold nutrient-rich water from the deep.

Zonation. A distribution pattern in which particular forms of life occur in distinct belts. In marine environments, zonation is often the result of variations in light, temperature, and exposure to wave action.

Zooxanthellae. The dinoflagellates that live symbiotically in the tissues of coral polyps and some other marine invertebrates.

Zooplankton. A collective term for all the single-celled and small multicelled animals that float in the ocean unable to move against tides or currents but able to move up and down the water column.

Bibliography

Introduction to the Ocean Environment

American Museum of Natural History. 2006. *Ocean.* New York: DK Publishing.
Barnes, R. S. K., and R. N. Hughes. 1999. *An Introduction to Marine Ecology*, 3rd ed. Malden, MA: Blackwell Science.
Bertness, Mark D., S. D. Gaines, and M. E. Hay, eds. 2001. *Marine Community Ecology*. Sunderland, MA: Sinauer Associates, Inc.
CIA. 2007. "Arctic Ocean." The World Factbook. https://www.cia.gov/library/publications/the-world-factbook/geos/xq.html.
CIA. 2007. "Atlantic Ocean." The World Factbook. https://www.cia.gov/library/publications/the-world-factbook/geos/zh.html.
CIA. 2007. "Indian Ocean." The World Factbook. https://www.cia.gov/library/publications/the-world-factbook/geos/xo.html.
CIA. 2007. "Pacific Ocean." The World Factbook. https://www.cia.gov/library/publications/the-world-factbook/geos/zn.html.
CIA. 2007. "Southern Ocean." The World Factbook. https://www.cia.gov/library/publications/the-world-factbook/geos/oo.html.
Earle, Sylvia A. 2001. *National Geographic Atlas of the Ocean: The Deep Frontier.* Washington, DC: National Geographic Society.
Kaiser, M. J., M. J. Attrill, S. Jennings, D. N. Thomas, D. K. A. Barnes, N. V. C. Polunin, D. G. Raffaelli, and P. J. leB. Williams. 2005. *Marine Ecology: Processes, Systems, and Impacts.* New York: Oxford University Press.
Longhurst, Alan. 1998. *Ecological Geography of the Sea.* San Diego: Academic Press.
Miller, C. B. 2004. *Biological Oceanography.* Malden, MA: Blackwell Publishing.

Olson, David M., and Eric Dinerstein. 2002. "The Global 200: Priority Ecoregions for Global Conservation." *Annals of the Missouri Botanical Garden* 89: 199–224. http://www.worldwildlife.org/science/pubs/annals_of_missouri.pdf.

Spalding, M. D., H. E. Fox, G. R. Allen, N. Davidson, Z. A. Ferdaña, M. Finlayson, B. Halpern, M. A. Jorge, A. Lombana, S. A. Lourie, K. D. Martin, E. McManus, J. Molnar, C. A. Recchia, and J. Robertson. 2007. "Marine Ecoregions of the World: A Bioregionalization of Coastal and Shelf Areas." *Bioscience* 57 (7): 573–583. www.worldwildlife.org?MEOW/pdfs/meow_biosci.pdf.

Tyler, P. A., ed. 2003. *Ecosystems of the Deep Oceans.* Ecosystems of the World, 28. Amsterdam: Elsevier.

Coast Biome

Chapman, V. J., ed. 1977. *Wet Coastal Ecosystems.* Ecosystems of the World, 1. Amsterdam: Elsevier.

Connell, Joseph H. 1961. "The Influence of Interspecific Competition and Other Factors on the Distribution of the Barnacle *Chlathamalus stellatus.*" *Ecology* 42: 710–723.

Daiber, Franklin. 1977. "Salt-Marsh Animals." In *Wet Coastal Ecosystems,* ed. V. J. Chapman, 79–108. Ecosystems of the World, 1. Amsterdam: Elsevier.

Department of Primary Industries and Fisheries, Queensland, Australia. 2006. "Know Your Mangroves 1–6." DPI&F Note. http://www2.dpi.qld.gov.au/fishweb/2626.html; http://www2.dpi.qld.gov.au/fishweb/2635.html; http://www2.dpi.qld.gov.au/fishweb/2637.html; http://www2.dpi.qld.gov.au/fishweb/2638.html; http://www2.dpi.qld.gov.au/fishweb/2638.html; http://www2.dpi.qld.gov.au/fishweb/2644.html.

Ellison, Aaron M., and Elizabeth J. Farnsworth. 2001. "Mangrove Communities." In *Marine Community Ecology,* eds. Mark D. Bertness, S. D. Gaines, and M. E. Hay, 423–442. Sunderland, MA: Sinauer Associates, Inc.

Field, J. G., and C. L. Griffiths. 1991. "Littoral and Sublittoral Ecosystems of Southern Africa." In *Intertidal and Littoral Ecosystems,* eds. A. C. Mathieson and P. H. Nienhuis, 323–346. Ecosystems of the World, 24. Amsterdam: Elsevier.

Hardin, David S. 1992. "Laws of Nature: Wildlife Management Legislation in Colonial Virginia." In *The American Environment: Interpretations of Past Geographies,* eds. Lary M. Dilsaver and Craig E. Colten, 137–162. Lanham, MD: Rowman and Littlefield.

Kaiser, M. J., M. J. Attrill, S. Jennings, D. N. Thomas, D. K. A. Barnes, N. V. C. Polunin, D. G. Raffaelli, and P. J. leB. Williams. 2005. *Marine Ecology: Processes, Systems, and Impacts.* New York: Oxford University Press.

Koehl, Mimi. 2006. *Wave-swept Shore: The Rigors of Life on a Rocky Coast.* Berkeley: University of California Press.

Knox, George A. 2001. *The Ecology of Seashores.* Boca Raton, FL: CRC Press LLC.

Lenihan, Hunter S., and Fiorenza Micheli. 2001. "Soft-Sediment Communities." In *Marine Community Ecology,* eds. Mark D. Bertness, S. D. Gaines, and M. E. Hay, 253–287. Sunderland, MA: Sinauer Associates, Inc.

Lippson, Alice Jane, and Robert L. Lippson. 1984. *Life in Chesapeake Bay.* Baltimore: Johns Hopkins University Press.

Little, Colin. 2000. *The Biology of Soft Shores and Estuaries.* New York: Oxford University Press.

Little, Colin, and J. A. Kitching. 1996. *The Biology of Rocky Shores.* New York: Oxford University Press.

Mann, K. H. 2000. *Ecology of Coastal Waters, with Implications for Management*, 2nd ed. Malden, MA: Blackwell Science.

Paine, R. T. 1966. "Food Web Complexity and Species Diversity." *American Naturalist* 100: 65–75.

Pennings, Steven C., and Mark D. Bertness. 2001. "Salt Marsh Communities." In *Marine Community Ecology,* eds. Mark D. Bertness, S. D. Gaines, and M. E. Hay, 289–316. Sunderland, MA: Sinauer Associates, Inc.

Rahman, Laskar Muqsudur. 2000. "The Sundarbans: A Unique Wilderness of the World." USDA Forest Service Proceedings. Rocky Mountain Research Station Online Publication RMS-P-15-Vol. 2. www.fs.fed.us/rm/pubs/rmrs_p015_2/rmrs_p015_2_143_148.pdf.

Russell, G. 1991. "Vertical Distribution." In *Intertidal and Littoral Ecosystems,* eds. A. C. Mathieson and P. H. Nienhuis, 43–65. Ecosystems of the World, 24. Amsterdam: Elsevier.

Steers J. A. 1977. Physiography." In *Wet Coastal Ecosystems,* ed. V. J. Chapman, 31–60. Ecosystems of the World, 1. Amsterdam: Elsevier.

Teal, John M. 1962. "Energy Flow in the Salt Marsh Ecosystem of Georgia." *Ecology* 43: 614–624.

West, Robert C. 1977. "Tidal Salt Marsh and Mangal Formations of Middle and South America." In *Wet Coastal Ecosystems,* ed. V. J. Chapman, 193–213. Ecosystems of the World, 1. Amsterdam: Elsevier.

Witman, Jon D., and Paul K. Dayton. 2001. "Rocky Subtidal Communities." In *Marine Community Ecology,* eds. Mark D. Bertness, S. D. Gaines, and M. E. Hay, 339–366. Sunderland, MA: Sinauer Associates, Inc.

World Wildlife Fund. 2001. "WildWorld: Terrestrial Ecoregions of the World." Australasian mangroves: http://www.nationalgeographic.com/wildworld/profiles/terrestrial_aa.html; Afrotropical mangroves: http://www.nationalgeographic.com/wildworld/profiles/terrestrial_at.html#mangrove); Indo-Malayan mangroves: http://www.nationalgeographic.com/wildworld/profiles/terrestrial_im.html#mangrove; Nearctic mangroves: http://www.nationalgeographic.com/wildworld/profiles/terrestrial_.na.html#mangrove; Neotropical mangroves: http://www.nationalgeographic.com/wildworld/profiles/terrestrial_nt.html#mangrove.

Zann, Leon P., compiler. 1995. "Mangrove Ecosystems in Australia: Structure, Function and Status." State of the Marine Environment Report for Australia: The Marine Environment—Technical Annex 1. Sydney: Australian Institute of Marine Science. http://www.environment.gov.au/coasts/publications/somer/annex1/mangrove.html.

Continental Shelf Biome

American Museum of Natural History. 1998. "Will the Fish Return? How Gear and Greed Emptied Georges Bank." AMNH BioBulletin. http://www.amnh.org/sciencebulletins/biobulletin/biobulletin/story1208.html.

Barnes, R. S. K., and R. N. Hughes. 1999. *An Introduction to Marine Ecology*, 3rd ed. Malden, MA: Blackwell Science.

Birkeland, C., ed. 1997. *Life and Death of Coral Reefs.* New York: Chapman & Hall.

Carpenter, R. C. 1997. "Invertebrate Predators and Grazers." In *Life and Death of Coral Reefs,* ed. C. Birkeland, 198–229. New York: Chapman & Hall.

Census of Marine Life Gulf of Maine Area Program. 2007. "Georges Bank and Great South Channel." http://research.usm.maine.edu/gulfofmaine-census/biodiversity/geography-characteristics/physioregions.

Done, T. J. 1983. "Coral Zonation: Its Nature and Significance." In *Perspectives on Coral Reefs,* ed. D. J. Barnes, 107–147. Manuka: Australian Institute of Marine Science.

Fish and Agriculture Organization. 2005. "Fishery Country Profile, The Republic of South Africa." http://www.fao.org/fi/fcp/en/ZAF/profile.htm.

Fisheries and Oceans Canada. 2006. "The Grand Banks and the Flemish Cap." Overfishing and International Fisheries and Oceans Governance. http://www.dfo-mpo.gc.ca/overfishing-surpeche/media/bk_grandbanks_e.htm.

Fréon, Pierre. 2006. "Tropical Marine Ecosystems: Large Upwelling Ecosystems of the World." Les dossiers thématiques de l'IRD, Suds enligne. http://www.mpl.ird.fr/suds-en-ligne/ecosys/ang_ecosys/upwelling/upwelling.htm.

Glynn, Peter W. 1997. "Bioerosion and Coral Reef Growth: A Dynamic Balance." In *Life and Death of Coral Reefs,* ed. C. Birkeland, 68–95. New York: Chapman & Hall.

Gubbay, Susan, C. Maria Baker, and Brain J Bett. 2002. "The Darwin Mounds and the Dogger Bank." A report to WWF-UK. http://www.ngo.grida.no/wwfneap/Projects/Reports/darwin_dogger_mgmt.pdf.

Kaiser, M. J., M. J. Attrill, S. Jennings, D. N. Thomas, D. K. A. Barnes, N. V. C. Polunin, D. G. Raffaelli, and P. J. leB. Williams. 2005. *Marine Ecology: Processes, Systems, and Impacts*. New York: Oxford University Press.

Knowlton, Nancy, and Jeremy Jackson. 2001. "The Ecology of Coral Reefs." In *Marine Community Ecology,* eds. Mark D. Bertness, S. D. Gaines, and M. E. Hay, 395–422. Sunderland, MA: Sinauer Associates, Inc.

Lippson, Alice Jane, and Robert L. Lippson. 1984. *Life in Chesapeake Bay*. Baltimore: Johns Hopkins University Press.

Paulay, Gustav. 1997. "Diversity and Distribution of Reef Organisms." In *Life and Death of Coral Reefs,* ed. C. Birkeland, 298–353. New York: Chapman & Hall.

Pitkin, Linda. 2001. *Coral Fish.* Washington, DC: Smithsonian Institution Press.

Probyn, T. A., B. A. Mitchell-Innes, P. C. Brown, L. Hutchings, and R. A. Carter. 1994. "A Review of Primary Production and Related Processes on the Agulhas Bank." *South African Journal of Science* 90 (3): 166–173.

Raloff, Janet. 2007. "Slime Dwellers." *Science News* 171: 346–348.

Sætersdal, G., G. Bianchi, T. Strømme, and S. C. Venema. 1999. "The DR. FRIDTJOF NANSEN Programme 1975–1993. Investigations of Fishery Resources in Developing Countries. History of the Programme and Review of Results." FAO Fisheries Technical Paper No. 391. Rome, Food and Agriculture Organization. http://www.fao.org/docrep/004/X3950E/X3950E01.htm.

Sale, Peter, ed. 1991. *The Ecology of Fishes on Coral Reefs.* New York: Academic Press.

Schott, F. A., M. Dengler, and R. Schoenefeldt. 2002. "The Shallow Overturning Circulation of the Indian Ocean." *Progress in Oceanography* 53: 57–103.

Shannon, Vere, G. Hempel, P. Malanotte-Rizzoli, C. Moloney, and J. Woods, eds. 2006. *Benguela: Predicting a Large Marine Ecosystem.* Amsterdam: Elsevier.

Takasuka, A., Y. Oozeki, and I. Aoki. 2007. "Optimal Growth Temperature Hypothesis: Why Do Anchovy Flourish and Sardine Collapse or Vice Versa Under the Same Ocean Regime?" *Canadian Journal of Fisheries and Aquatic Sciences* 64 (5): 768–776.

Thirteen/Online. 2007. "Sharkland." Thirteen/WNET New York and Educational Broadcasting Corporation. http://www.pbs.org/wnet/nature/sharkland/index.html.

Van der Lingen, C. D., L. J. Shannon, P. Cury, A. Kreiner, C. L. Moloney, J.-P. Roux, and F. Vaz-Velho. 2006. "Resource and Ecosystem Variability, Including Regime Shifts, in the Bengula Current System." In *Benguela: Predicting a Large Marine Ecosystem,* eds. V. Shannon, G. Hempel, P. Malanotte-Rizzoli, C. Moloney, and J. Woods, 147–184. Amsterdam: Elsevier.

Waggoner, Ben M., Allen Collins, and David Smith. 1994–2006. "Anthozoa Systematics." University of California Museum of Paleontology. http://www.ucmp.berkeley.edu/cnidaria/anthozoasy.html.

Williams, Susan L., and Kenneth L. Heck, Jr. 2001. "Seagrass Community Ecology." In *Marine Community Ecology,* eds. Mark D. Bertness, S. D. Gaines, and M. E. Hay, 315–337. Sunderland, MA: Sinauer Associates, Inc.

Deep Sea Biome

Alaska Science Outreach. 2004. "Corals in Alaska. Exploring Corals of the Aleutian Seas." http://www.alaskascienceoutreach.com/coralsite/corals.html.

Angel, Martin V. 2003. "The Pelagic Environment of the Open Ocean." In *Ecosystems of the Deep Oceans*, ed. P. A. Tyler, 39–79. Ecosystems of the World, 28. Amsterdam: Elsevier.

Asare, Amma. n.d. "Bioluminescence." http://www.milton.edu/academics/pages/marine bio/biolum.html.

Bennett, Bruce A., Craig R. Smith, Bryce Glaser, and Hilary L. Maybaum. 1994. "Faunal Community Structure of a Chemoautotrophic Assemblage on Whale Bones in the Deep Northeast Pacific Ocean." *Marine Ecology Research Series* 108: 205–203. http://www.int-res.com/articles/meps/108/m108p205.pdf.

CenSeam: a Global Census of Marine Life on Seamounts (Content Partner); National Oceanic and Atmospheric Administration (Content source); J. Emmett Duffy, topic ed. 2007. "Seamount." In *Encyclopedia of Earth,* ed. J. Cleveland Cutler. Washington, DC: Environmental Information Coalition, National Council for Science and the Environment. http://www.eoearth.org/article/Seamount.

Etter, R. J., and L. S. Mullineaux. 2003. "Deep-Sea Communities." In *Marine Community Ecology,* eds. Mark D. Bertness, S. D. Gaines, and M. E. Hay, 367–393. Sunderland, MA: Sinauer Associates, Inc.

Fiorenza, Micheli, Charles H. Peterson, Lauren S. Mullineaux, Charles R. Fisher, Susan W. Mills, Gorka Sancho, Galen A. Johnson, and Hunter S. Lenihan. 2002. "Predation Structures Communities at Deep-Sea Hydrothermal Vents." *Ecological Monographs* 72 (3): 365–382.

Haddock, S. H. D., C. M. McDougall, and J. F. Case, 1997. "The Bioluminescence Web Page." http://lifesci.ucsb.edu/~biolum.

Kaiser, M. J., M. J. Attrill, S. Jennings, D. N. Thomas, D. K. A. Barnes, N. V. C. Polumim, D. G. Raffaelli, and P. J. leB. Williams. 2005. *Marine Ecology: Processes, Systems, and Impacts*. New York: Oxford University Press.

Morgan, Lance E. 2005. "What Are Deep-Sea Corals?" *Current. The Journal of Marine Education: Special Issue on Deep Sea Corals* 21 (4): 2–4. http://www.mcbi.org/what/current.htm.

Morgan, Lance E. 2005. "The Intertwined Fates of Precious Corals and Monk Seals." *Current. The Journal of Marine Education: Special Issue on Deep Sea Corals* 21 (4): 12. http://www.mcbi.org/what/current.htm.

NOAA Ocean Explorer. 2005. "Precious Corals." Northwestern Hawaiian Islands Exploration. http://www.oceanexplorer.noaa.gov/explorations/02hawaii/background/corals/corals.html.

Reed, John K., and Steve W. Ros. 2005. "Deep-Water Reefs Off the Southeastern U.S.: Recent Discoveries and Research." *Current. The Journal of Marine Education: Special Issue on Deep Sea Corals* 21 (4): 33–37. http://www.mcbi.org/what/current.htm.

Rogers, A. D. 2004. "The Biology, Ecology and Vulnerability of Seamount Communities." International Union for Conservation of Nature & Natural Resource. http://www.iucn.org/THEMES/MARINE/pdf/AlexRogers-CBDCOP7-Seamounts-Complete1.pdf.

SIMoN. 2005. "Seamounts Overview." Monterey Bay National Marine Sanctuary. http://www.mbnms-simon.org/sections/seamounts/overview.php?sec=s.

Thistle, David. 2003. "Deep-Sea Floor: An Overview." In *Ecosystems of the Deep Oceans*, ed. P. A. Tyler, 3–37. Ecosystems of the World, 28. Amsterdam: Elsevier.

Tsao, Fan. 2005. "Deep-Sea Corals Are Long-Lived Historians." *Current. The Journal of Marine Education: Special Issue on Deep Sea Corals* 21 (4): 22–23. http://www.mcbi.org/what/current.htm.

Tsao, Fan, and Lance E. Morgan. 2005. "Corals That Live on Mountaintops." *Current. The Journal of Marine Education: Special Issue on Deep Sea Corals* 21 (4): 9–11. http://www.mcbi.org/what/current.htm.

Tunnicliffe, Verena, S. Kim Juniper, and Myriam Sibuet. 2003. "Reducing Environments of the Deep-Sea Floor." In *Ecosystems of the Deep Oceans*, ed. P. A. Tyler, 81–110. Ecosystems of the World, 28. Amsterdam: Elsevier.

Tyler, P. A. 2003. "Introduction." In *Ecosystems of the Deep Oceans*, ed. P. A. Tyler, 1–3. Ecosystems of the World, 28. Amsterdam: Elsevier.

Index

About the Author

SUSAN L. WOODWARD received her Ph.D. in geography from the University of California, Los Angeles, in 1976. She taught undergraduate courses in biogeography and physical geography for twenty-two years at Radford University in Virginia before retiring in 2006. Author of *Biomes of Earth*, published by Greenwood Press in 2003, she continues to learn and write about our natural environment. Her travels have allowed her to see firsthand some of the world's major grassland biomes in North America, South America, Russia, China, and southern Africa.